DIGITAL TECHNIQUES

Student Textbook
Book 1

Revised By: **Lee Anne Farr**
Educational Media Designer

EB-6201A
595-3509-05

Digital Techniques, Third Edition

Not affiliated with D.C. Heath, Inc.

ISBN 0-87119-221-7

Contents

COURSE INTRODUCTION IV

COURSE OBJECTIVES VII

COURSE OUTLINE IX

UNIT ONE — Introduction to Digital Techniques 1-1

UNIT TWO — Semiconductor Devices for Digital Circuits 2-1

UNIT THREE — Digital Logic Circuits 3-1

UNIT FOUR — Digital Integrated Circuits 4-1

UNIT FIVE — Boolean Algebra 5-1

UNIT SIX — Flip-Flops and Registers 6-1

UNIT SEVEN — Sequential Logic Circuits: Counters, Shift Registers and Clocks 7-1

UNIT EIGHT — Combinational Logic Circuits 8-1

UNIT NINE — Semiconductor Memories 9-1

UNIT TEN — Data Conversion 10-1

UNIT ELEVEN — Digital Troubleshooting 11-1

INDEX I-1

Introduction

This is the computer age and if you are to succeed or excel in electronics, you must have a knowledge of digital techniques. All computers and most other electronic circuits use digital techniques. The application of the material in this course will be beneficial, if not essential to your understanding of digital equipment. This course will teach you the concepts, terminology, components, and circuits that combine to form the basic digital system.

Digital techniques are so widely used today that it is almost impossible to think of electronic equipment without them. Digital techniques are used in virtually every area of electronics. They have greatly improved electronic methods and have resulted in practical electronic equipment with amazing capability, and there is potential for further improvements and advances. As an electronic engineer, technician, or hobbyist, you can benefit by knowing digital techniques. This program will provide you with a solid understanding of digital methods and a guide to their application.

After completing this course, you will be familiar with a wide range of integrated circuits, their uses and characteristics. You will also have a working knowledge of semiconductor memories, Boolean algebra, logic circuits, memory devices, data conversion, and digital troubleshooting.

How do you gauge your learning? Let the "**objectives**" be your guide. These carefully constructed objectives are the framework for the course. When you can meet all of the objectives, you have satisfied the requirements of the course. You'll find two types of objectives in this course: broad, "**Course Objectives**" are listed following this introduction. More specific "**Unit Objectives**" are listed near the front of each unit. When you can satisfy these unit objectives, you've learned everything that was intended from the units; no matter how easy it seemed.

Course Objectives

When you complete this program, you will have the following skills and knowledge. You will be able to:

1. Identify the two types of electrical signals.

2. Convert between number systems and perform binary arithmetic.

3. Recognize the most commonly used binary codes.

4. Name the major components used in implementing digital circuits and explain how they operate.

5. Explain the operation of digital logic gates.

6. Identify the more commonly used integrated circuit families used in digital equipment and discuss their operation, characteristics, and features.

7. Use Boolean algebra and Karnaugh maps to express logic operations and minimize logic equations.

8. Explain the operation of flip-flops.

9. Discuss the operation and application of binary and BCD counters, shift registers, and other sequential logic circuits.

10. Name the most frequently used combinational logic circuits and explain their operation.

11. Design both combinational and sequential logic circuits for a given application, from definition and concept, to the selection of the integrated circuits.

12. Identify the various types of semiconductor memories (RAMs, ROMs, EPROMS, etc.), explain how they operate and give examples as to how they are used.

13. Name the various types of data conversion such as digital-to-analog converters, analog-to-digital converts, multiplexers, and sample/hold circuits. Tell how they operate and give examples of their application.

14. Troubleshoot digital circuits using standard test equipment and special instruments such as logic probes, logic and signature analyzers.

Course Outline

Unit 1
Introduction to Digital Techniques

- Introduction
- Unit Objectives
- Digital Techniques
  - Contrasting Analog and Digital Devices and Techniques
  - Where are Digital Techniques Used?
  - Why Use Digital Techniques?
- Number Systems
  - Decimal Number System
  - Binary Number System
  - Octal Number System
  - Hexadecimal Number System
  - Converting Between the Binary and Decimal Number Systems
  - Conversion From Decimal to Hexadecimal
  - Converting Between the Hexadecimal and Binary Number Systems
- Binary Arithmetic
  - Binary Addition
  - Binary Subtraction
  - Binary Multiplication
  - Binary Division
  - Representing Negative Numbers
  - Two's Complement Arithmetic
    - Ten's Complement Arithmetic
    - Two's Complement Subtraction
- Binary Codes
  - Binary Coded Decimal
  - Gray Code
  - ASCII Code
- Data Representation
  - Electromechanical Devices
  - Transistors
  - Logic Levels
  - Positive and Negative Logic
  - Parallel vs Serial Data Representation
- Appendix — Table of Powers of 2

Unit 2
Semiconductor Devices For Digital Circuits

- Introduction
- Unit Objectives
- The Bipolar Transistor Switch
    - Modes of Operation
        - Cut-off
        - Linear
        - Saturation
    - Saturated Switching Circuits
    - Switching Speed
    - Non-Saturating Switching Circuits
- Designing a Saturated Switch Logic Inverter
    - Procedure
    - Example Application 1
    - Example Application 2
- MOS Field-Effect Transistors (MOSFETs)
    - The N-Channel MOSFET
    - The P-Channel MOSFET
    - Bipolars vs MOSFET's
    - MOSFET Circuits

Unit 3
Digital Logic Circuits

- Introduction
- Unit Objectives
- Types of Logic Circuits
- The Inverter
- Decision-Making Logic Elements
    - The AND Gate
    - The OR Gate
- The Dual Nature of Logic Gates
- NAND/NOR Gates
    - NAND Gate
    - NOR Gate
    - How NAND/NOR Gates Are Used
- Practical Logic Circuits
    - Relays and switches
    - Discrete Component Logic Circuits
    - Integrated Circuits
- Appendix Positive and Negative
    - Logic Equivalent Circuits

Unit 4
Digital Integrated Circuits

- Introduction
- Unit Objectives
- Logic Circuit Characteristics
  - Logic Levels
  - Propagation Delay
  - Power Dissipation
  - The Speed-Power Trade-Off
  - Noise Immunity
  - Fan Out
- Integrated Circuits
  - Manufacturing Methods
    - Monolithic
    - Thin and Thick Film Techniques
    - Hybrid Circuits
  - Application
  - Function
  - Integrated Circuit Packaging
    - TO5
    - Flat-Pack
    - DIP
  - Temperature Ranges
- Transistor–Transistor Logic (TTL)
  - Circuit Operation
  - Special TTL Variations
    - Low Power TTL
    - High Speed TTL
    - Schottky TTL
    - Three State TTL and Data Busses
- Emitter–Coupled Logic (ECL)
  - Circuit Operation
  - Circuit Characteristics
- Metal Oxide Semiconductor Integrated Circuits (MOS)
  - PMOS and NMOS Circuits
  - Complementary MOS (CMOS)
- Integrated Injection Logic
  - Circuit Description
  - Characteristics and Application
- Selecting a Digital Integrated Circuit for a Specific Application
  - Trends
  - Complex Functions
  - Trade-Offs

Unit 5
Boolean Algebra

- Introduction
- Unit Objectives
- Relating Digital Logic Circuits and Boolean Equations
  - Review of Basic Functions
  - Boolean Formats
  - Sum-of-Products
  - Product-of-Sums
  - Relating Circuits and Equations
- Truth Tables
- Boolean Rules
- DeMorgan's Theorem
- Minimizing Logic Circuits
- Using NAND/NOR Gates
- NOR Logic Equivalent Circuits
- NAND Logic Equivalent Circuits
- Rules of Boolean-Summary
- Karnaugh Mapping
  - Two Input Variables
  - Three Input Variables
  - Four Input Variables
  - "Don't Care" States

Unit 6
Flip-Flops and Registers

- Introduction
- Unit Objectives
- RS Flip-Flops
- D Flip-Flops
  - Storage Registers
- JK Flip-Flops

Unit 7

Sequential Logic Circuits: Counters, Shift Registers, And Clocks

- Introduction
- Unit Objectives
- Counters
  - Binary Counters
    - Frequency Dividers
    - Maximum Count
    - Down Counters
    - Up-Down Counter
    - Synchronous Counters
    - Counter Control Functions
  - Typical Integrated Circuit Counters
  - BCD Counters
    - Cascading BCD Counters
    - The BCD Counter as a Frequency Divider
    - Typical Integrated Circuit BCD Counter
  - Special Counters
    - Modulo 3 Counter
    - Modulo 5 Counter
    - Modulo N Counter with MSI
- Shift Registers
  - Shift Register Operation
  - Bipolar Logic Shift Registers
  - Shift Register Applications
    - Serial-to-Parallel Conversion
    - Scaling Operations
    - Shift Register Memory
    - Sequencer/Ring Counter
    - Counters
  - MOS Shift Registers
    - Dynamic MOS Shift Registers
    - Static MOS Shift Registers
- Clocks and One Shots
  - Clock Oscillator Circuits
    - Discrete Component Circuits
    - IC Clock Circuits
    - Two-Phase Clocks
  - One-Shot Multivibrators
    - Discrete Component One-Shot Circuit
    - Integrated One-Shots
  - One-Shot Applications

Unit 8
Combinational Logic Circuits

- Introduction
- Unit Objectives
- Decoders
    - BCD to Decimal Decoder
    - Octal and Hex Decoders
    - BCD to 7-Segment Decoder
- Encoders
- Multiplexers
    - Multiplexers Operation
    - Multiplexer Applications
        - Parallel to Serial Conversion
        - Serial Binary Word Generator
        - Boolean Function Generator
- Demultiplexers
- Exclusive OR
    - Exclusive NOR
    - Applications of the Exclusive OR
        - Binary Adder
        - Parity Generator/Checker
        - Binary Comparators
- Code Converters
- Read Only Memories (ROMs)
    - ROM Operation
    - ROM Construction
        - Diode Matrix ROM
        - Bipolar ROM
        - MOS ROM's
        - Access Time
    - ROM Applications
        - Random Logic
        - Code Conversion
        - Arithmetic Operations
    - Microprogramming
- Programmable Logic Arrays

Unit 9
Semiconductor Memories

Introduction
Unit Objectives
Memory Types and Organization
- Memory Classification
- Memory Organization
  - Sequential Access
  - Random Access

Memory Characteristics and Specifications
- Volatility
- Access Time
- Memory Size
- Memory Configuration
- Device Technology

Read/Write Memories
- Static Memories
  - Read
  - Write
  - Comparing Bipolar and MOS RAMs
  - Static RAM Organization
  - Alternate Organizations
  - Typical Memory Configurations
- Dynamic Memories
  - Dynamic Cells
  - Three Transistor Cell
  - One Transistor Cell
  - Dynamic RAM Organization
    - Read Operation
    - Write Operation
    - Refresh
  - 64K and Larger Dynamic RAMs

Programmable Read Only Memories (PROMs)
- Bipolar PROMs
  - Nichrome Fuse
  - Silicon Fuse
  - Typical Bipolar PROMs
- MOS PROMs
  - Light Erasable PROM
  - Electrically Erasable PROM
  - PROM Programmers

Unit 10
Data Conversion

Introduction
Unit Objectives
Purpose of Data Conversion
Digital-to-Analog Conversion (DAC)
- Binary Weighted Resistor DAC
- Improved Weighted Resistor DAC
- R/2R Ladder DAC
- Typical DACs
- DAC Specifications and Error Sources
- Multiplying DACs

Analog-to-Digital Conversion (ADC)
- Comparators
- Counter-Ramp Feedback ADC
- Successive Approximation Converter
- Flash Converter
- Dual Slope ADC
- Voltage-to-Frequency Conversion
- ADC Specifications
- Sampling and Multiplexing

Unit 11
Digital Troubleshooting

Introduction
Unit Objectives
Typical Problems in Digital Circuits
- Operator Problems
- Construction Problems
- Defective Components
- Mechanical Problems
- Power Supplies
- Timing Problems
- Environmental Problems
- Noise
- Design Errors
- Software

Digital IC Problems
- External IC Problems
- Internal IC Problems

Digital Test Instruments
- Multimeters
- Oscilloscopes
- Logic Clips and Monitors
- Logic Probe
- Logic Pulser
- Current Tracer
- Logic Analyzers
- Signature Analyzer

Procedures for Digital Troubleshooting
- Data Collection
- Isolating the Problem
- Making the Repair
- Testing

Unit 1
Introduction to Digital Techniques

Contents

Introduction 1-3

Unit Objectives 1-5

Digital Techniques 1-6

Number Systems 1-13

Binary Arithmetic 1-32

Binary Codes 1-49

Data Representation 1-57

Summary 1-65

Introduction

Digital techniques are an integral part of our modern society. Digital systems are used extensively in our homes and communities, indeed, everywhere you look you can find some application of digital techniques.

You are familiar with the decimal number system and use it every day. Other number systems, however, are used in digital systems and you must become familiar with these systems. They include Binary, Octal, and Hexadecimal. By the time you finish this unit, you will be familiar with each of these number systems. In addition, you will learn how to convert between the systems.

In many digital applications, decimal numbers and some special characters are *coded* into some type of binary code. The type of code used depends on the application. Four binary codes are described—Pure Binary Code, Binary Coded Decimal, Gray Code, and the American Standard Code for Information Interchange (ASCII).

After you learn the basics of binary number systems and codes, we'll show you how they are used by the electronic components within a digital circuit.

Examine the Unit Objectives listed in the next section to see what you will learn in this unit.

Unit Objectives

When you complete this Unit you will have the following knowledge and capabilities:

1. You will be able to distinguish between analog and digital signals.

2. You will be able to list at least five examples of areas using digital techniques.

3. You will be able to distinguish between the four number systems—decimal, binary, octal, and hexadecimal.

4. Given any number, you will be able to convert it to its equivalent in another number system.

5. Given any two binary numbers, you will be able to add, subtract, multiply or divide them.

6. Given any decimal number, you will be able to convert it into its binary coded decimal (BCD) equivalent.

7. Given a BCD number you will be able to convert it into its decimal equivalent.

8. You will be able to list four popular digital codes.

9. You will be able to list the two key ways binary data is represented with digital hardware.

10. You will be able to list the advantages and disadvantages of both serial and parallel methods of binary data transmission.

11. You will be able to identify binary signals as being either positive or negative logic.

There are two basic types of electronic signals and techniques, analog and digital. Analog signals are the most familiar type. An analog signal is an AC or DC voltage or current that varies smoothly or continuously. It is one that does not change abruptly or in steps. An analog signal can exist in a wide variety of forms. Several types of analog signals are shown in Figure 1-1.

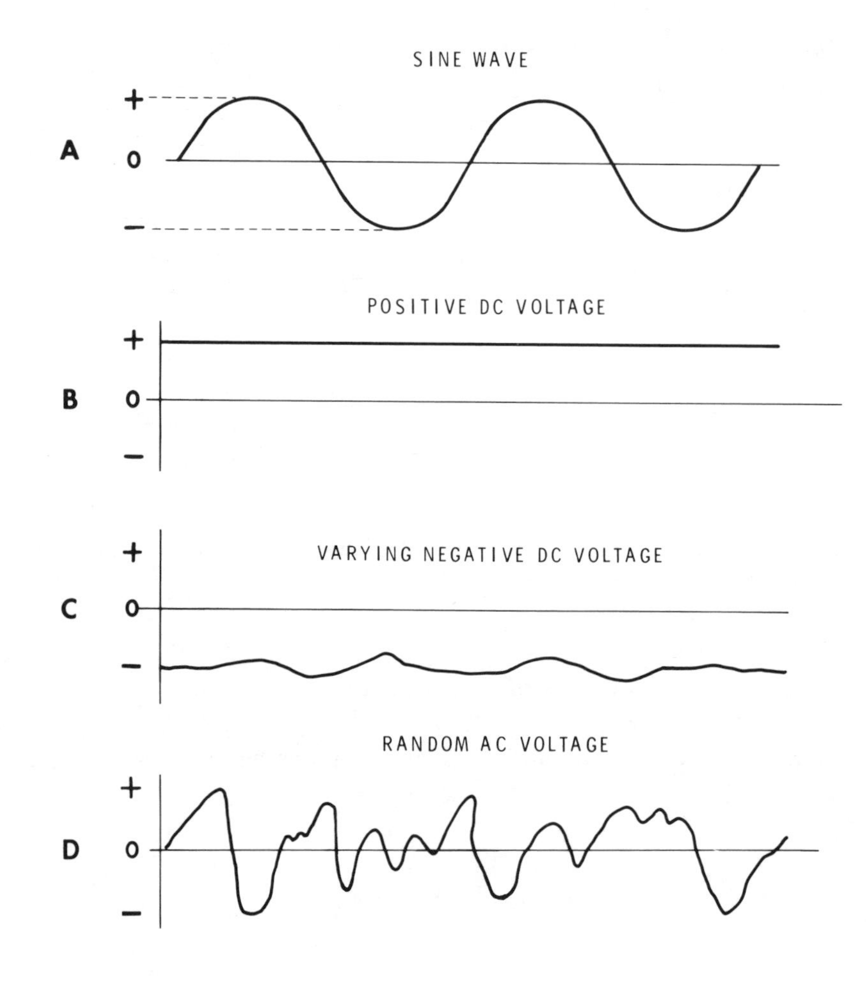

Figure 1-1
Types of Analog signals.

Figure 1-1A shows the most common type of analog signal, a sine wave. A significant number of electronic signals are sinusoidal. Radio signals and audio tones are examples. A fixed DC voltage is also an analog signal. Figure 1-1B shows a constant positive DC voltage. Another type of analog signal is a varying DC voltage or current. A changing negative DC voltage is illustrated in Figure 1-1C. Any random but continuously varying voltage waveform is considered to be analog. The signal shown in Figure 1-1D is only one of an infinite variety of such signals. Electronic circuits that process these analog signals are called linear circuits.

Digital signals are essentially a series of pulses or rapidly changing voltage levels that vary in discrete steps or increments. Digital signals are pulses of voltage that usually switch between two fixed levels. Figure 1-2 shows several types of digital signals. Notice how these signals switch between two distinct voltage levels. In Figure 1-2A, the two levels are 0 (ground) and +5 volts. In Figure 1-2B, the levels are 0 (ground) and –6 volts. In Figure 1-2C the signal alternates between the +3 and –3 volt levels. This two-level, off-on or up-down fast switching characteristic is fundamental of all digital signals. Electronic circuits that process these digital signals are called digital, logic, or pulse circuits.

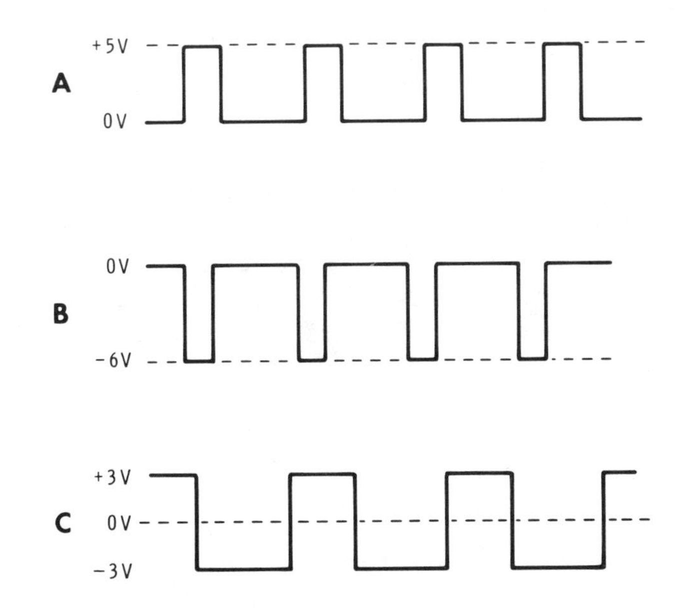

Figure 1-2
Types of Digital signals.

Contrasting Analog and Digital Devices and Techniques

Now let's further define analog and digital methods in terms of devices and ideas that are already quite familiar to you. For example, a light bulb can be either an analog or digital device depending upon how it is used. The amount of current through a light bulb can be set to any level less than its maximum rated value. We can vary the current through it continuously and its brightness will vary. Used in this way the light bulb is an analog device. The brilliance of the lamp is proportional to the current through it. There are virtually an infinite number of brightness levels.

The lamp can also be used as a digital device where the current through it and its brightness varies in discrete steps. The most common way of using the light bulb as a digital device is to give it two brilliance levels, usually off and on. The important point is that the lamp has two states. Because of this off-on characteristic, we say that the lamp is binary in nature. The term binary designates any two-state device or signal.

Another example of an analog device is a typical clock or watch. It indicates the time continuously by the positions of the hands on a calibrated dial. The second hand sweeps smoothly and continuously around in an analog fashion as do both hour and minute hands. To determine the exact time, you must estimate the positions of the hands. Your ability to read the time accurately is limited by the precision of the dial calibration increments. Digital clocks overcome this problem. On a digital clock, you read the time directly from decimal number display readouts in discrete increments of hours, minutes and seconds. The accuracy is greatly improved and you gain the added convenience of a direct number display.

Where Are Digital Techniques Used?

Perhaps the greatest use of digital techniques today is in computers. Digital computers are used in virtually all areas of business and industry. They are extremely useful machines that can save man a tremendous amount of effort and greatly extend his capabilities.

A typical microcomputer.

Over the years digital computers have grown in capability, but have become smaller, cheaper and easier to use. As a result, their use has increased tremendously. The small, low-cost but very powerful microcomputer has put digital and computer techniques within the reach of nearly everyone. A microcomputer can be quickly and easily designed into a system to replace more conventional equipment and circuitry for control, computation and automation.

Advanced semiconductor technology has given us a component known as a microprocessor. These microprocessors are complete digital computers in a single miniature integrated circuit package. Microprocessors can often be used to replace conventional digital circuits. Like all digital computers, the microprocessor must be programmed to carry out its specified function.

Digital techniques are employed in almost every imaginable area. Communications, transportation, banking, business, medicine, stores, schools, factories—all use digital techniques in one way or another. Even in your own home there are several items that are digital in nature. Of course, stereo and television equipment have become digitized. Most major appliances are now using digital techniques. Security systems, energy management systems, computerized shopping, banking, meal planning, stock market portfolio management—the list is nearly endless.

Why Use Digital Techniques?

The primary reason for the widespread use of digital techniques has been the availability of low cost, digital integrated circuits (ICs). Advances in integrated circuit technology have produced many excellent low cost digital circuits. Such circuits are small, inexpensive and very reliable. Medium scale and large scale (MSI and LSI) integrated devices can replace entire circuits and instruments. Electronic equipment designers recognize the availability of such devices and have begun to take advantage of them. While digital techniques have been known for years, it took integrated circuits to make them practical.

By using digital IC's many equipment improvements have been made. Reductions in size, weight, cost and power consumption usually result when analog techniques are replaced by digital methods.

A large scale integrated circuit.
(Photo courtesy MOSTEK.)

Self-Test Review

1. Analog Signals vary ______________ while digital signals vary in ____________.

2. Turning a lamp on and off is using it as a _______________ device.

3. How many discrete voltage levels do most digital signals have?
____

4. The most widespread use of digital techniques is in ____________ .

5. List 3 advantages of digital methods over analog techniques.

   a. ____
   b. ____
   c. ____

6. The single factor most influential in the increased use of digital techniques was the:

   a. recognition of the deficiencies in analog methods.
   b. development of integrated circuits.
   c. discovery of digital methods.
   d. developments resulting from the space program.

7. A constant DC voltage is:

   a. an analog signal.
   b. a digital signal.
   c. either a. or b. depending upon how it is defined.

8. The waveform below is:

   a. analog.
   b. digital.

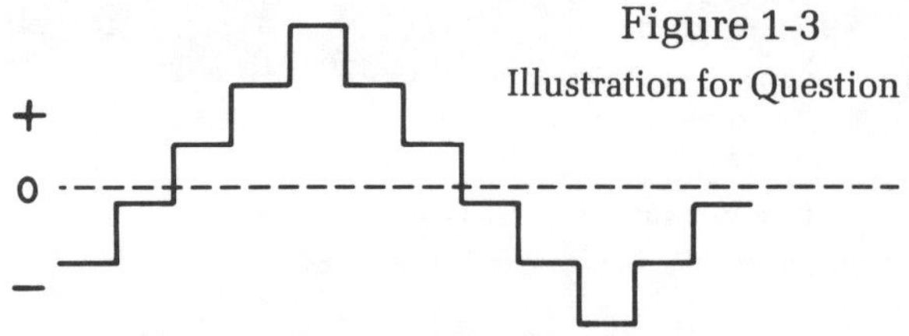

+
0
–

Figure 1-3
Illustration for Question 8.

Number Systems

All digital circuits, instruments, and systems work with numbers that represent specific quantities. For example, the analog voltage measured by a digital voltmeter is converted into digital form and displayed as a specific decimal number. The number that you enter into an electronic calculator is stored and used in the calculation you specify. The digital computer that prints your payroll check works with numbers, specifically your salary, the number of hours you work and the various deductions. As you can see, numbers or quantities are the basic source for an end product of most digital equipment. Figure 1-4 shows how most digital equipment accepts input numbers, processes them and generates number outputs. The actual form of the input and output numbers depends on the application. They may be in a binary, decimal, octal, or hexadecimal form. In some applications the input and/or output may be in analog form despite the digital processing.

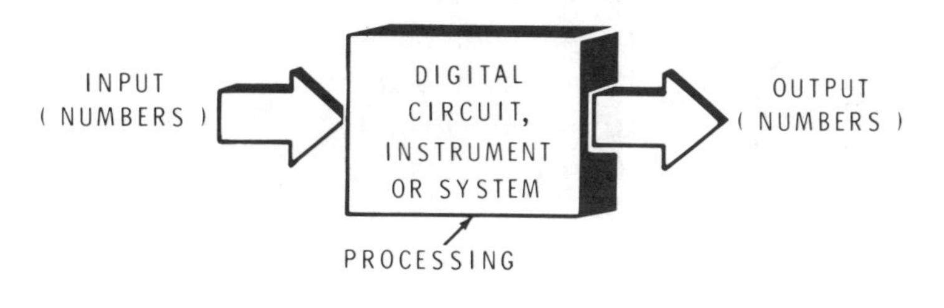

Figure 1-4

A general block diagram of any digital system.

Decimal Number System

A basic distinguishing feature of a number system is its **base** or **radix**. The base indicates the number of characters or digits used to represent quantities in that number system. The decimal number system has a base or radix of 10 because we use the ten digits 0 through 9 to represent quantities. When a number system is used where the base is not known, a subscript is used to show the base. For example, the number 4603_{10} is derived from a number system with a base of 10.

Positional Notation

The decimal number system is positional or weighted. This means each digit position in a number carriers a particular weight which determines the magnitude of that number. Each position has a weight determined by some power of the number system base, in this case 10. The positional weights are 10^0 (units)*, 10^1 (tens), 10^2 (hundreds), etc. Refer to Figure 1-5 for a condensed listing of powers of 10.

$$
\begin{aligned}
10^0 &= 1 \\
10^1 &= 10 \\
10^2 &= 100 \\
10^3 &= 1{,}000 \\
10^4 &= 10{,}000 \\
10^5 &= 100{,}000 \\
10^6 &= 1{,}000{,}000 \\
10^7 &= 10{,}000{,}000 \\
10^8 &= 100{,}000{,}000 \\
10^9 &= 1{,}000{,}000{,}000
\end{aligned}
$$

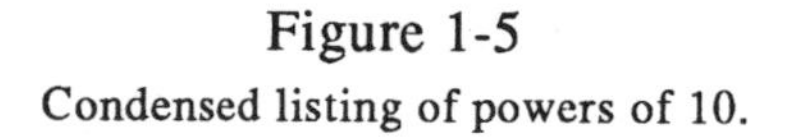

Figure 1-5
Condensed listing of powers of 10.

We evaluate the total quantity of a number by considering the specific digits and the weights of their positions. For example, the decimal number 4603 is written in the shorthand notation with which we are all familiar. This number can also be expressed with positional notation.

$$
\begin{aligned}
&(4 \times 10^3) + (6 \times 10^2) + (0 \times 10^1) + (3 \times 10^0) = \\
&(4 \times 1000) + (6 \times 100) + (0 \times 10) + (3 \times 1) = \\
&4000 + 600 + 0 + 3 = 4603_{10}
\end{aligned}
$$

To determine the value of a number, multiply each digit by the weight of its position and add the results.

*Any number with an exponent of zero is equal to one.

Fractional Numbers

So far, only **integer** or whole numbers have been discussed. An integer is any of the natural numbers, the negatives of these numbers, or zero (that is, 0, 1, 4, 7, etc.). Thus, an integer represents a whole or complete number. But, it is often necessary to express quantities in terms of fractional parts of a whole number.

Decimal fractions are numbers whose positions have weights that are

negative powers of ten such as $10^{-1} = \frac{1}{10} = 0.1$, $10^{-2} = \frac{1}{100} = 0.01$, etc.

Figure 1-6 provides a condensed listing of negative powers of 10 (decimal fractions).

$$10^{-1} = \frac{1}{10} = 0.1$$

$$10^{-2} = \frac{1}{100} = 0.01$$

$$10^{-3} = \frac{1}{1000} = 0.001$$

$$10^{-4} = \frac{1}{10{,}000} = 0.0001$$

$$10^{-5} = \frac{1}{100{,}000} = 0.00001$$

$$10^{-6} = \frac{1}{1{,}000{,}000} = 0.000001$$

Figure 1-6
Condensed listing of negative powers of 10.

A radix point (decimal point for base 10 numbers) separates the integer and fractional parts of a number. The integer or whole portion is to the left of the decimal point and has positional weights of units, tens, hundreds, etc. The fractional part of the number is to the right of the decimal point and has positional weights of tenths, hundredths, thousandths, etc. To illustrate this, the decimal number 278.94 can be written with positional notation as shown below.

$$(2 \times 10^2) + (7 \times 10^1) + (8 \times 10^0) + (9 \times 10^{-1}) + (4 \times 10^{-2}) =$$
$$(2 \times 100) + (7 \times 10) + (8 \times 1) + (9 \times 1/10) + (4 \times 1/100) =$$
$$200 + 70 + 8 + 0.9 + 0.04 = 278.94_{10}$$

In this example, the left-most digit (2×10^2) is the **most significant digit** or MSD because it carries the greatest weight in determining the value of the number. The right-most digit, called the **least significant digit** or LSD, has the lowest weight in determining the value of the number.

Binary Number System

The simplest number system that uses positional notation is the binary number system. As the name implies, a **binary** system contains only two elements or states. In a number system this is expressed as a base of 2, using the digits 0 and 1. These two digits have the same basic value as 0 and 1 in the decimal number system.

Positional Notation

As with the decimal number system, each bit (digit) position of a binary number carriers a particular weight which determines the magnitude of that number. The weight of each position is determined by some power of the number system base (in this example, 2). To evaluate the total quantity of a number, consider the specific bits and the weights of their positions. (Refer to Figure 1-7 for a condensed listing of powers of 2.) For example, the binary number 110101 can be written with positional notation as follows:

$$(1 \times 2^5) + (1 \times 2^4) + (0 \times 2^3) + (1 \times 2^2) + (0 \times 2^1) + (1 \times 2^0)$$

To determine the decimal value of the binary number 110101, multiply each bit by its positional weight and add the results.

$$(1 \times 32) + (1 \times 16) + (0 \times 8) + (1 \times 4) + (0 \times 2) + (1 \times 1) =$$
$$32 + 16 + 0 + 4 + 0 + 1 = 53_{10}$$

$2^0 = 1_{10}$	$2^6 = 64_{10}$
$2^1 = 2_{10}$	$2^7 = 128_{10}$
$2^2 = 4_{10}$	$2^8 = 256_{10}$
$2^3 = 8_{10}$	$2^9 = 512_{10}$
$2^4 = 16_{10}$	$2^{10} = 1024_{10}$
$2^5 = 32_{10}$	$2^{11} = 2048_{10}$

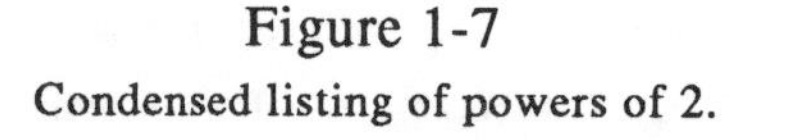

Figure 1-7
Condensed listing of powers of 2.

Fractional binary numbers are expressed as negative powers of 2. Figure 1-8 provides a condensed listing of negative powers of 2. In positional notation, the binary number 0.1101 can be expressed as follows:

$$(1 \times 2^{-1}) + (1 \times 2^{-2}) + (0 \times 2^{-3}) + (1 \times 2^{-4})$$

To determine the decimal value of the binary number 0.1101, multiply each bit by its positional weight and add the results.

$$(1 \times 1/2) + (1 \times 1/4) + (0 \times 1/8) + (1 \times 1/16) =$$
$$0.5 + 0.25 + 0 + 0.0625 = 0.8125_{10}$$

In the binary number system, the radix point is called the binary point.

$$2^{-1} = \frac{1}{2} = 0.5_{10}$$
$$2^{-2} = \frac{1}{4} = 0.25_{10}$$
$$2^{-3} = \frac{1}{8} = 0.125_{10}$$
$$2^{-4} = \frac{1}{16} = 0.0625_{10}$$
$$2^{-5} = \frac{1}{32} = 0.03125_{10}$$
$$2^{-6} = \frac{1}{64} = 0.015625_{10}$$
$$2^{-7} = \frac{1}{128} = 0.0078125_{10}$$
$$2^{-8} = \frac{1}{256} = 0.00390625_{10}$$

Figure 1-8
Condensed listing of negative powers of 2.

Binary Number Sizes

Binary numbers are also referred to as binary words. An 8-bit binary number is also an 8-bit word. You will also see the term byte used to refer to binary words. Most digital circuits and equipment use a fixed word size. The size of this word determines the maximum magnitude and resolution with which numbers can be represented. The number of bits in a word determine the number of discrete states that can exist and the maximum decimal number value that can be represented.

The formula below indicates the number of states that can be represented with a given number of bits.

$N = 2^n$ N = total number of states.
n = number of bits in the word.

For example, with a 4-bit word, we can represent a maximum of

$$N = 2^n = 2^4 = 2 \times 2 \times 2 \times 2 = 16$$

This means that by using 4-bit positions, we can create a total of 16 different binary bit patterns or number combinations. These are shown in Table I along with their decimal equivalents.

TABLE I

DECIMAL	BINARY
0	0000
1	0001
2	0010
3	0011
4	0100
5	0101
6	0110
7	0111
8	1000
9	1001
10	1010
11	1011
12	1100
13	1101
14	1110
15	1111

Binary and decimal number equivalents for a 4-bit word.

As Table 1 indicates, we represent the numbers 0 through 15 using the binary number weighting [illegible]. The maximum decimal number that can be represented is one less than the total number of states. The largest decimal number value (N) that can be represented for a given number of bits (n) is expressed with the formula below.

$$N = 2^n - 1$$

For example, with a 6-bit number we can represent a maximum value of:

$$N = 2^6 - 1 = 64 - 1 = 63$$

If you know the maximum decimal quantity (N) that you wish to represent with a binary number, you can determine the required number of bits (B) with the expression given below.

$$B = 3.32 \log_{10}(N + 1)$$

The common logarithm can be obtained from a set of tables, a slide rule or an electronic calculator with log capability. For example, if the maximum decimal number that you need to represent is 500, the number of bits required is:

$$B = 3.32 \log_{10}(500 + 1)$$
$$B = 3.32 \log_{10}501$$
$$B = 3.32\ (2.6998377)$$
$$B = 8.96$$

Of course, you cannot implement fractional bits so the total number of bits required is the next highest whole number. Therefore, to represent the number 500, you would need a total of nine bits. Using the previously given expression, you can determine that, with a total of nine bits, the maximum number you can represent is:

$$N = 2^n - 1 = 2^9 - 1 = 512 - 1 = 511$$

The Appendix at the end of this unit contains a table of numbers that are powers of 2. It will help you to quickly determine the relationship between decimal number size and binary word bit length.

Octal Number System

Octal is another number system that is often used with microprocessors. It has a base (radix) of 8, and uses the digits 0 through 7. These eight digits have the same basic value as the digits 0 through 7 in the decimal number system.

Positional Notation

As with the binary number system, each digit position of an octal number carries a positional weight which determines the magnitude of that number. The weight of each position is determined by some power of the number system base (in this example, 8). To evaluate the total quantity of a number, consider the specific digits and the weights of their positions. Refer to Figure 1-9 for a condensed listing of powers of 8. For example, the octal number 372.01 can be written with positional notation as follows:

$$(3 \times 8^2) + (7 \times 8^1) + (2 \times 8^0) + (0 \times 8^{-1}) + (1 \times 8^{-2})$$

The decimal value of the octal number 372.01 is determined by multiplying each digit by its positional weight and adding the results. As with decimal and binary numbers, the radix (octal) point separates the integer from the fractional part of the number.

$$(3 \times 64) + (7 \times 8) + (2 \times 1) + (0 \times 0.125) + (1 \times 0.015625) =$$
$$192 + 56 + 2 + 0 + 0.015625 = 250.015625_{10}$$

$$8^{-4} = \frac{1}{4096} = 0.000244140625_{10}$$

$$8^{-3} = \frac{1}{512} = 0.001953125_{10}$$

$$8^{-2} = \frac{1}{64} = 0.015625_{10}$$

$$8^{-1} = \frac{1}{8} = 0.125_{10}$$

$$1_{10} = 8^0$$
$$8_{10} = 8^1$$
$$64_{10} = 8^2$$
$$512_{10} = 8^3$$
$$4096_{10} = 8^4$$
$$32768_{10} = 8^5$$
$$262144_{10} = 8^6$$

Figure 1-9
Condensed listing of powers of 8.

Since the octal number system is not in widespread use anymore, it will not be described in further detail.

Hexadecimal Number System

Hexadecimal is another number system that is often used with microprocessors. As the name implies, hexadecimal has a base (radix) of 16_{10}. It uses the digits 0 through 9 and the letters A through F.

The letters are used because it is necessary to represent 16_{10} different values with a single digit for each value. Therefore, the letters A through F are used to represent the number values 10_{10} through 15_{10}. The following discussion will compare the decimal number system with the hexadecimal number system.

All of the numbers 0 through 9 are of equal value between systems ($0_{10} = 0_{16}$, $3_{10} = 3_{16}$, $9_{10} = 9_{16}$, etc.). For numbers greater than 9, this relationship exists: $10_{10} = A_{16}$, $11_{10} = B_{16}$, $12_{10} = C_{16}$, $13_{10} = D_{16}$, $14_{10} = E_{16}$, and $15_{10} = F_{16}$. Using letters in counting may appear awkward until you become familiar with the system. Figure 1-10 illustrates the relationship between decimal, hexadecimal, and binary integers, while Figure 1-11 illustrates the relationship between decimal, hexadecimal, and binary fractions.

DECIMAL	HEXADECIMAL	BINARY
0	0	0
1	1	1
2	2	10
3	3	11
4	4	100
5	5	101
6	6	110
7	7	111
8	8	1000
9	9	1001
10	A	1010
11	B	1011
12	C	1100
13	D	1101
14	E	1110
15	F	1111
16	10	10000

Figure 1-10

Sample comparison of decimal, hexadecimal, and binary integers.

DECIMAL	HEXADECIMAL	BINARY
0.00390625	0.01	0.00000001
0.0078125	0.02	0.0000001
0.01171875	0.03	0.00000011
0.015625	0.04	0.000001
0.01953125	0.05	0.00000101
0.0234375	0.06	0.0000011
0.02734375	0.07	0.00000111
0.03125	0.08	0.00001
0.03515625	0.09	0.00001001
0.0390625	0.0A	0.0000101
0.04296875	0.0B	0.00001011
0.046875	0.0C	0.00001100
0.05078125	0.0D	0.00001101
0.0546875	0.0E	0.0000111
0.05859375	0.0F	0.00001111

Figure 1-11
Sample comparison of decimal, hexadecimal, and binary fractions.

As with the previous number systems, each digit position of a hexadecimal number carries a positional weight which determines the magnitude of that number. The weight of each position is determined by some power of the number system base (in this example, 16_{10}). The total quantity of a number can be evaluated by considering the specific digits and the weights of their positions. (Refer to Figure 1-12 for a condensed listing of powers of 16_{10}.) For example, the hexadecimal number E5D7.A3 can be written with positional notation as follows:

$$(E \times 16^3) + (5 \times 16^2) + (D \times 16^1) + (7 \times 16^0) + (A \times 16^{-1}) + (3 \times 16^{-2})$$

The decimal value of the hexadecimal number E5D7.A3 is determined by multiplying each digit by its positional weight and adding the results. As with the previous number systems, the radix (hexadecimal) point separates the integer from the fractional part of the number.

$$(14 \times 4096) + (5 \times 256) + (13 \times 16) + (7 \times 1) + (10 \times 1/16) + (3 \times 1/256) =$$
$$57344 + 1280 + 208 + 7 + 0.625 + 0.01171875 =$$
$$58839.63671875_{10}$$

$$16^{-4} = \frac{1}{65536} = 0.0000152587890625_{10}$$

$$16^{-3} = \frac{1}{4096} = 0.000244140625_{10}$$

$$16^{-2} = \frac{1}{256} = 0.00390625_{10}$$

$$16^{-1} = \frac{1}{16} = 0.0625_{10}$$

$$1_{10} = 16^0$$
$$16_{10} = 16^1$$
$$256_{10} = 16^2$$
$$4096_{10} = 16^3$$
$$65536_{10} = 16^4$$
$$1048576_{10} = 16^5$$
$$16777216_{10} = 16^6$$

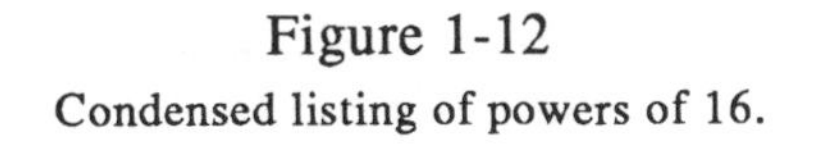

Figure 1-12
Condensed listing of powers of 16.

Converting Between The Binary and Decimal Number Systems

In working with digital equipment, you will often need to determine the decimal value of binary numbers. In addition, you will also find it necessary to convert a specific decimal number into its binary equivalent. Let's see how such conversions are accomplished.

Binary to Decimal

To convert a binary number into its decimal equivalent you simply add together the weights of the positions in the number where binary 1's occur. The weights of the integer and fractional positions are indicated below.

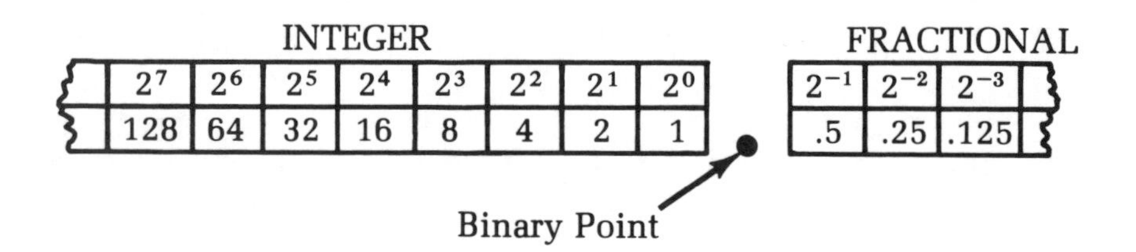

As an example, let's convert the binary number 1010 into its decimal equivalent. Since no binary point is shown, the number is assumed to be a whole number where the binary point is to the right of the number. The right-most bit, called the least significant bit or LSB, has the lowest integer weight of $2^0 = 1$. The left-most bit is the most significant bit (MSB) because it carries the greatest weight in determining the value of the number. In this example, it has a weight of $2^3 = 8$. To evaluate the number we add together the weights of the positions where binary 1's appear. In this example, 1's occur in the 2^3 and 2^1 positions. The decimal equivalent is ten.

Binary Number	1	0	1	0	
Position Weights	2^3	2^2	2^1	2^0	
Decimal Equivalent	8 +	0 +	2 +	0	= 10

As a further illustration of this process, let's convert the binary number 101101.11 into its decimal equivalent.

Binary Number	1	0	1	1	0	1	.1	1
Position Weights	2^5	2^4	2^3	2^2	2^1	2^0	2^{-1}	2^{-2}
Decimal Equivalent	32 +	0 +	8 +	4 +	0 +	1 +	.5 +	.25=45.75

Note that you can disregard the position weights where binary 0s occur since they add nothing to the number value.

After you solve a few practice problems, you will quickly catch on to this procedure.

Decimal to Binary

A decimal integer number can be converted to a different base or radix through successive divisions by the desired base. To convert a decimal integer number to its binary equivalent, successively divide the number by 2 and note the remainders. When you divide by 2, the remainder will always be 1 or 0.

The remainders form the equivalent binary number.

As an example, the decimal number 25 is converted into its binary equivalent.

$25 \div 2 = 12$	with remainder 1	←	LSB
$12 \div 2 = 6$	0		
$6 \div 2 = 3$	0		
$3 \div 2 = 1$	1		
$1 \div 2 = 0$	1	←	MSB

Divide the decimal number by 2 and note the remainder. Then divide the quotient by 2 and again note the remainder. Then divide the quotient by 2 and again note the remainder. Continue this division process until 0 results. Then collect remainders beginning with the last or most significant bit (MSB) and proceed to the first or least significant bit (LSB). The number $11001_2 = 25_{10}$. Notice that the remainders are collected in the reverse order. That is, the first remainder becomes the least significant bit, while the last remainder becomes the most significant bit.

To convert a decimal fraction to a different base or radix, multiply the fraction successively by the desired base and record any integers produced by the multiplication as an overflow. For example, to convert the decimal fraction 0.3125 into its binary equivalent, multiply repeatedly by 2.

$0.3125 \times 2 = 0.625 = 0.625$	with overflow 0	←	MSB
$0.6250 \times 2 = 1.250 = 0.250$	1		
$0.2500 \times 2 = 0.500 = 0.500$	0		
$0.5000 \times 2 = 1.000 = 0$	1	←	LSB

These multiplications will result in numbers with a 1 or 0 in the units position (the position to the left of the decimal point). By recording the value of the units position, you can construct the equivalent binary fraction. This units position value is called the "overflow." Therefore, when 0.3125 is multiplied by 2, the overflow is 0. This becomes the most significant bit (MSB) of the binary equivalent fraction. Then 0.625 is multiplied by 2. Since the product is 1.25, the overflow is 1. When there is an overflow of 1, it is effectively subtracted from the product when the value is recorded. Therefore, only 0.25 is multiplied by 2 in the next multiplication process. This method continues until an overflow with no fraction results. It is important to note that you can not always obtain 0 when you multiply by 2. Therefore, you should only continue the conversion process to the precision you desire. Collect the conversion overflows beginning at the radix (binary) point with the MSB and proceed to the LSB. This is the same order in which the overflows were produced. The number $0.0101_2 = 0.3125_{10}$.

If the decimal number contains both an integer and fraction, you must separate the integer and fraction using the decimal point as the break point. Then perform the appropriate conversion process on each number portion. After you convert the binary integer and binary fraction, recombine them. For example, the decimal number 14.375 is converted into its binary equivalent.

$14.375_{10} = 14_{10} + 0.375_{10}$

$14 \div 2 = 7$	with remainder	0	←	LSB
$7 \div 2 = 3$		1		
$3 \div 2 = 1$		1		
$1 \div 2 = 0$		1	←	MSB

$\boxed{14_{10} = 1110_2}$

$0.375 \times 2 = 0.75 = 0.75$	with overflow	0	←	MSB
$0.750 \times 2 = 1.50 = 0.50$		1		
$0.500 \times 2 = 1.00 = 0$		1	←	LSB

$\boxed{0.375_{10} = 0.011_2}$

$14.375_{10} = 14_{10} + 0.375_{10} = 1110_2 + 0.011_2 = 1110.011_2.$

Conversion From Decimal to Hexadecimal

Decimal to hexadecimal conversion is accomplished in the same manner as decimal to binary, but with a base number of 16_{10}. As an example, the decimal number 156 is converted into its hexadecimal equivalent.

$156 \div 16 = 9$	with remainder	$12 = C$	←	LSD
$9 \div 16 = 0$		$9 = 9$	←	MSD

Divide the decimal number by 16_{10} and note the remainder. If the remainder exceeds 9, convert the 2-digit number to its hexadecimal equivalent (12_{10} = C in this example). Then divide the quotient by 16 and again note the remainder. Continue dividing until a quotient of 0 results. Then collect the remainders beginning with the last or most significant digit (MSD) and proceed to the first or least significant digit (LSD). The number $9C_{16} = 156_{10}$. NOTE: The letter H after a number is sometimes used to indicate hexadecimal.

To convert a decimal fraction to a hexadecimal fraction, multiply the fraction successively by 16_{10} (hexadecimal base). As an example, the decimal fraction 0.78125 is converted into its hexadecimal equivalent.

$0.78125 \times 16 = 12.5 = 0.5$	with overflow	$12 = C$	←	MSD
$0.50000 \times 16 = 8.0 = 0$		$8 = 8$	←	LSD

Multiply the decimal by 16_{10}. If the product exceeds one, subtract the integer (overflow) from the product. If the "overflow" exceeds 9, convert the 2-digit number to its hexadecimal equivalent. Then multiply the product fraction by 16_{10} and again note any overflow. Continue multiplying until an overflow, with 0 for a fraction, results. Remember, you can not always obtain 0 when you multiply by 16. Therefore, you should only continue the conversion to the precision you desire. Collect the conversion overflows beginning at the radix point with the MSD and proceed to the LSD. The number $0.C8_{16} = 0.78125_{10}$.

As shown in this section, conversion of an integer from decimal to hexadecimal requires a different technique than for conversion of a fraction. Therefore, when you convert a hexadecimal number composed of an integer and a fraction, you must separate the integer and fraction, then perform the appropriate operation on each. After you convert them, you must recombine the integer and fraction. For example, the decimal number 124.78125 is converted into its hexadecimal equivalent.

$124.78125_{10} = 124_{10} + 0.78125_{10}$

$124 \div 16 = 7$	with remainder	$12 = C$	←	LSD
$7 \div 16 = 0$		$7 = 7$	←	MSD

$\boxed{124_{10} = 7C_{16}}$

$0.78125 \times 16 = 12.5 = 0.5$	overflow	$12 = C$	←	MSD
$0.50000 \times 16 = 8.0 = 0$		$8 = 8$	←	LSD

$\boxed{0.78125_{10} = 0.C8_{16}}$

$$124.78125_{10} = 124_{10} + 0.78125_{10} = 7C_{16} + 0.C8_{16} = 7C.C8_{16}$$

First separate the decimal integer and fraction. Then convert the integer and fraction to hexadecimal.

Finally, recombine the integer and fraction.

Converting Between the Hexadecimal and Binary Number Systems

The hexadecimal number system is an excellent shorthand form to express large binary quantities. Figures 1-10 and 1-11 illustrate the relationship between hexadecimal and binary integers and fractions.

As you know, four bits of a binary number exactly equal 16_{10} value combinations. Therefore, you can represent a 4-bit binary number with a 1-digit hexadecimal number:

$$1101_2 = (1 \times 2^3) + (1 \times 2^2) + (0 \times 2^1) + (1 \times 2^0) = 8 + 4 + 0 + 1 = 13_{10} = D_{16}$$

Because of this relationship, converting binary to hexadecimal is simple and straightforward. For example, binary number 10110110 is converted into its hexadecimal equivalent.

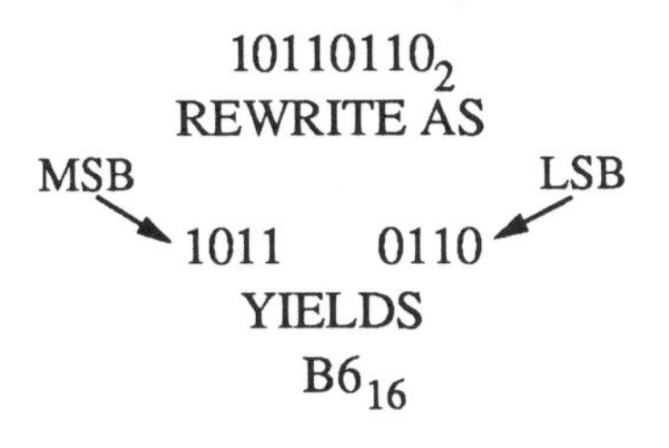

To convert a binary number to hexadecimal, first separate the number into groups containing four bits, beginning with the least significant bit. Then convert each 4-bit group into its hexadecimal equivalent. Don't forget to use letter digits as required. This gives you a hexadecimal number equal in value to the binary number.

Binary fractions can also be converted to their hexadecimal equivalents using the same process, with one exception; the binary bits are separated into groups of four, beginning with the most significant bit (at the radix point). For example, the binary fraction 0.01011011 is converted into its hexadecimal equivalent.

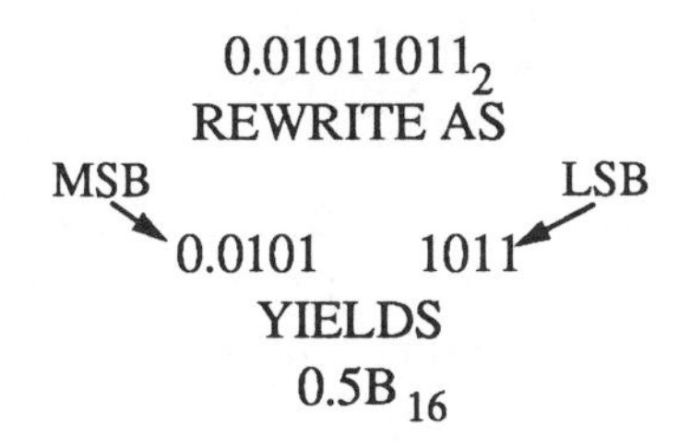

Again, you must separate the binary number into groups of four, beginning with the radix point. Then convert each 4-bit group into its hexadecimal equivalent. This gives you a hexadecimal number equal in value to the binary number.

Zeros may be added to fill out the binary number for calculation. However, when you add zeros to a binary integer, place them to the left of the MSB. In a binary fraction, zeros are placed to the right of the LSB. Never, under any circumstances, move the radix to perform conversion.

Now, a binary number containing both an integer and a fraction (110110101.01110111) will be converted into its hexadecimal equivalent.

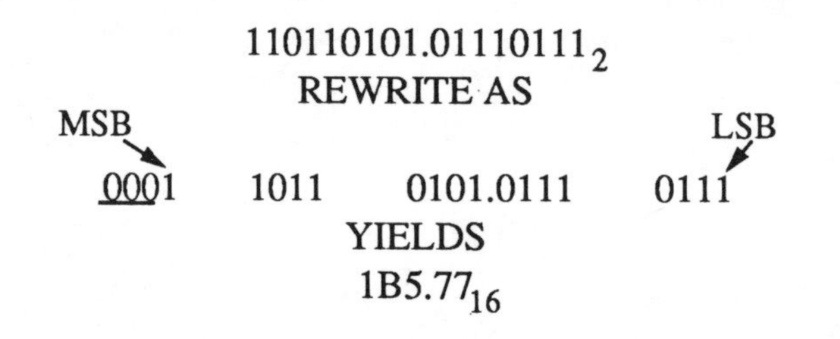

The integer part of the number is separated into groups of four, **beginning** at the radix point. Note that three zeros were added to the third group to complete the group. The fractional part of the number is separated into groups of four, **beginning** at the radix point. (No zeros were needed to complete the fractional groups.) The integer and fractional 4-bit groups are then converted to hexadecimal. The number $110110101.01110111_2 = 1B5.77_{16}$. **Never** shift the radix point in order to form 4-bit groups.

Converting hexadecimal to binary is just the opposite of the previous process; simply convert each hexadecimal number into its 4-bit binary equivalent. For example, convert the hexadecimal number 8F.41 into its binary equivalent.

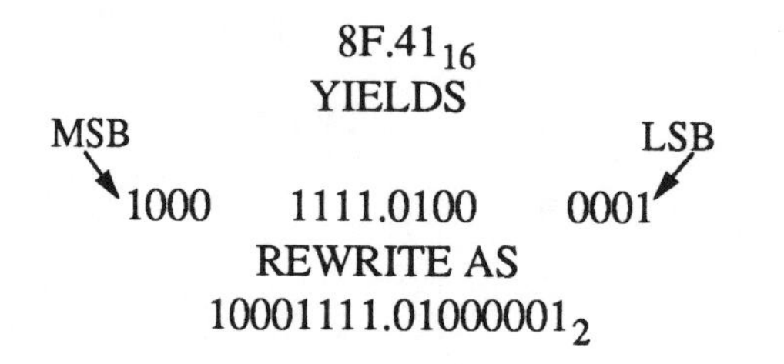

Convert each hexadecimal digit into a 4-bit binary number. Then condense the 4-bit groups to form the binary value equal to the hexadecimal value. The number $8F.41_{16} = 10001111.01000001_2$.

Self-Test Review

9. The radix of the binary number system is ________________.

10. What is the largest decimal number that can be represented with 8-bits?

11. How many discrete states can be represented with 6-bits?

12. How many bits does it take to represent the number 3875_{10} in binary?

13. What number system uses only the digits 0 through 7?

14. Convert the following:

    a. 100101101_2 to decimal. ____________________
    b. 11100.1001_2 to decimal. ____________________
    c. 22.62_{10} to binary. ____________________
    d. 764_{10} to binary. ____________________

15. Convert the following:

    a. $C73A.1E_{16}$ to decimal. ____________________
    b. $38DF_{16}$ to decimal. ____________________
    c. 581_{10} to hexadecimal. ____________________
    d. 68.57_{10} to hexadecimal ____________________

16. Convert the following:

    a. 1100101_2 to hexadecimal. ____________________
    b. 100.0110_2 to hexadecimal. ____________________
    c. $4C21_{16}$ to binary. ____________________
    d. $E72.A4_{16}$ to binary. ____________________

Binary Arithmetic

A number system can be used to perform two basic operations: addition and subtraction. But by using addition and subtraction, you can then perform multiplication, division, and any other numerical operation. For simplicity, we will use decimal arithmetic as a guide.

Binary Addition

Binary addition is performed somewhat like decimal addition. If two decimal numbers, 56719_{10} and 31863_{10} for example, are added together, the sum 88582_{10} is obtained. You can analyze the details of this operation in the following manner.

NOTE: In the following explanations, the term "first column" refers to the first column of figures you work with in the problem — the column on the right (9, 3, and 2 in the following example). The term "second column" refers to the second column you work with, etc.

Carry:	00101
Addend:	56719
Augend:	+ 31863
Sum:	88582

Adding the first column, decimal numbers 9 and 3, gives the sum of 12. This is expressed in the sum as the digit 2 with a carry of 1. The carry is then added to the next column. Adding the second column decimal numbers 1 and 6, and carry from the first column, 1, gives the sum of 8, with no carry. This process continues until all of the columns (including carries) have been added. The sum represents the numeric value of the addend and the augend. (The addend is the number to be added to another number, while the augend is the number to which the addend is added.)

When you add two binary numbers, you perform the same operation. The example below summarizes the four rules of addition with binary numbers.

1. 0 + 0 = 0
2. 0 + 1 = 1
3. 1 + 1 = 0 with a carry of 1
4. 1 + 1 + 1 = 1 with a carry of 1

To illustrate the process of binary addition, let's add 1101_2 to 1101_2.

Carry:	1101
Addend:	1101_2
Augend:	$+1101_2$
Sum:	11010_2

In the first column, 1 plus 1 equals 0 with a carry of 1 to the second column. This agrees with rule 3.

In the second column, 0 plus 0 equals 0 with no carry. The carry from the first column is added to this. Thus, 0 plus 1 equals 1 with no carry. These two additions in the second column give a total sum of 1 with a carry of 0. Rules 1 and 2 were used to obtain the sum.

In column three, 1 plus 1 equals 0 with a carry of 1. To this sum, the carry from the second column is added. This yields a third column sum of 0 with a carry of 1 to column four. Rules 3 and 1 were used to obtain the sum.

In column four, 1 plus 1 equals 0 with a carry of 1. To this sum, the carry from the third column is added. This yields a fourth column sum of 1 with a carry to the fifth column. Rule 4 allows you to add three binary 1's and obtain 1 with a carry of 1.

In column five, there is no addend or augend. Therefore, you can assume rule 2 and add the carry to obtain the sum of 1. Thus, the sum of 1101_2 plus 1101_2 equals 11010_2. You can verify this by converting the binary numbers to decimal numbers and adding.

Now study the following two examples of binary addition, where 10001111_2 is added to 10110101_2 and 111011_2 is added to 11001100_2.

Carry:	10111111
Addend:	10110101_2
Augend:	$+ 10001111_2$
Sum:	101000100_2

Carry:	11111000
Addend:	11001100_2
Augend:	$+ 00111011_2$
Sum:	100000111_2

Binary Subtraction

Binary subtraction is performed exactly like decimal subtraction. Therefore, before you attempt binary subtraction, you should reexamine decimal subtraction. You know that in decimal arithmetic, if 5486 is subtracted from 8303, the difference 2817 is obtained.

Minuend after borrow		7	12	9	13
Minuend:		8	3	0	3
Subtrahend:	−	5	4	8	6
Difference:		2	8	1	7

Because the digit 6 in the subtrahend is larger than the digit 3 in the minuend, a 1 is borrowed from the next high-order digit in the minuend. If that digit is a 0, as in this example, 1 is borrowed from the next high-order digit that contains a number other than 0. That digit is reduced by 1 (from 3 to 2 in our example) and the digits skipped in the minuend are given the value 9. This is equivalent to removing 1 from 30 with the result of 29, as in our example. In the decimal system, the digit borrowed has the value of 10. Therefore, the minuend digit now has the value 13, and 6 from 13 equals 7.

Whenever 1 is borrowed from a higher-order digit, the borrow is equal in value to the radix or base of the number system. As you know, the radix or base of the decimal number system is 10, and the radix or base in the binary system is 2. Therefore, a borrow in the decimal number system equals 10, while a borrow in the binary number system equals 2.

When you subtract one binary number from another, you use the same method described for decimal subtraction. This is summarized by the following for binary subtraction.

1. $0 - 0 = 0$
2. $1 - 1 = 0$
3. $1 - 0 = 1$
4. $0 - 1 = 1$ with a borrow of 1.

To illustrate the process of binary subtraction, let's subtract 1101_2 from 11011_2.

Minuend after borrow:	0	10	10			
Minuend:	1	1	0	1	1	
Subtrahend:	−	1	1	0	1	
Difference:		1	1	1	0	

The "minuend after borrow" now shows the value of each minuend digit after a borrow occurs. **Remember that binary 10 equals decimal 2.**

In the first column, 1 from 1 equals 0 (rule 2). Then, 0 from 1 in the second column equals 1 (rule 3). In the third column, 1 from 0 requires a borrow from the fourth column. Thus, 1 from 10 equals 1 (rule 4). The minuend in the fourth column is now 0, from the previous borrow. Therefore, a borrow is required from the fifth column, so that 1 from 10 in the fourth column equals 1 (rule 4). Because of the previous borrow, the minuend in the fifth column is now 0 and the subtrahend is 0 (nonexistent), so that 0 from 0 equals 0 (rule 1). The 0 in the fifth column is not shown in the difference because it is not a significant bit. Thus, the difference between 11011_2 and 1101_2 is 1110_2. You can verify this by converting the binary number to a decimal number and subtracting.

As a further example of binary subtraction, subtract 00100101_2 from 11000100_2, as shown below. Then proceed to the next example and subtract 10111010_2 from 11101110_2.

Minuend after borrow:			0	1	1	1	10	1	10
Minuend:		1	1	0	0	0	1	0	0
Subtrahend:	−	0	0	1	0	0	1	0	1
Difference:		1	0	0	1	1	1	1	1

Minuend after borrow:			0	10	10				
Minuend:		1	1	1	0	1	1	1	0
Subtrahend:	−	1	0	1	1	1	0	1	0
Difference:		0	0	1	1	0	1	0	0

When a borrow is required in the minuend, 1 is obtained from the next high-order bit that contains a 1. That bit then becomes 0, and all bits skipped (0 value bits) are given the value of 1. This is equivalent to removing 1 from 1000_2 with the result of 0111_2.

Binary Multiplication

Multiplication is a short method of adding a number to itself as many times as it is specified by the multiplier. However, if you were to multiply 324_{10} by 223_{10} you would probably use the following method.

Multiplicand:	324
Multiplier:	× 223
First partial product:	972
Second partial product:	648
Third partial product:	648
Carry:	0121
Final product:	72252

Using the short form of multiplication, you multiply the multiplicand by each digit of the multiplier and then sum the partial products to obtain the final product. Note that, for convenience, the additive carries are set down under the partial products rather than over them as in normal addition.

Binary multiplication follows the same general principles as decimal multiplication. However, with only two possible multiplier bits (1 or 0), binary multiplication is a much simpler process. The example below lists the rules of binary multiplication. These rules will be used to multiply 1111_2 by 1101_2.

1. $0 \times 0 = 0$
2. $0 \times 1 = 0$
3. $1 \times 0 = 0$
4. $1 \times 1 = 1$

Multiplicand:	1111
Multiplier:	× 1101
First partial product:	1111
Second partial product:	0000
Carry:	0000
Sum of partial products:	1111
Third partial product:	1111
Carry:	111100
Sum of partial products:	1001011
Fourth partial product:	1111
Carry:	1111000
Final product:	11000011

As with decimal multiplication, you multiply the multiplicand by each bit in the multiplier and add the partial sums. First you multiply 1111_2 by the least significant multiplier bit (1) and set down the partial product so the least significant bit (LSB) is under the multiplier bit. Then you multiply the multiplicand by the next multiplier bit (0) and set down the partial product so the LSB is under the multiplier bit. Now that there are two partial products, they should be added. Although it is possible to add more than two binary numbers, keeping track of multiple carries may become confusing. Therefore, for these examples, add only two partial products at a time.

Notice that the first partial product is identical to the multiplicand. The second partial product is all zeros. Since the binary number system contains only ones and zeros, the partial product will always equal either the multiplicand or zero. Because of this, you can obtain the third partial product by copying the multiplicand. Begin with the LSB under the third multiplier bit. Add this value to the previous partial sum. Now obtain the fourth partial product by copying the multiplicand. Begin with the LSB under the fourth multiplier bit. Add this value to the previous partial sum. This is the final product. Again, you can verify the result by converting the binary numbers to decimal.

Reexamine the illustration for the previous multiplication example and you will notice that binary multiplication is a process of shift and add. For each 1 bit in the multiplier you copy down the multiplicand, beginning with the LSB under the bit. You can ignore any zeros in the multiplier. But do not make the mistake of setting down the multiplicand under the 0 bit.

To make sure you fully understand binary multiplication, multiply 1001_2 by 1100_2 and then multiply 1101_2 by 1111_2.

Multiplicand:	1001
Multiplier:	× 1100
First partial product:	0000
Second partial product:	0000
Carry:	0000
Sum of partial products:	00000
Third partial product:	1001
Carry:	00000
Sum of partial products:	100100
Fourth partial product:	1001
Carry:	000000
Final product:	1101100

Multiplicand:	1101
Multiplier:	× 1111
First partial product:	1101
Second partial product:	1101
Carry:	11000
Sum of partial products:	100111
Third partial product:	1101
Carry:	100100
Sum of partial products:	1011011
Fourth partial product	1101
Carry:	1111000
Final product:	11000011

In the first of these examples, the two zeros in the multiplier were included in the multiplication process. This was to insure that the multiplicand was copied down under the proper multiplier bits. The multiplication process could have been represented in this manner:

Multiplicand:	1001
Multiplier:	× 1100
Third partial product:	100100
Fourth partial product:	1001
Carry	000000
Final product:	1101100

Remember, just as in decimal multiplication, you must keep track of any zeros by setting a zero in the product under the 0 bit in the multiplier. This is very important when the zero occupies the LSB.

Binary Division

Division is the reverse of multiplication. Therefore, it is a procedure for determining how many times one number can be subtracted from another. The process you are probably familiar with is called "long" division. If you were to divide decimal 181 by 45, you would obtain the quotient, 4 - 1/45, as follows:

	004	Quotient
Divisor 45	)181	Dividend
	180	
	1	Remainder

Using long division, you would examine the most significant digit in the dividend and determine if the divisor was smaller in value. In this example, the divisor is larger, so the quotient is zero. Next, you examine the two most significant digits, and here again, the divisor is larger, so the quotient is again zero. Finally, you examine the whole dividend and discover it is approximately four times the divisor value. Therefore, you give the quotient a value of 4. Next, you subtract the product of 45 and 4 (180) from the dividend. The difference of 1 represents a fraction of the divisor. This fraction is added to the quotient to produce the correct answer of 4 - 1/45.

Binary division is performed in a similar manner. However, binary division is a simpler process since the number base is two rather than ten. First, let's divide 100011_2 by 101_2.

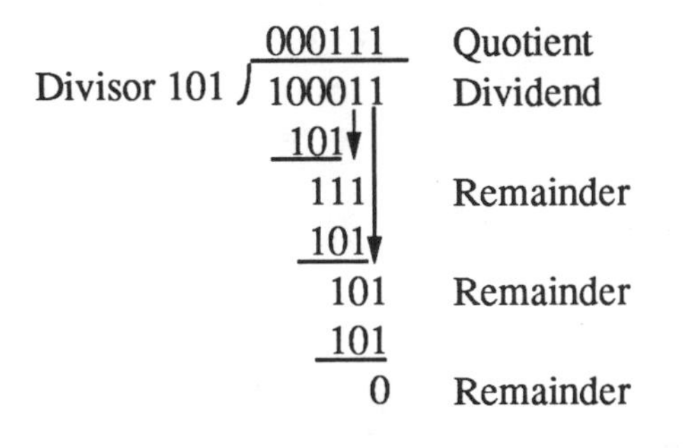

Using long division, you examine the dividend beginning with the MSB and determine the number of bits required to exceed the value of the divisor. When you find this value, place a 1 in the quotient and subtract the divisor from the selected dividend value. Then carry the next least significant bit in the dividend down to the remainder. If you can subtract the divisor from the new remainder, place a 1 in the quotient. Then subtract the divisor from the remainder and carry the next least significant bit in the dividend (LSB in this example) down to the remainder. If the divisor can be subtracted from the new remainder, place a 1 in the quotient and subtract the divisor from the remainder. Continue the process until all of the dividend bits have been carried down. Then express any remainder as a fraction of the divisor in the quotient. Thus, 100011_2 divided by 101_2 equals 111_2. You can verify the answer by converting the binary number to decimal.

To make sure you fully understand binary division, work out the following examples of long division. Divide 101000_2 by 1000_2 and then divide 100111_2 by 110_2.

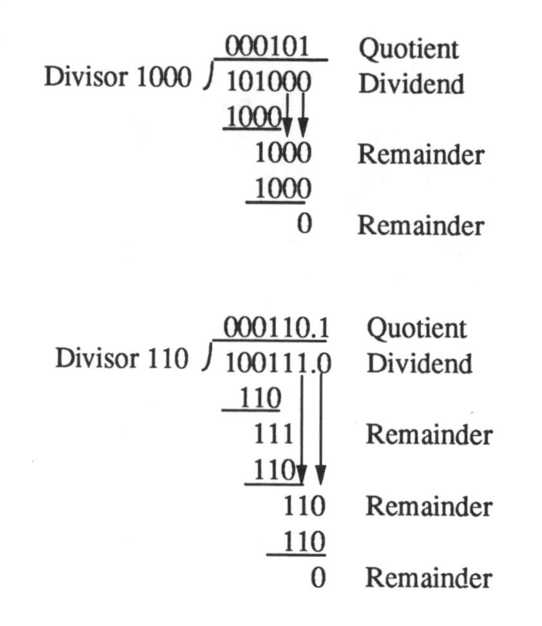

In the second example, the quotient was not a whole number, but rather a whole number plus a fraction (remainder divided by the divisor). The answer 110 - 11/110 is correct. You could have left the answer in this form or, as in the example, continue the division process until the remainder was zero. This is made possible by adding a sufficient number of zeros after the binary point to permit division by the divisor. In the previous example, only one zero was added after the binary point As in the decimal number system, adding zeros after the binary point in the binary number system, will not affect the value of the number. Note that some numbers cannot be solved in this manner (e.g., decimal 1/3).

Representing Negative Numbers

Until now, we have been examining binary arithmetic using unsigned numbers. However, you must be able to express both positive and negative (signed) numbers. Over the years, three methods have been developed for representing signed numbers — Sign and Magnitude, One's Complement, and Two's Complement. Of these, only one method has survived. The two older methods will be briefly examined first, followed by the system that is used today.

Sign And Magnitude

Using this system, a binary number contained both the sign (+ or –) and the value of the number. Using 8-bit numbers, positive and negative values were expressed as follows:

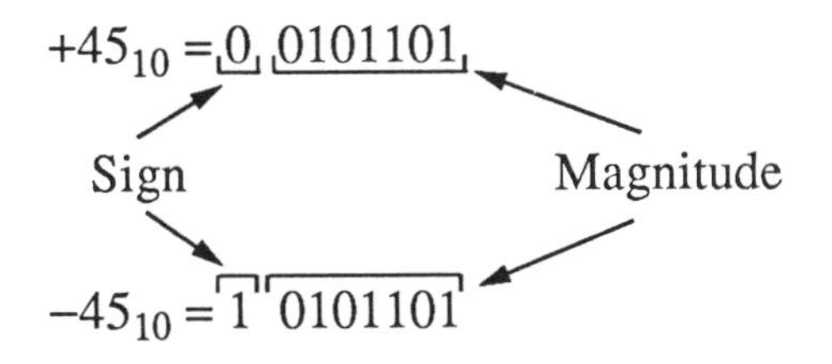

The MSB of the binary number indicated the sign, while the remaining bits contained the value of the number. As you can see, a zero sign bit indicated a positive value, while a one sign bit indicated a negative value.

While this method of representing negative numbers may seem logical, its popularity was short lived. Because it required complex and slow arithmetic circuitry, it was quickly abandoned.

One's Complement

Another method of representing negative numbers became popular in the early days of computers. It was called the one's complement method. Using this system, positive numbers were represented in the same way as in the sign-magnitude system. That is, the MSB in any number was considered to be a sign bit. A sign bit of 0 represented positive. Using 8-bit numbers, positive values were represented like this:

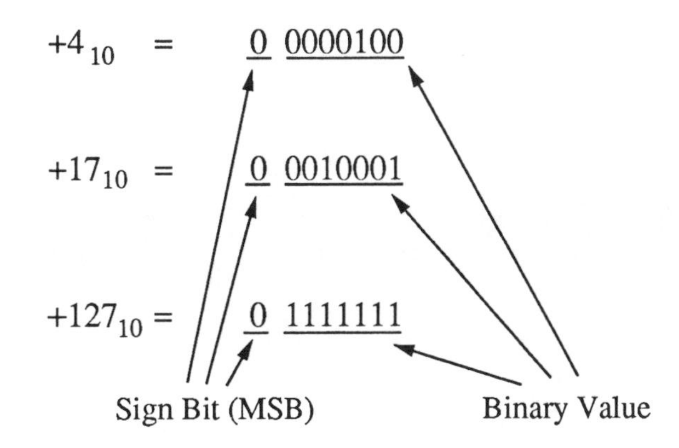

Negative numbers were represented by the one's complement of the positive value. The one's complement of a number is formed by changing all the 0's to 1's and all the 1's to 0's. As previously shown, $+4_{10}$ is represented as 0 0000100. By changing all 0's to 1's and all 1's to 0's, the representation for -4_{10} was formed. In this case:

$$-4_{10} = \underline{1}\ \underline{1111011}_2$$

Notice that all the bits, including the sign bit, were inverted. In the same way:

$$-17_{10} = \underline{1}\ \underline{1101110}_2$$

$$-127_{10} = \underline{1}\ \underline{0000000}_2$$

Two's Complement

The current method used to represent signed numbers is called two's complement. In this system, positive numbers are represented just as they were with the sign-and-magnitude method and the one's complement method. That is, it uses the same bit pattern for all positive values up to $+127_{10}$. However, negative numbers are represented as the two's complement of positive numbers.

The two's complement of a number is formed by taking the one's complement and then adding 1. For example, if you work with 8-bit numbers and use the two's complement system, $+4_{10}$ is represented by 00000100_2. To find -4_{10}, you must take the two's complement of this number. You do this by first taking the one's complement, which is 11111011_2. Next, add 1 to form the two's complement:

$$\begin{array}{r} 11111011_2 \\ +\quad\quad 1\ \ \\ \hline 11111100_2 \end{array}$$

Thus, the two's complement representation of -4_{10} is 11111100_2.

To be sure you have the idea, look at a second example. How do you express -17_{10} as an 8-bit two's complement number? Start with the binary representation of $+17_{10}$, which is 00010001_2. Take the one's complement by changing all the 0's to 1's and 1's to 0's. Thus, the one's complement of $+17_{10}$ is 11101110_2. Next find the two's complement by adding 1:

$$\begin{array}{r} 11101110_2 \\ +\qquad\quad 1 \\ \hline 11101111_2 \end{array}$$

Figure 1-13 compares unsigned, two's complement and one's complement numbers. Several 8-bit patterns are shown in the left column, while the other three columns show the decimal number represented by these patterns.

BIT PATTERN	UNSIGNED BINARY	2's COMPLEMENT	1's COMPLEMENT
00000000	0	0	+0
00000001	1	+1	+1
00000010	2	+2	+2
00000011	3	+3	+3
•	•	•	•
•	•	•	•
•	•	•	•
•	•	•	•
01111100	124	+124	+124
01111101	125	+125	+125
01111110	126	+126	+126
01111111	127	+127	+127
10000000	128	–128	–127
10000001	129	–127	–126
10000010	130	–126	–125
10000011	131	–125	–124
•	•	•	•
•	•	•	•
•	•	•	•
•	•	•	•
11111100	252	–4	–3
11111101	253	–3	–2
11111110	254	–2	–1
11111111	255	–1	–0

Figure 1-13
Table of bit pattern values for unsigned binary, 2's complement and 1's complement numbers.

In the 1's complement column, notice that the range of numbers is from -127_{10} to $+127_{10}$ and that there are two representations of zero.

In the 2's complement column the range of 8-bit two's complement numbers is from -128_{10} to $+127_{10}$. Notice also that there is only one representation for zero.

If this table included all 256_{10} possible 8-bit patterns, you could look up any pattern to see what number it represents. The patterns that have 0 as their MSB are easy to determine without a table (the pattern represents the binary number directly). But what decimal number is represented by the two's complement number 11110011? You should know that this represents some negative number because the MSB is a 1.

Actually, you can determine the value very easily by taking the two's complement to find the equivalent positive number. Remember, you find the two's complement by taking the one's complement and adding 1. The one's complement is 00001100_2. Thus, the two's complement is:

$$\begin{array}{r} 00001100_2 \\ \underline{+ \qquad\quad 1} \\ 00001101_2 \end{array} \text{ or } +13_{10}$$

Since the two's complement of 11110011_2 represents $+13_{10}$, then 11110011_2 must equal -13_{10}.

Two's Complement Arithmetic

In the previous discussion you saw that signed numbers are represented in two's complement form. Now you will see why.

In digital electronic devices, such as computers, simple circuits cost less and operate faster than more complex ones. Two's complement numbers are used with arithmetic because they allow the simplest, cheapest, fastest circuits.

A characteristic of the two's complement system is that both signed and unsigned numbers can be added by the same circuit. For example, suppose you wish to add the unsigned numbers 132_{10} and 14_{10}. The addition would look like this:

Addend:	10000100	132_{10}
Augend:	00001110	$+ 14_{10}$
Sum:	10010010	146_{10}

Now look at the example given previously again. If you assume that the inputs are two's complement signed numbers, then the addend, augend, and sum are:

Addend:	10000100	-124_{10}
Augend:	00001110	$+14_{10}$
Sum:	10010010	-110_{10}

Notice that the bit patterns are the same. Only the meaning of the bit patterns have changed. The advantage of two's complement is that the bit patterns can be interpreted either way. This allows us to work with either signed or unsigned numbers without requiring different circuits for each.

Using two's complement arithmetic simplifies the required circuitry by allowing subtraction using an adder circuit. To see how this works, it may be helpful to look at a similar process with the decimal number system. The decimal equivalent of two's complement is called ten's complement. Since you are more familiar with the decimal number system, let's briefly examine ten's complement arithmetic.

Ten's Complement Arithmetic

An easy way to illustrate ten's complement is to consider an analogy. Visualize an automobile odometer or mileage indicator. Generally, this is a 6-digit device that indicates mileage between 00,000.0 and 99,999.9 miles. Let's ignore the tenths digit and concentrate on the other five.

In an automobile, the odometer generally operates in only one direction, forward. However, consider what happens if it is turned backwards instead. Starting at +3 miles, the count would proceed backwards as follows:

00,003
00,002
00,001
00,000
99,999
99,998
99,997
etc.

It is easy to visualize that 99,999 represents –1 mile. Also 99,998 represents –2 miles: 99,997 represents –3 miles; etc. This is how signed numbers are represented in ten's complement form.

Once you accept this system for representing positive and negative numbers, you can perform arithmetic with these signed numbers. For example, if you add +3 and −2, the result is +1. Using the system developed above, +3 is represented by 00003 while −2 is represented by 99,998. Thus, the addition looks like this:

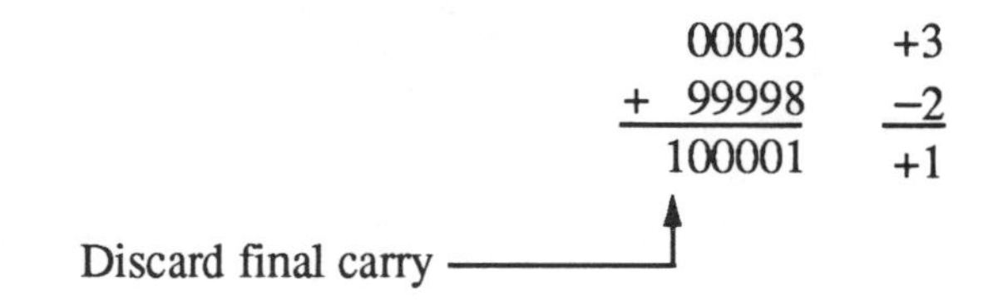

If you now discard the final carry on the left side of the sum, the answer is 00001, the representation of +1. You can also find the ten's complement of a digit by subtracting the digit from ten. For example, the ten's complement of 6 is 4 since 10 − 6 = 4. To complement a number containing more than one digit, raise ten to a power equal to the total number of digits, then subtract the number from it. As an example, to obtain the ten's complement of 654_{10} first raise ten to the third power since there are three digits in the number. Then subtract 654 from the result.

$$\begin{array}{rcr} 10^3 & = & 1000 \\ & & -654 \\ \hline & & 346 \end{array}$$

Thus, the ten's complement of 654_{10} is 346_{10}.

Once you find the ten's complement, you can subtract one number from another by an indirect method using only addition. Most of us have learned to subtract like this:

Minuend:	973
Subtrahend:	−654
Difference:	319

However, you can arrive at the same answer by using ten's complement of the subtrahend and adding. Recall that the ten's complement of 654_{10} is 346_{10}. Let's compare these two methods of subtraction:

STANDARD METHOD		TEN'S COMPLEMENT METHOD	
Minuend	973	973	Minuend
Subtrahend	−654	+346	Ten's complement of Subtrahend
Difference	319	1319	Difference

↑ Discard final carry

Notice that when you use the ten's complement method, the answer is too large, by 1000_{10}. However, you can still arrive at the correct answer by simply discarding the final carry.

While the ten's complement method of subtraction works, it is not readily used because it is more complex than the standard method. In fact, it does not eliminate subtraction entirely since the ten's complement itself is found by subtraction.

The binary equivalent of ten's complement is two's complement. It overcomes the disadvantage of ten's complement in that the two's complement can be formed without any subtraction at all. Recall that you can form the two's complement of a binary number by changing all the 0's to 1's and all the 1's to 0's and then adding one. Let's examine two's complement arithmetic in more detail.

Two's Complement Subtraction

As in ten's complement arithmetic, you can form the two's complement by subtracting from a power of the base or radix (two) or by finding the one's complement and adding one. Once the two's complement is formed, subtraction is performed indirectly by adding the two's complement of the subtrahend to the minuend.

To illustrate this point, observe the following two ways of subtracting 26_{10} from 69_{10}. The standard method of subtraction looks like this:

Minuend	01000101_2	69
Subtrahend	-00011010_2	−26
Difference	00101011_2	43

While this method works fine on paper, it's of little use to a computer since it has no subtraction circuitry. However, it can still perform subtraction by the indirect method of adding the two's complement of the subtrahend to the minuend:

	Minuend	01000101
Two's complement of	Subtrahend	+11100110
	Difference	100101011

Discard final carry ⟶ (points to the leading 1 of 100101011)

This illustrates a major reason for using the two's complement system to represent signed numbers. It allows a computer to subtract and add with the same circuit.

17. Perform the following binary computations.

a.
$$\begin{array}{r} 11010110 \\ +11100011 \\ \hline \end{array}$$

b.
$$\begin{array}{r} 11010111.01 \\ +\ 01110010.11 \\ \hline \end{array}$$

c.
$$\begin{array}{r} 111011 \\ -101010 \\ \hline \end{array}$$

d.
$$\begin{array}{r} 10000111.11 \\ -01111010.01 \\ \hline \end{array}$$

e.
$$\begin{array}{r} 11011 \\ \times\ 101 \\ \hline \end{array}$$

f.
$$\begin{array}{r} 1011 \\ \times\ 110 \\ \hline \end{array}$$

g. $110\overline{)11010011}$

h. $1011\overline{)11001101}$

18. What are the three methods used to represent signed numbers?

a. ______________________________
b. ______________________________
c. ______________________________

19. What is the two's complement of 10001001_2?

Binary Codes

The general term given for the process of converting a decimal number into its binary equivalent is coding. We can express a decimal number as an equivalent binary code or binary number. The binary number system, as discussed, is known as the pure binary code. We give it this name to distinguish it from other types of binary codes. In this section you will see some of the other types of binary codes used in digital systems.

Binary Coded Decimal

Because the decimal number system is so familiar, it is easy to use. The binary number system is less convenient to use because we are not as intimately familiar with it. It is difficult to quickly glance at a binary number and recognize its decimal equivalent. For example, the binary number 1010011 represents the decimal number 83. You certainly cannot tell immediately by looking at the number what its decimal value is. However, you know that within a few minutes, using the procedures described earlier, that you could readily calculate its decimal value. The amount of time that it takes you to convert or recognize a binary number quantity is a distinct disadvantage in working with this code despite the numerous hardware advantages. Digital engineers recognized this problem early and developed a special form of binary code that was more compatible with the decimal system. Because so many digital devices, instruments and equipment use decimal input and output, this special code has become very widely used and accepted. This special compromise code is known as binary coded decimal (BCD). The BCD code combines some of the characteristics of both the binary and decimal number systems.

The BCD code is a system that represents the decimal digits 0 through 9 with a four-bit binary code. This BCD code uses the standard 8421 position weighting system of the pure binary code. The standard 8421 BCD code and the decimal equivalents are shown in Table II. As with the pure binary code, you can convert the BCD numbers into their decimal equivalents by simply adding together the weights of the bit positions where the binary 1's occur. Since 9 is the largest character used as a digit in the decimal number system, the 4-bit binary numbers representing the decimal numbers 10 through 15 are invalid in the BCD system.

TABLE II
8421 BCD CODE

DECIMAL	BCD
0	0000
1	0001
2	0010
3	0011
4	0100
5	0101
6	0110
7	0111
8	1000
9	1001

To represent a decimal number in BCD notation you simply substitute the appropriate four-bit code for each decimal digit. For example, the number 834 in BCD would be 1000 0011 0100. Each decimal digit is represented by its equivalent 8421 four-bit code. A space is left between each four-bit group in order to avoid confusing the BCD format with the pure binary code.

The beauty of the BCD code is that the ten BCD code combinations are very easily remembered. Once you begin to work with binary numbers on a regular basis, you will find that the BCD numbers will come to you as quickly and automatically as decimal numbers. For that reason, by simply glancing at the BCD representation of a decimal number you can make the conversion almost as quickly as if it were already in decimal form.

While the BCD code does help to simplify the man-machine interface it is less efficient than the pure binary code. It takes more bits to represent a given decimal number in BCD than it does with pure binary notation. For example, the decimal number 83 in pure binary form is 1010011. In BCD code the decimal number 83 is written as 1000 0011. In the pure binary code it takes only a 7-bit word to represent the number 83. In BCD form it takes 8-bits. The inefficiency arises from the fact that for each bit in a data word there is usually a certain amount of digital circuitry associated with it. The extra circuitry associated with the BCD code costs more, increases equipment complexity, and consumes more power. Arithmetic operations with BCD numbers are also more time-consuming and complex than those with pure binary numbers. As you recall, with four bits of binary information we can represent a total of $2^4 = 16$ different states or the decimal number equivalents 0 through 15. In the BCD system we waste six of these states (10-15), thus compounding the inefficiency. Therefore, when we use the BCD number system, we trade off some efficiency for the improved communications between the digital equipment and the human operator.

Besides the standard pure binary coded form, the BCD numbering system is by far the most widely used digital code. You will find one or the other in most of the applications that you encounter. However, there are several other codes that are used for special applications. Let's consider some of these.

Gray Code

The Gray Code is a widely used non-weighted code system. Also known as the cyclic, unit distance or reflective code, the Gray code can exist in either the pure binary or BCD formats. The Gray code is shown in Table III. As with the pure binary code, the first ten codes are used in BCD operations. Notice that there is a change in only one bit from one code number to the next in sequence. You can get a better idea about the Gray code sequence by comparing it to the standard four-bit 8421 pure binary code also shown in Table III. For example, consider the change from 7 (0111) to 8(1000) in the pure binary code. When this change takes place all bits change. Bits that were 1's are changed to 0's and 0's are changed to 1's. Now, notice the code change from 7 to 8 in the Gray code. Here 7(0100) changes to 8 (1100). Only the first bit changes.

TABLE III
THE GRAY CODE

DECIMAL	GRAY	PURE BINARY
0	0000	0000
1	0001	0001
2	0011	0010
3	0010	0011
4	0110	0100
5	0111	0101
6	0101	0110
7	0100	0111
8	1100	1000
9	1101	1001
10	1111	1010
11	1110	1011
12	1010	1100
13	1011	1101
14	1001	1110
15	1000	1111

The Gray code is generally known as an error-minimizing code because it greatly reduces the possibility of ambiguity in the electronic circuitry, when changing from one state to the next. When binary codes are implemented with electronic circuitry, it takes a finite period of time for bits to change from 0 to 1 or 1 to 0. These state changes can create timing and speed problems. This is particularly true in the standard 8421 codes where many bits change from one combination to the next. When the Gray code is used, however, the timing and speed errors are greatly minimized because only one bit changes at a time. This permits code circuitry to operate at higher speeds with fewer errors.

The biggest disadvantage of the Gray code is that it is difficult to use in arithmetic computations. Where numbers must be added, subtracted or used in other computations, the Gray code is not applicable. In order to perform arithmetic operations the Gray code number must generally be converted into pure binary form.

ASCII Code

The American Standard Code for Information Interchange (ASCII) code is a special form of BCD code that is widely used in digital computers and data communications equipment. It is a 7-bit binary code that is used in transferring data between computers and their external peripheral devices and in communicating data by radio and telephone lines. With 7-bits we can represent a total of $2^7 = 128$ different states or characters. The ASCII code is used to represent the decimal numbers 0 through 9. The letters of the alphabet (both upper and lower case), and other special characters such as punctuation marks and codes that are used to control various computer peripheral devices and communication circuits. The standard ASCII code is shown in Table IV.

TABLE IV

AMERICAN STANDARD CODE FOR INFORMATION INTERCHANGE

ROW	COLUMN	0	1	2	3	4	5	6	7
	BITS 4321 ↓ 765 ⇨	000	001	010	011	100	101	110	111
0	0000	NUL	DLE	SP	0	@	P	`	p
1	0001	SOH	DC1	!	1	A	Q	a	q
2	0010	STX	DC2	"	2	B	R	b	r
3	0011	ETX	DC3	#	3	C	S	c	s
4	0100	EOT	DC4	$	4	D	T	d	t
5	0101	ENQ	NAK	%	5	E	U	e	u
6	0110	ACK	SYN	&	6	F	V	f	v
7	0111	BEL	ETB	'	7	G	W	g	w
8	1000	BS	CAN	(	8	H	X	h	x
9	1001	HT	EM	)	9	I	Y	i	y
10	1010	LF	SUB	*	:	J	Z	j	z
11	1011	VT	ESC	+	;	K	[	k	{
12	1100	FF	FS	,	<	L	\	l	¦
13	1101	CR	GS	-	=	M	]	m	}
14	1110	SO	RS	.	>	N	^	n	~
15	1111	SI	US	/	?	O	_	o	DEL

Explanation of special control functions in columns 0, 1, 2 and 7.

NUL *Null*
SOH *Start of Heading*
STX *Start of Text*
ETX *End of Text*
EOT *End of Transmission*
ENQ *Enquiry*
ACK *Acknowledge*
BEL *Bell (audible signal)*
BS *Backspace*
HT *Horizontal Tab (punched card skip)*
LF *Line Feed*
VT *Vertical Tab*
FF *Form Feed*
CR *Carriage Return*
SO *Shift Out*
SI *Shift In*
SP *Space (blank)*

DLE *Data Link Escape*
DC1 *Device Control 1*
DC2 *Device Control 2*
DC3 *Device Control 3*
DC4 *Device Control 4*
NAK *Negative Acknowledge*
SYN *Synchronous Idle*
ETB *End of Transmission Block*
CAN *Cancel*
EM *End of Medium*
SUB *Substitute*
ESC *Escape*
FS *File Separator*
GS *Group Separator*
RS *Record Separator*
US *Unit Separator*
DEL *Delete*

The 7-bit ASCII code for each number, letter or control function is made up of a 3-bit group followed by a 4-bit group. Figure 1-14 shows the arrangement of these two groups and the numbering sequence. The 3-bit group is on the left and bit 1 is the LSB. Note how these groups are arranged in rows and columns in Table IV.

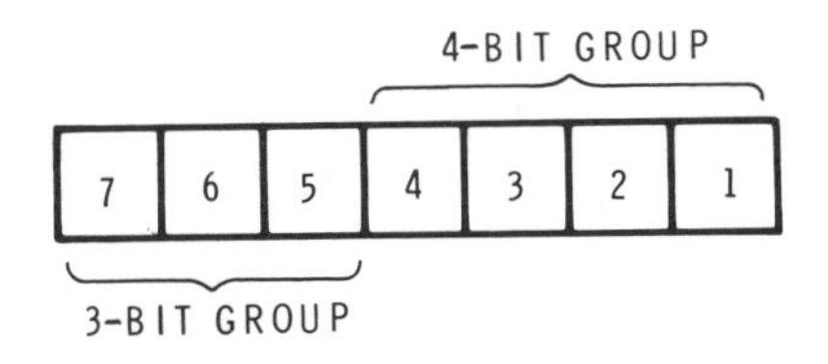

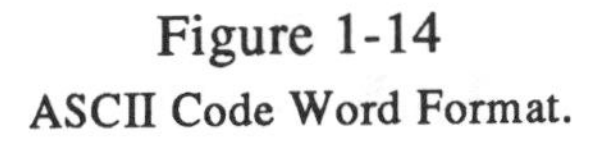

Figure 1-14
ASCII Code Word Format.

To determine the ASCII code for a given number, letter, or control operation, you locate that item in the table. Then you use the three and four-bit codes associated with the column and row in which the item is located. For example, the ASCII code for the letter L is 1001100. It is located in column 4, row 12. The most significant 3-bit group is 100, while the least significant four-bit group is 1100. The complete code is 1001100.

There are both 6 and 8-bit special versions of the ASCII code. In addition, the International Business Machines Corporation (IBM) uses another 8-bit coding system called Extended Binary Coded Decimal Interchange Code (EBCDIC) instead of ASCII, for its mainframe peripheral and data communications operations.

20. The BCD code is better than the binary code because:

    a. it uses less bits.
    b. it is more compatible with the decimal number system.
    c. it is more adaptable to arithmetic computations.
    d. there are more different coding schemes available.

21. Convert the following decimal numbers to 8421 BCD code.

    a. 1049.
    b. 267.
    c. 835.

22. Convert the following 8421 BCD code numbers to decimal.

    a. 1001 0110 0010.
    b. 0111 0001 0100 0011.
    c. 1010 1001 1000.
    d. 1000 0000 0101.

23. Which code is best for minimum hardware errors?

    a. ASCII.
    b. 8421 BCD.
    c. pure binary.
    d. Gray.

24. Which BCD code is used for data communications?

    a. Gray.
    b. 8421.
    c. ASCII.

25. The ASCII code is used primarily in ____________________ and ____________________.

26. What is the ASCII code for the letter "f"?________________ .

Data Representation

Now that you understand the reason for using the binary number system and are familiar with some of the binary coding schemes used in digital equipment, you are ready to consider the actual hardware means of implementing these binary numbers. By hardware we mean the electronic components and circuits that are used to represent and manipulate the binary numbers used in the digital system. It is relatively easy to represent a binary number with electronic components. The component, to represent a specific bit in a binary word, must be capable of assuming two distinct states. One of the states will represent a binary 0 and the other a binary 1.

Electromechanical Devices

Switches and relays are ideal for representing binary data. A closed switch or relay contact can represent a binary 1 while the open switch or contact can represent a binary 0. Of course these logic representations can also be reversed. Switches and relays are still widely used to implement digital systems or parts of digital equipment. They are used in places where static binary conditions are required or very low speed operation can be tolerated.

Early digital equipment such as computers and test instruments used relays to represent binary numbers. But the relays were soon replaced by vacuum tubes in many applications. Each bit was represented by a vacuum tube that was either conducting or cut-off. When the tube was conducting it represented one binary state and when it was cut-off it represented the other binary state. Vacuum tubes worked well in digital applications. They achieved operating speeds significantly higher than that of relays. However, because of their large size, high power consumption and speed limitations, they have been replaced by solid state devices.

Transistors

Today the most common way of representing binary data in digital equipment is with a transistor. A transistor can readily assume two distinct states, conducting and cut-off. When a transistor is cut-off it is essentially an open circuit. When a transistor is conducting heavily, it acts as a very low resistance and accurately simulates a closed switch. Most digital circuitry in use today uses saturated bipolar switching transistors for data representation. Non-saturated bipolar transistor switches are also used in many applications where high speed operation is desirable. Keep in mind that both discrete component and integrated circuit transistors are used in digital applications.

The enhancement mode metal oxide semiconductor field-effect transistor (MOSFET) is also widely used as a two state switch to represent binary data. This type of transistor is the key element in MOS and complementary MOS (CMOS) integrated circuits.

Logic Levels

The basic element for representing a single bit of data is a switch: mechanical, electromechanical or electronic. The on-off nature of a switch makes it perfect for binary data representation. The exact relationship between the state of the switch and the bit represented by this switch is arbitrary. In actual digital hardware we are not so much concerned with whether the transistor is off or on. Instead the bit assignments are generally represented by voltage levels. The switching element controls these voltage levels. For example, a binary 0 may be represented by 0 volts or ground. A binary 1 may by represented by +5 volts. Depending upon the equipment power supplies available, the exact circuitry used, and the application, almost any voltage level assignments can be used.

Figure 1-6 shows two ways in which a bipolar transistor can be used to produce two distinct voltage levels. In Figure 1-6A, the transistor is connected as a shunt switch. This means that the transistor is in parallel with the output. When the transistor is not conducting, the output voltage is +5 volts as seen through collector resistor Rc. When the transistor is conducting it acts as a very low resistance or near short circuit. At this time the output is some low positive voltage level near ground or zero volts. The switching of the transistor of course is controlled by the application of the appropriate base signal. Switching times in the nanosecond (10^{-9} seconds) region are possible with modern transistors.

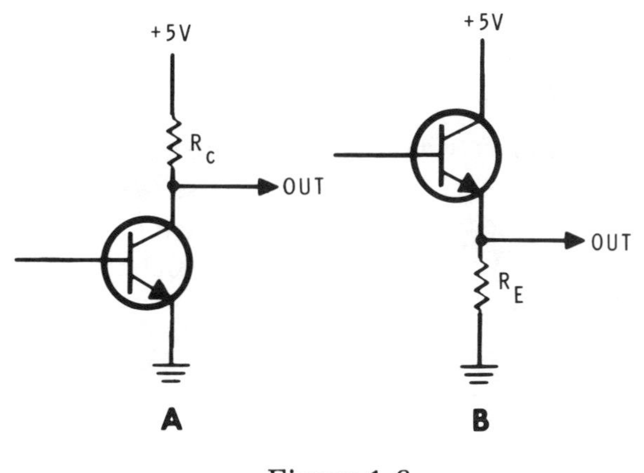

Figure 1-6
Bipolar transistor logic switches, (A) shunt switch (B) series switch.

In Figure 1-6B the transistor is connected as a series switch. When the transistor is cut off, the output is zero volts or ground as seen across resistor R_E. When the transistor conducts, it acts as a very low impedance and connects the +5 volts supply line to the output. Again the operation of the transistor is controlled by applying the appropriate signal to the base. You will find both series and shunt transistor switches used in digital circuits.

Positive and Negative Logic

There are two basic types of logic level representation, positive logic and negative logic. When the most positive of two voltage levels is assigned the binary 1 state, we say that positive logic is being used. When the negative or least positive of two voltage levels is assigned to the binary 1 state, we say that negative logic is being used. Indicated below are several examples of both positive and negative logic level assignments. Keep in mind that the assignments are strictly arbitrary and are selected by the designer when the circuit or equipment is designed.

Positive Logic	Negative Logic
binary 0 = +.2V. binary 1 = +3.4V.	binary 0 = +3.4V. binary 1 = +.2V.
binary 0 = −6V. binary 1 = 0V.	binary 0 = 0V. binary 1 = −6V.
binary 0 = +1V. binary 1 = +15V.	binary 0 = +15V. binary 1 = +1V.

Parallel vs. Serial Data Representation

There are two basic ways in which digital numbers are transmitted, processed or otherwise manipulated. These methods are designated as serial and parallel. In the serial methods of data handling, each bit of a binary word or number is processed serially one at a time. In a parallel system all bits of a word or a number are processed simultaneously.

Serial Data

Figure 1-7 shows a binary number represented in a serial data format. The binary number exists as a series of voltage levels representing the binary 1s and 0s. These voltage level changes occur at a single point in a circuit or on a single line. Each bit of the word exists for a specific interval of time. The time interval allotted to each bit is in this example, one millisecond. The most significant bit (MSB) is the one at the far left. It occurs first since time is considered to be increasing from left to right. Because this is an 8-bit binary word, it takes 8 milliseconds for the entire word to occur or be transmitted. Positive logic level assignments are used. By observing the voltage levels at a specific point or on the transmission line, the number can be determined. The number is 10110010. This is the binary equivalent of the decimal number 178.

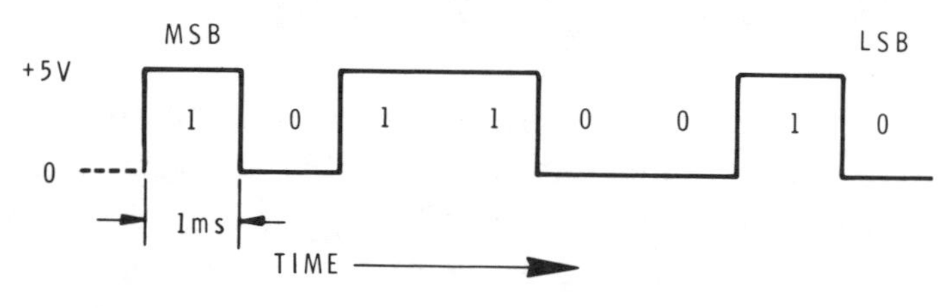

Figure 1-7
The serial binary word 10110010.

The primary advantage of the serial binary data representation is that it requires only a single line or channel for transmitting it from one place to another. In addition, since each bit on the single line occurs separately from the others, only one set of digital circuitry is generally needed to process this data. For these reasons, serial data representation is the simplest and most economical of the two types. Its primary disadvantage is that the transmission and processing time required for a serial word is significant since the bits occur one after the other. Despite this time penalty, serial data representation is widely used because of its economy and simplicity.

Parallel Data

The other method of representing, transmitting and processing binary data is designated as parallel. The reason for this is that all bits of a binary word or number are transmitted or processed simultaneously. For this reason a separate line or channel is required for each bit of the word in transmitting that word from one point to another. Refer to Figure 1-8. Here the 8-bit digital word 10110010 is available as voltage levels on eight separate output lines. Since all of the bits of the word are available at the same time, digital circuitry must be provided to process or otherwise manipulate each of the bits in the word simultaneously. The transmission and processing of parallel data, therefore, is more complex and expensive than that required for serial data. However, the clear advantage of parallel data transmission is its speed. All bits are processed at the same time and, therefore, the time required for handling of the data is very short. For high speed applications requiring rapid processing, parallel digital techniques are preferred.

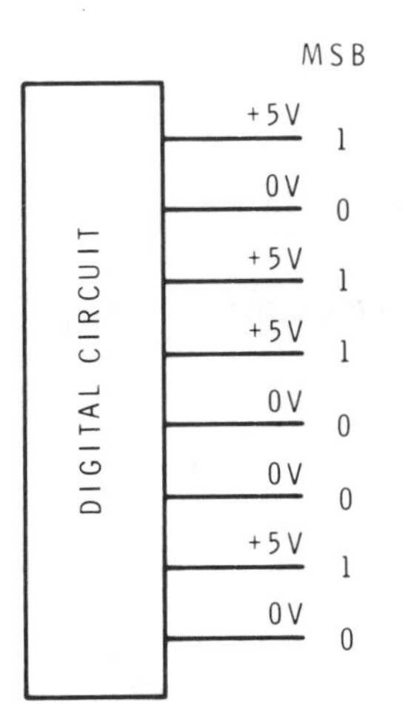

Figure 1-8
The parallel binary word 10110010.

Self-Test Review

27. The basic component used to represent a binary digit is a ________________.

28. The two types of transistors used to implement digital circuits are ________________________ and ________________________.

29. Designate the following logic level assignments as being either positive or negative.

    a. binary 0 = +3
       binary 1 = −3
    b. binary 0 = +0.8
       binary 1 = +1.8

30. Serial data transmission is faster than parallel data transfers.

    a. True.
    b. False.

31. The following voltage levels appear on six parallel data lines designated A through F.

    A = +5V, B = +5V, C = 0V, D = +5V, E = 0V, F = +5V

    Using positive logic and assuming bit A is the LSB, what is the decimal number equivalent?

Appendix

Table of Powers of 2

2^n	n	2^{-n}
1	0	1.0
2	1	0.5
4	2	0.25
8	3	0.125
16	4	0.062 5
32	5	0.031 25
64	6	0.015 625
128	7	0.007 812 5
256	8	0.003 906 25
512	9	0.001 953 125
1 024	10	0.000 976 562 5
2 048	11	0.000 488 281 25
4 096	12	0.000 244 140 625
8 192	13	0.000 122 070 312 5
16 384	14	0.000 061 035 156 25
32 768	15	0.000 030 517 578 125
65 536	16	0.000 015 258 789 062 5

n = number of bits

Summary

Electronic circuits are divided into two categories, analog (linear) and digital (discrete levels). This course is concerned with digital circuits. A digital circuit has either of two possible values (binary 0 or binary 1). Analog signals usually vary smoothly, or at a linear rate, and can have an infinite number of values. That is, an analog signal can have as many values as there are points on a curve.

All digital circuitry works with binary values that can be used to represent different numbers. The type of number used depends on the application. There are four main number systems—decimal, binary, octal, and hexadecimal. Each number system is distinguished by its base, or radix. The base indicates how many digits a system uses to represent quantities—decimal uses 10 digits (0-9), binary uses 2 digits (0-1), octal uses 8 digits (0-7), and hexadecimal uses 16 digits (0-F).

The maximum number that can be represented in any number system is $R^N - 1$. This is the radix raised to a power (where N is the number of digits). The minus 1 is because all number systems start at 0.

A binary word is usually defined as 8-bits long and is called a byte. In some cases, a binary word is 16-bits long, and in this case, the word is said to contain two bytes of information.

When working with digital systems it can become necessary to convert between the different number systems. A decimal integer number can be converted to a different base through successive divisions by the desired base. To convert any number to decimal you simply multiply each digit by the weight of its position and add the results. Since the binary number system is used extensively in digital devices, understanding binary arithmetic is essential. By using binary addition and subtraction you can perform binary multiplication and division. Three methods have been developed to represent negative numbers—Sign and Magnitude, One's Complement, and Two's Complement. Two's complement is the current method used to represent a negative number. The two's complement is formed by taking the one's complement of a number and adding one.

In the Binary Coded Decimal (BCD) system, the binary bits (either 0 or 1) are arranged to have a numerical value that can be read in the decimal system. In the BCD system 1010, 1011, 1100, 1101, 1110, and 1111 are invalid codes as they represent the decimal numbers 10, 11, 12, 13, 14, and 15. In the decimal number system it requires two digits to express numbers greater than 9. In the BCD system a single digit is made up of four binary bits.

Other popular variations of binary codes used are the gray code and ASCII code. The ASCII code is the most widely used code for data transmission. It uses a seven-bit binary number. The seven-bit number is divided into three bits (bits 5, 6, and 7) that indicate a column in a standard table. Bits 1, 2, 3, and 4 indicate a row in the standard table. The cross reference between row and column pin-points a specific character in the ASCII table. In the gray code only one bit is allowed to switch at any one time. This is extremely helpful in detecting transmission errors. It is used as a parity check and to validate data received.

Switches, relays, and transistors can be used for representing binary data in digital equipment. Of these, the transistor is most commonly used.

There are two types of logic levels—positive and negative. When the binary 1 state is the most positive of the two voltage levels, positive logic is being used. When the binary 1 state is the most negative of the two voltage levels, negative logic is being used.

Digital information or digital signals are normally processed by digital circuits. The information (digital data) can be sent or received either in the series mode (one digital bit after the other) or in the parallel mode (all the bits in a binary word at one time), or a combination of serial and parallel inputs or outputs. Serial transmission is the slowest, because it can only transfer one binary bit of information at a time.

Unit 2
Semiconductor Devices For Digital Circuits

Contents

Introduction 2-3

Unit Objectives. 2-5

The Bipolar Transistor Switch. 2-6

Designing a Saturated Switch Logic Inverter. .2-17

MOS Field-Effect Transistors 2-27

Summary 2-33

Introduction

At the heart of all modern digital circuits are semiconductor devices like diodes and transistors. Your ability to understand digital circuits and apply them to practical situations depends directly on a knowledge of semiconductors. The purpose of this Unit is to provide you with a solid background in semiconductor fundamentals as they apply to digital circuits, both discrete components as well as integrated circuits. Our discussion here will focus on practical operation and application rather than detailed coverage of internal device physics.

The "Unit Objectives" will tell you exactly what you will learn in this Unit.

Unit Objectives

When you complete Unit 2 on semiconductor devices, you will have the knowledge and skills indicated below. You will be able to:

1. Identify from a list the symbols used to represent PNP and NPN bipolar transistors and P- and N-channel enhancement mode MOSFETs.

2. List the advantages in using MOSFETs in digital circuitry over bipolar transistors.

3. Explain the operation of both bipolar transistors and MOSFETs.

4. Name and explain the three operating modes of a bipolar transistor.

5. Determine the proper bias on a bipolar transistor for saturated operation.

6. Explain the operation of a logic inverter circuit.

7. Design a saturated bipolar transistor switching circuit.

The Bipolar Transistor Switch

The basic component used in implementing any digital logic circuit is a switch. Modern digital integrated circuits use a high speed transistor switch as the primary component. There are two basic types of transistor switches used in implementing digital integrated circuits, the bipolar transistor and the metal oxide semiconductor field effect transistor (MOSFET). An understanding of these two devices is pertinent to the operation, capabilities, and limitations of the various types of digital integrated circuits.

The primary function of a transistor switch in a digital logic circuit is to alternately connect and disconnect a load to and from the circuit power supply. In doing this, the transistor switch produces two distinct voltage levels across the load which represent the binary 0 and binary 1 states. The transistor switch should make and break these connections as quickly and efficiently as possible.

The most commonly used digital switch is the bipolar transistor. In digital applications, the bipolar transistor operates as an off/on or two state device. In one state the transistor is non-conducting or cut-off and acts as essentially an open circuit. In the other state, the transistor is conducting heavily and acts as a very low resistance, approaching a short circuit. A two state logic input signal is applied to the transistor to produce this on/off operation.

Modes of Operation

A bipolar transistor has three basic regions or modes of operation: cut-off, linear or active, and saturation. All three of these modes are used in digital circuits, the cut-off and linear mode in non-saturated bipolar circuits and the cut-off and saturation modes in saturated bipolar circuits.

Cut-Off

In the cut-off mode the transistor is nonconducting. Both the emitter-base (E-B) and collector-base (C-B) junctions are reverse-biased or not biased at all to produce the cut-off state. In theory, no emitter or collector current flows, and the transistor acts as an open circuit between emitter and collector. In most practical transistors, however, the cut-off is not perfect. Because of imperfections in the semiconductor material out of which the device is made, some leakage current flows. In most modern transistors this leakage current is extremely low and for most practical applications can be neglected. However, where very high temperature operation is expected the leakage current becomes a more important consideration. In silicon transistors, the leakage current nearly doubles for each 10° C rise in temperature.

Linear

The linear or active mode of operation is characterized by a forward-biased emitter-base junction and a reverse-biased collector-base junction. In this mode, the transistor does conduct. Emitter and collector currents flow. The emitter and collector currents are directly proportional to the base current variations. The emitter and collector currents are simply amplified versions of the base current variation. In this mode of operation, the transistor functions as a variable resistance and is used to amplify or otherwise process analog signals. This region is of concern in non-saturating digital integrated circuits.

Saturation

The third mode of bipolar transistor operation is saturation. In this mode, both the emitter-base and collector-base junctions are forward-biased. The transistor conducts heavily and acts as a very low resistance. The resistance between the emitter and collector is very low, approaching that of a short circuit.

In digital applications, the bipolar transistor is usually switched between the cut-off and saturation states. As it switches, the transistor passes quickly through the linear region. The primary responsibility of the designer of a digital circuit is to see that the bipolar transistor switches as quickly as possible between cut-off and saturation and that these two states are as stable as possible. In non-saturating digital circuits, the transistors switch between cut-off and the linear region. Again, high speed is the primary requirement.

Saturated Switching Circuits

Figure 2-1 shows the most common form of saturated bipolar transistor logic switch. Here, the transistor is connected as a shunt switch since it is in parallel with the output load R_L. This circuit is also known as a transistor logic inverter.

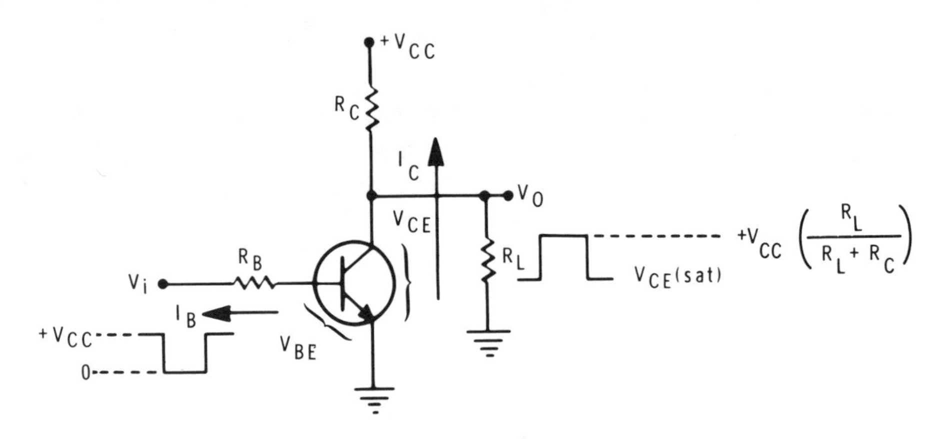

Figure 2-1
Basic transistor switching circuit.

With an input voltage V_i of zero volts or ground, the transistor is cut-off. The emitter-base junction is not forward-biased, therefore, the transistor does not conduct. The only collector current flowing at this time is a minute leakage current. The output voltage V_O, with no load, is equal to the supply voltage V_{CC} as seen through collector resistor R_C. If a finite resistive load R_L is connected between the output and ground V_O will be some value less than V_{CC} and dependent upon the division ratio between R_C and R_L.

$$V_O = V_{CC} \left(\frac{R_L}{R_C + R_L}\right)$$

When an input voltage V_i of sufficient amplitude is applied to base resistor R_B, the emitter-base junction will become forward-biased and the transistor will conduct. The transistor will be in the linear or saturation regions depending upon the size of V_i, the value of R_B and the DC forward current transfer ratio h_{FE} (also known as the DC current gain or Beta) of the transistor.

Figure 2-2 shows the typical input and output waveforms of a transistor switching circuit. The input switches between zero volts (LOW) and V_i (HIGH). When the input is LOW, the transistor is cut-off and output voltage V_o is approximately equal to V_{CC} (HIGH). When the input is HIGH, the transistor saturates and acts as a low resistance. The output voltage V_o is the collector-emitter saturation voltage V_{CE} (sat) which is only a few tenths of a volt (LOW). As you can see, the output is HIGH when the input is LOW, and the output is LOW when the input is HIGH. The input and output signals are always opposite one another. This is the reason for the name inverter.

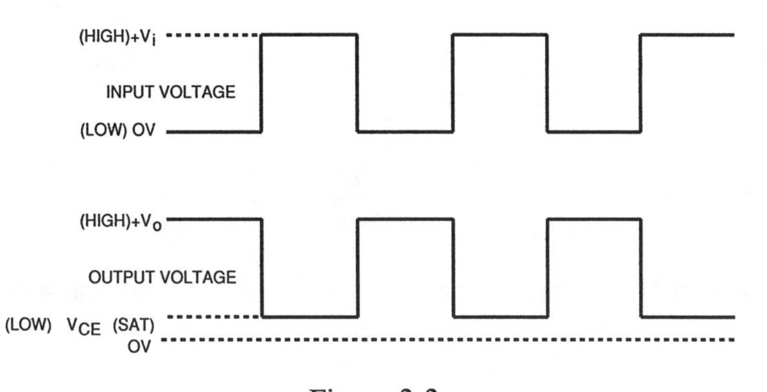

Figure 2-2
Input and output waveforms of a shunt transistor switching circuit.

In a digital circuit the magnitude of V_i and R_B are such that sufficient base current flows in order to cause the transistor to saturate. This condition occurs when the actual base current I_B is greater than the ratio of the collector current I_C to the gain (Beta or h_{FE}).

$$I_B > \frac{I_C}{h_{FE}} \text{ (for saturation)}$$

The base current is a direct function of the applied input voltage V_i and the value of the base resistor R_B. This relationship is

$$I_B = \frac{V_i - V_{BE}}{R_B}$$

where V_{BE} is the voltage across the forward biased emitter-base junction.

The ratio of the collector current (I_c) to the base current (I_B) in a common emitter circuit is known as the DC forward current transfer ratio or h_{FE}. This ratio

$$h_{FE} = \frac{I_C}{I_B}$$

expresses the effective gain of the device or the ability of the base current to control the larger collector current. The greater this ratio, the higher the gain.

By algebraically rearranging this expression, we can calculate the base current for a given collector current and gain.

$$I_B = \frac{I_C}{h_{FE}}$$

If we design the circuit so that the base current is greater than this ratio, the transistor will saturate. That is, both emitter-base and collector-base junctions will become forward-biased. In this state the transistor is conducting heavily and the resistance between the emitter and collector is very low. For typical switching transistors this value of resistance is in the 5 to 30 ohms range. The voltage drop between the collector and emitter during saturation V_{CE} (sat) is only several tenths of a volt. This is very low compared to the supply voltage V_{CC} and therefore for most practical purposes is considered to be nearly zero volts.

During saturation the amount of emitter and collector current flowing becomes basically a function of the value of the supply voltage V_{CC} and the collector resistance R_C. Because the voltage drop across the transistor is essentially zero, the collector current can be found from the expression

$$I_C = \frac{V_{CC} - V_{CE}\,(\text{sat})}{R_C} \approx \frac{V_{CC}}{R_C}$$

This relationship holds true only if sufficient base current flows to saturate the transistor. If the value of the base current is less than the ratio of I_C/h_{FE}, the transistor will be operating in the linear region. The emitter-base junction will be forward-biased but the collector base junction will be reverse-biased. The collector-emitter voltage V_{CE} will be correspondingly higher.

There are two ways you can determine whether a transistor is saturated or operating in the linear region. The first method is to measure the junction potentials on the transistor. When measuring these voltages it is important to note the polarity of each transistor element with respect to the other. By knowing the magnitudes of the junction voltages and their relative polarities you can establish the state of the transistor.

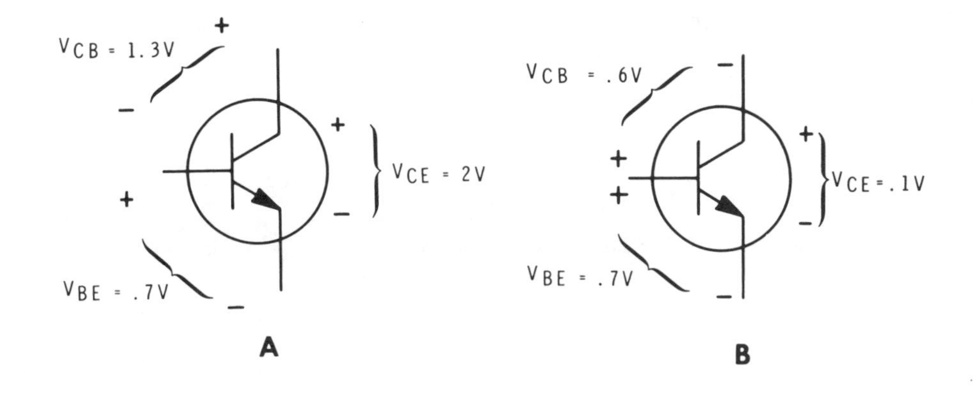

Figure 2-3
Polarity and voltage relationships in a conducting transistor (A) linear operation and (B) saturation.

Figure 2-3 shows typical junction voltages for an NPN transistor both in the saturated and unsaturated states. The transistor in Figure 2-3A is operating in the linear or active region. The emitter-base junction is forward-biased because junction voltage V_{BE} is of the proper polarity. A conducting junction in a silicon transistor typically has a voltage drop of approximately .7 volt. Observing the collector-base junction we see that the voltage across it (V_{CB}) is 1.3 volts with the collector being more positive than the base. This indicates a reverse-biased condition on the collector-base junction. The voltage drop between the emitter and collector V_{CE} is two volts. Note the relationship between V_{CE}, V_{BE}, and V_{CB}.

$$V_{CE} = V_{BE} + V_{CB}$$

In Figure 2-3B, the transistor is saturated. Again V_{BE} is approximately .7 volt with the polarity indicated. The big difference however is the polarity change in V_{CB}. Here the base is more positive than the collector indicating a forward biased condition on this junction. The junction voltage drop is approximately .6 volt. Again note that the collector-emitter voltage V_{CE} is the *algebraic* sum of (or difference between) V_{CB} and V_{BE} and in this case is only $.7 - .6 = .1$ volt. Because of this low voltage drop the effective resistance of the transistor is extremely low. Another beneficial characteristic of saturated operation is that the low collector-emitter voltage greatly minimizes the power dissipation in the conducting transistor. The power dissipation is

$$P = V_{CE} \bullet I_C$$

With V_{CE} so low during saturation, the power dissipation is also very low even though the collector current may be large.

The other method of determining whether or not a transistor is in saturation is to find both the base and collector current through actual circuit measurements and then determine if the base current is less than or greater than the ratio of the collector current and the DC current gain h_{FE}. As indicated before, if $I_B > I_C/h_{FE}$ then the transistor is saturated. If $I_B < I_C/h_{FE}$, the transistor is operating in its active region. The actual value of h_{FE} depends upon the type of transistor being used, the current level in the transistor, its temperature and other factors. The current gain value varies even among transistors of the same type. To ensure saturation in a switching transistor, designers generally make the base resistor small enough to produce a base current with a given minimum logic input voltage that is greater than the I_C/h_{FE} ratio. This safety factor is necessary in order to ensure saturation under all conditions. When the base current is greater than the I_C/h_{FE} ratio, we say that we are overdriving the base.

Self-Test Review

1. The voltage drop across a conducting PN junction in a silicon transistor is approximately ________________ volts.

2. The collector and base currents in a transistor inverter are measured and found to be I_C = 10 ma, I_B = .5 ma. The transistor h_{FE} is 15. Is the transistor saturated?______________________________

3. A PNP transistor has the following junction voltages V_{BE} = .7 volts, base negative with respect to emitter. V_{CB} = .5 volts, collector positive with respect to base. Is the transistor saturated?____________

4. When a transistor is saturated it acts as a(n):

   a. very low resistance.
   b. very high resistance.
   c. open circuit.
   d. variable resistance.

5. To act as an open circuit, a transistor must be operating in which mode?

   a. linear.
   b. saturation.
   c. cut-off.

6. Another name for a saturated shunt transistor switch is ________ .

Switching Speed

One of the most important characteristics of a logic circuit is its ability to switch rapidly between the binary logic levels. This switching speed is affected by the transistor characteristics, the circuit component values, stray capacitance and inductance, the current and voltage levels in the circuit and the specific circuit configuration. When the input signal to a digital circuit changes from one logic level to the other, the output of the circuit does not change instantaneously. Instead, there is a delay time existing between the change in the input signal and the corresponding change in the output. This time lag is generally referred to as propagation delay.

The turn-on time of a transistor is primarily a function of the transistor characteristics and the amount of base drive applied to the circuit. A heavy base current helps to ensure a rapid turn-on.

The turn-off time delay is affected mainly by the transistor characteristics. The turn-off of the transistor is delayed because of storage time. When a transistor is saturated, an excess of minority carriers (holes in an NPN and electrons in a PNP transistor) build up in the collector-base junction region. This charge storage keeps the transistor conducting even with the base drive removed. It takes a finite period of time for this charge to be removed so that the transistor begins to come out of saturation. This storage time is a function of the transistor characteristics and the amount of base drive.

By using the proper transistors, circuit configuration, and component values, the switching delay times can be significantly reduced. Despite all of the factors that limit the switching speed, modern high-speed switching transistors can change from one state to the next in only a matter of nanoseconds (10^{-9} seconds).

Non-Saturating Switching Circuits

The most serious limitation to the switching speed of a bipolar transistor is the storage time associated with the condition of saturation. The charge storage build up in the collector-base region during saturation takes a finite time to be cleared away, in order to turn the transistor off. This storage time is the most significant part of the turn-off time and therefore any means of minimizing it will greatly increase the switching speed of the transistor. Special bipolar switching transistors have been designed to help minimize this storage time effect, and external circuitry can be adjusted to minimize it to some degree. The obvious way to increase switching speeds, therefore, is to avoid saturation. By keeping the transistor from going into saturation no charge storage occurs. Therefore very high switching speeds can be achieved. A number of logic circuits have been designed using non-saturating bipolar transistor switches. The transistors switch between the cut-off and linear regions. Such circuits are capable of switching at frequencies as high as 1 GHz.

Self-Test Review

7. The finite time that it takes transistor logic switches to turn on and off is called _____________ _________.

8. The turn-on delay is a function of transistor characteristics and __________ __________.

9. The turn-off delay is caused primarily by _______________ __________.

10. Non-saturating logic circuits have a faster switching speed than saturated circuits.

    a. True.
    b. False.

Designing A Saturated Switch Logic Inverter

While most modern digital equipment is implemented with integrated circuits, it is sometimes necessary or desirable to supplement the IC with a discrete component circuit to perform a special function. This includes things such as logic level conversion, driving an indicator light such as an incandescent lamp or light emitting diode (LED) or operating a relay. All of these circuits use a saturated bipolar transistor switch. Several examples are given in Figure 2-4.

The circuit in Figure 2-4A is simply an inverter where the input and output logic levels may or may not be equal. Such a circuit is useful in interfacing different types of logic circuits. In Figure 2-4B, the LED will light when an input voltage V_i is applied. The transistor acts as an on/off switch controlled by V_i. This is also true in the relay driver circuit of Figure 2-4C. Contacts A and B of relay K_1 are normally open (N.O.) when V_i is zero. When V_i becomes sufficiently positive, the transistor saturates and K_1 is energized. The magnetic field produced by the relay coil closes contacts A and B. Diode D_1 is used to protect the transistor when the input voltage is removed. When the transistor cuts off the magnetic field the coil collapses thereby inducing a high negative voltage spike that can damage the transistor. The voltage spike causes D_1 to conduct and clamp the collector voltage to a safe level.

Such circuits are so common that it is desirable to know how to design them. The procedure is simple as you will see here.

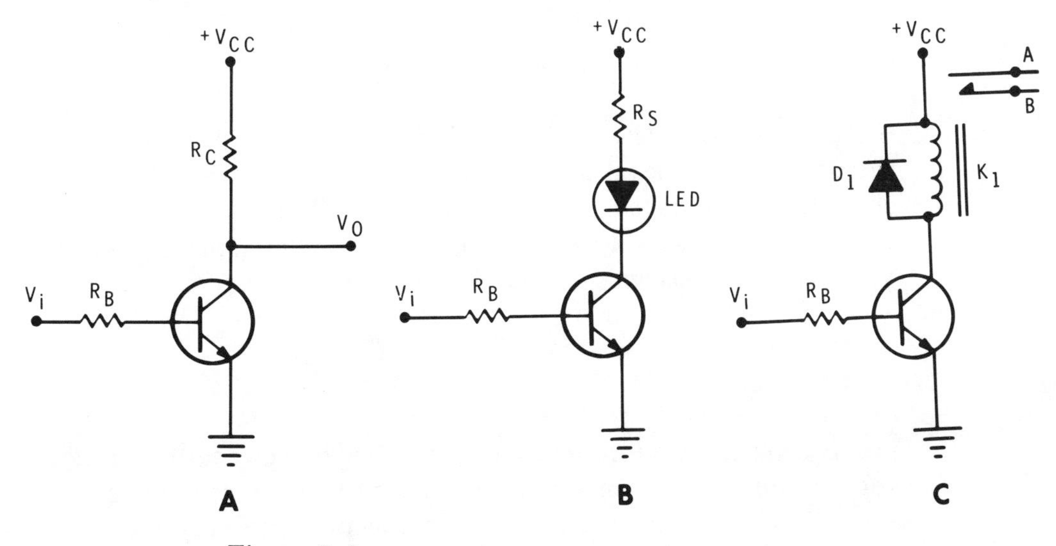

Figure 2-4
Bipolar transistor switch used as a logic inverter (A), An LED indicator driver (B), and a relay drive (C).

Procedure

1. Define the load.

   For a lamp or relay driver, the characteristics of the lamp or relay are given. These usually include a rated voltage (V_L), current and/or resistance. If the circuit is an inverter used to supply a signal to an external load, the load voltage and current or load resistance must be given.

2. Specify a supply voltage.

   The supply voltage (V_{CC}) will usually be equal to or higher than the desired load voltage. Normally, the circuit will operate from an existing supply of some standard value such as +5 volts, +12 volts, etc.

3. Select a suitable transistor.

   A wide variety of types are available. The exact application will guide you in its selection. A transistor designed for switching rather than linear applications is usually preferred. The voltage and current ratings will be determined by the load and supply characteristics. The collector current and voltage breakdown ratings should be at least twice the operating characteristics. Gain (h_{FE}) and operating speed requirements will be dictated by the application. The exact transistor characteristics can be determined from the manufacturer's data sheets.

4. Determine the value of any series dropping resistor.

   If the supply voltage is larger than the load (lamp, relay, etc.) voltage, then some series dropping resistor (R_S) will be needed. See Figure 2-4B. The voltage across this resistance will be the supply voltage (V_{CC}) less the load voltage (V_L) and the transistor saturation voltage V_{CE} (sat). The resistance can then be found with the expression

$$R_s = \frac{V_{CC} - V_L - V_{CE}\text{ (sat)}}{I_C}$$

   where I_C is the load current and the collector current. V_{CE} (sat) is very low and can be considered zero. Use the closest standard resistor value. This step does not apply to an inverter with only a collector resistor.

5. Specify an output voltage.

If the circuit being designed is an inverter with a shunt load, the desired output voltage (V_O) should be specified. It will be some value less than V_{CC} depending upon the values of R_C and R_L. See Figure 2-5.

$$V_O = V_{CC}\left(\frac{R_L}{R_C + R_L}\right)$$

If there is no shunt load, $V_O = V_{CC}$.

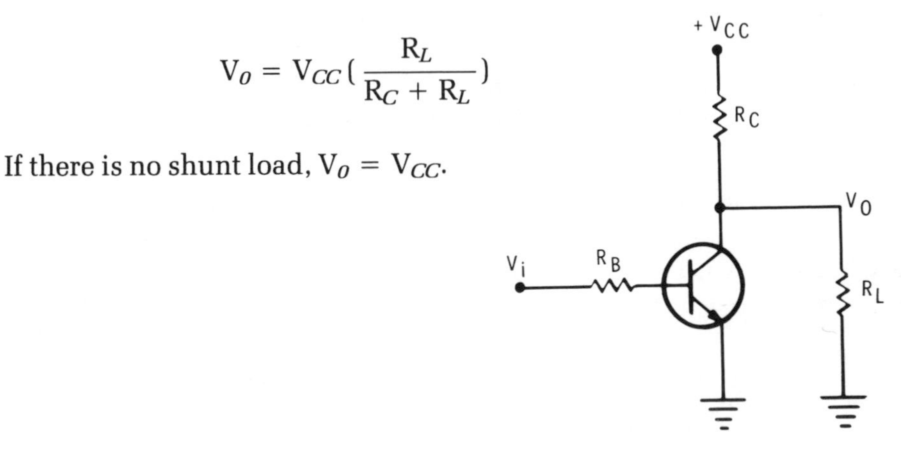

Figure 2-5
Logic inverter with shunt load.

6. Determine the value of the collector resistor.

If the circuit being designed is an inverter with a shunt load to ground, the collector resistor R_C value can be calculated if the supply voltage (V_{CC}), load resistance (R_L) and desired output voltage (V_O) are known.
Since

$$V_O = V_{CC}\left(\frac{R_L}{R_C + R_L}\right)$$

The collector resistance can be found by rearranging this expression.

$$R_C = \frac{R_L\,(V_{CC} - V_O)}{V_O}$$

Use the closest standard value of resistance.

7. Determine the collector current.

   This is the load current specified earlier for lamp or relay drivers. For the inverter arrangement described in Step 6, the current is

$$I_C = \frac{V_{CC} - V_{CE}\,(\text{sat})}{R_C} \approx \frac{V_{CC}}{R_C}$$

   Since V_{CE} (sat) is usually only several tenths of a volt it can be considered negligible or zero in the above expression.

8. Calculate the base current.

   Knowing the gain (h_{FE}) from the manufacturer's data sheet and the collector current (I_C), the base current (I_B) can be found.

$$h_{FE} = \frac{I_C}{I_B} \text{ therefore } I_B = I_C/h_{FE}$$

   Use the minimum value of h_{FE} quoted in the data sheet. To provide some overdrive and ensure saturation it is desirable to provide some safety factor by derating the h_{FE} by a factor of 2 (or more if desired). Therefore

$$I_B = \frac{I_C}{h_{FE}/2} \quad \text{or} \quad I_B = \frac{2\,I_C}{h_{FE}\,(\text{min})}$$

9. Calculate the base resistor.

   The base resistor (R_B) is found with the expression below.

$$R_B = \frac{V_i - V_{BE}}{I_B}$$

   Here V_i is the lowest expected value of base drive voltage. It is the binary 1 voltage level for positive logic. V_{BE} of course is the emitter-base voltage drop which is typically .7 volts for a silicon transistor.

If the circuit being designed is to be driven by another inverter as in Figure 2-6 its supply voltage and collector resistance should be considered.

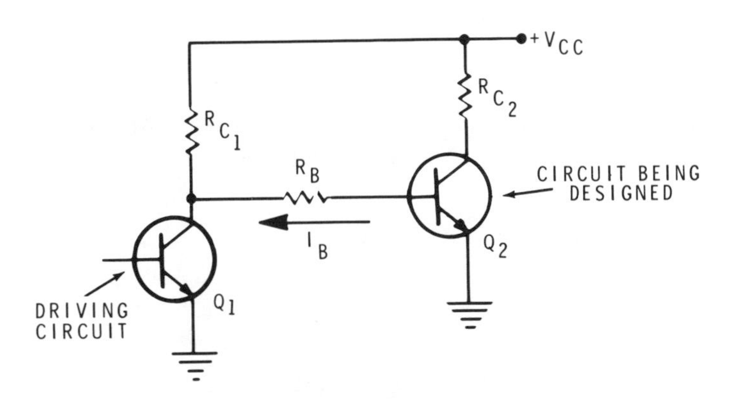

Figure 2-6

When Q_1 cuts off, the driver circuit will be activated by I_B flowing through R_B and the collector resistor R_{C1} of the driving circuit. In this case,

$$R_B = \frac{V_{CC} - I_B R_{C1} - V_{BE}}{I_B}$$

Use the closest lower standard resistance value.

The following examples will illustrate the procedure for two practical applications.

Example Application 1

Design a driver for an LED indicator. The steps below correspond to those in the procedure. See Figure 2-4B.

1. The load is a light emitting diode indicator whose normal brilliance is obtained with 20 ma of current. Its normal operating voltage, the load voltage drop (V_L), is 1.7 volts at this current value.

2. The supply voltage V_{CC} is +5 volts.

3. A type MPSA20 silicon transistor will be used. h_{FE} (min) = 100.

4. Since the LED voltage drop is less than the supply voltage a series dropping resistor is needed. The load (collector) current is 20 ma.

$$R_S = \frac{V_{CC} - V_L - V_{CE}\,(sat)}{I_C}$$

If we consider V_{CE} (sat) negligible then

$$R_S = \frac{5 - 1.7}{.02} = \frac{3.3}{.02} = 165 \text{ ohms}$$

A standard 150 or 180 ohm 10 percent resistor or 160 ohm 5 percent resistor could be used.

5. Not applicable.

6. Not applicable.

7. $I_C = 20$ ma or .02 amp.

8. $$I_B = \frac{2\,I_C}{h_{FE}} = \frac{2\,(.02)}{100} = \frac{.04}{100} = .4 \text{ ma} = 400\ \mu A$$

9. Assume the input voltage V_i = +3.5 volts. V_{BE} = .7 volts for a silicon transistor.

$$R_B = \frac{V_i - V_{BE}}{I_B} = \frac{3.5 - .7}{.0004} = 7000 \text{ ohms}$$

A standard 6.8K 10 percent value can be used.

See Figure 2-7

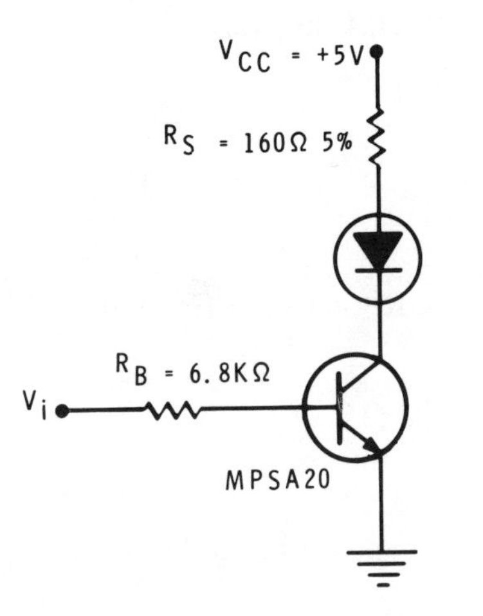

Figure 2-7
LED driver circuit: Example Application 1.

Example Application 2

Design an inverter circuit to apply +6 volts across a 600 ohm load. The supply voltage is +15 volts. The driving signal (V_i) is supplied by the +15 volt supply through a 1000 ohm collector resistor. See Figure 2-8.

1. R_L = 600 ohms, V_L = 6 volts.

2. V_{CC} = +15 volts.

3. Use an MPSA20 silicon transistor.

4. Not applicable.

5. V_O = 6 volts.

6. $$R_C = \frac{R_L\ (V_{CC} - V_O)}{V_O}$$

$$R_{C2} = \frac{600\ (15 - 6)}{6} = \frac{600\ (9)}{6} = 900 \text{ ohms}$$

A standard 910 ohm resistor could be used.

7. $$I_C = \frac{V_{CC}}{R_C} = \frac{15}{910} = .0165 \text{ or } 16.5 \text{ ma}$$

8. $$I_B = \frac{2\ I_C}{h_{FE}} = \frac{2\ (.0165)}{100} = .00033 \text{ amp} = .33 \text{ ma} = 330\mu A$$

9. $$R_B = \frac{V_{CC} - I_B R_{C1} - V_{BE}}{I_B}$$

$$R_B = \frac{15 - (.00033)(1000) - .7}{.00033} = \frac{13.97}{.00033} = 42{,}333 \text{ ohms}$$

A standard 39K ohm resistor could be used. See Figure 2-8.

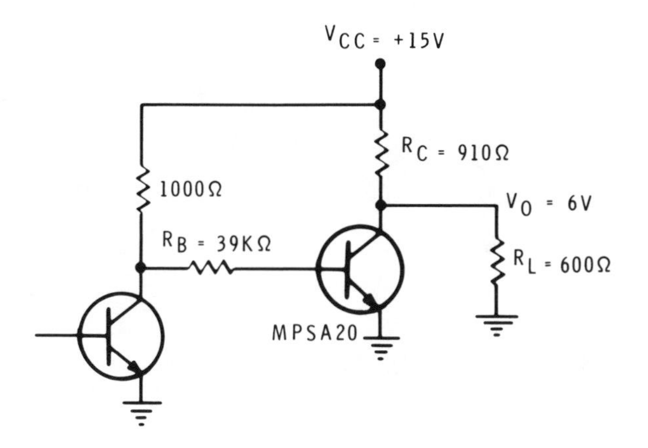

Figure 2-8
Inverter circuit: Example Application 2.

11. Design a transistor switch circuit that will energize a relay whose coil resistance is 400 ohms and current requirement is 30 ma. Use a supply voltage of +15 volts. The input voltage is +15 volts. Use an MPSA20 transistor. Draw the completed circuit and label all values.

MOS Field-Effect Transistors

Another transistor widely used in digital integrated circuits is the enhancement mode metal oxide semiconductor field-effect transistor (MOSFET). Also known as an insulated gate field-effect transistor (IGFET), this device offers numerous advantages over the bipolar transistor particularly for digital work and integrated circuits. Because the MOSFET is basically a simple device, it is more easily constructed than a bipolar transistor. Since it can be made smaller than bipolar devices it permits more circuitry to be produced on a given area of semiconductor material. The cost of an integrated circuit is directly proportional to the area of the semiconductor material used to construct the circuit and the complexity of the devices used. Simple, low cost, high density circuits are readily constructed with MOSFET components.

The N-Channel MOSFET

Figure 2-9 shows the basic construction of an N-channel enhancement mode MOSFET. It is constructed of a P-type silicon base or substrate into which is diffused two N-type semiconductor material areas. These form the source and drain elements of the transistor. On top of this is diffused a thin layer of silicon dioxide, a glass insulator which isolates the source and drain regions from the remainder of the device. On top of the silicon dioxide insulator is formed a third element called the gate. The silicon dioxide insulates the gate terminal from the P-type silicon material. The gate is simply a metallized diffusion such as aluminum or a silicon conductive material that forms a capacitor with the P-type silicon base, the silicon dioxide layer acting as the dielectric. The area beneath the gate dielectric and between the source and drain is known as the channel. If the drain is made positive with respect to the source, current will flow between the source and the drain. It is the level and polarity of the voltage between the source and the gate that determines the conductivity of the channel.

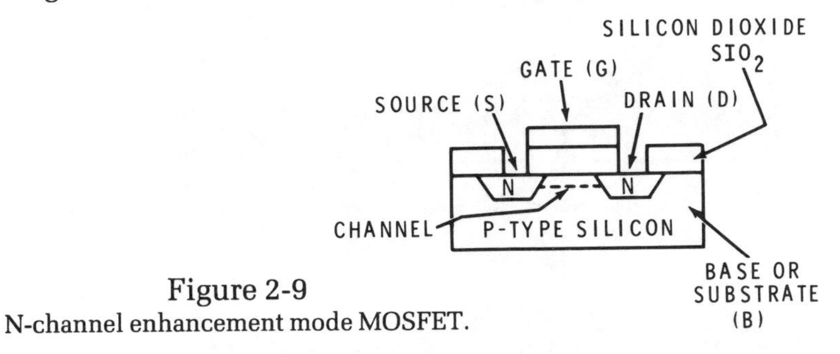

Figure 2-9
N-channel enhancement mode MOSFET.

With the gate source voltage equal to zero, no current flows between the source and the drain. The alternate N-type and P-type materials between source and drain effectively form two back-to-back diodes both of which are cut off. However, when the voltage applied between the gate and source exceeds a certain threshold level with the gate positive with respect to the source, an electric field will be established in the channel region. This causes the transistor to conduct and electrons will flow between the source and the drain.

The gate-source arrangement in the MOSFET acts as a capacitor. Applying a gate-source voltage charges this capacitor. The gate becomes positive and the area below the gate in the substrate becomes negative. The majority carriers in the P-type substrate (holes) will be depleted by the negative charge and the electron density will be enhanced. This negative charge in the P-type base establishes a channel for current flow between the two N-type regions. Removing the gate-source voltage or decreasing it below the threshold level will cause the conduction to cease.

The enhancement mode MOSFET is an excellent switch. When the gate voltage is below the threshold value, the resistance between the source and the drain is extremely high and very closely approximates an open circuit. When the gate voltage is above the threshold level, the transistor conducts and the resistance between the source and the drain is very low, approximating a short circuit. Such characteristics make the enhancement mode MOSFET ideal for digital circuits.

One of the primary benefits of the MOSFET over the standard bipolar transistor is that the input impedance between source and gate is extremely high. The input impedance between the source and gate is many thousands of megohms and, in effect, is more capacitive than resistive. This high input impedance minimizes the loading of one logic circuit on the next. Figure 2-10 shows the schematic symbol normally used to represent an N-channel enhancement mode MOSFET.

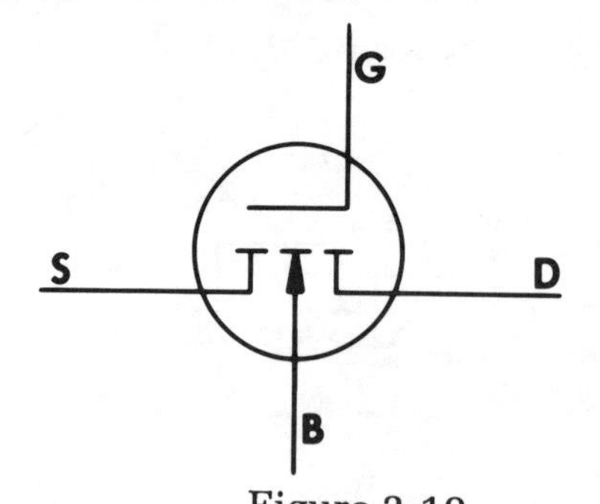

Figure 2-10

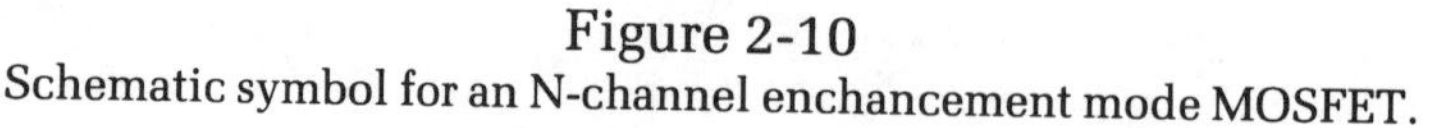
Schematic symbol for an N-channel enchancement mode MOSFET.

The P-Channel MOSFET

Figure 2-11 shows the construction of a P-channel enhancement mode MOSFET. It is similar in construction to the N-channel device. However, the substrate is N-type material, while the source and drain diffusions are P-type material. The symbol used to represent this device is shown in Figure 2-12. The operation of the P-channel MOSFET is similar to that for the N-channel device with the exception of the operating voltage polarities. Like the N-channel device, the P-channel MOSFET is normally off if the gate-to-source voltage is below a specific threshold value. When the gate voltage is made negative with respect to the source and is of an amplitude above the threshold level, the transistor will conduct and current will flow between the source and the drain. In the P-channel device, the current carriers are holes instead of electrons.

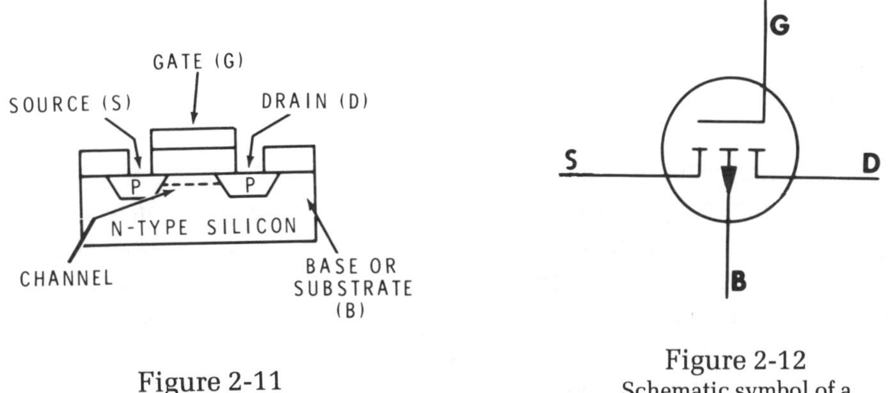

Figure 2-11
P-channel enhancement and MOSFET.

Figure 2-12
Schematic symbol of a P-channel enhancement mode MOSFET.

One of the most important characteristics of the enhancement mode MOSFET is its threshold voltage, that value of gate-source voltage required to cause the transistor to conduct. There are two basic types of threshold in common use; low threshold and high threshold. The high threshold devices are easier to make, and, therefore, are more common. This high threshold value is approximately three to four volts. There is circuitry available with a low threshold in the one to two volt region. Typically, P-channel devices have high thresholds, while N-channel devices have low thresholds.

Figure 2-13 shows a simplified schematic symbol often used to represent an enhancement mode MOSFET. Because of the complexity of the standard symbols, they are rarely used. The letter P or N is written adjacent to the symbol to designate whether it is a P-channel or an N-channel device.

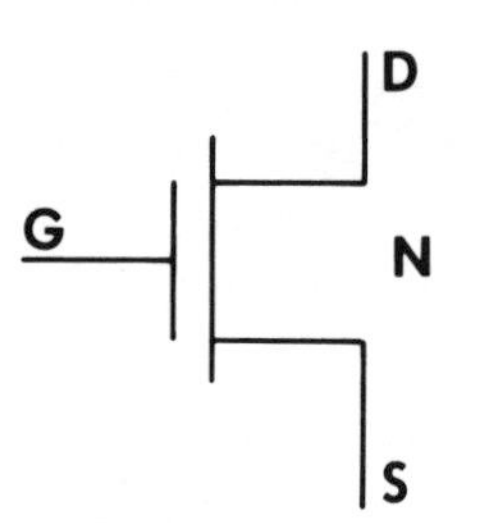

Figure 2-13
Simplified symbol of
enhancement mode MOSFET.

Bipolars vs. MOSFETs

The primary benefits of the MOSFET over the bipolar transistor are; small size, simplicity of construction, high input impedance and low power consumption. However, these advantages are somewhat offset by the major disadvantage; slow switching speeds. Because of the high impedance nature of the device and its capacitive characteristics, switching speeds are significantly lower than those for bipolar transistors. MOSFET switching speeds in the region below 100 nanoseconds have only recently been introduced. Nevertheless, the advantages of the MOSFET over the bipolar for many applications offset this switching speed disadvantage. Bipolar transistors are still faster and offer the further advantage of being able to handle high power applications.

MOSFET Circuits

Logic circuits are readily constructed with enhancement mode MOSFETs. Figure 2-14 shows an inverter circuit constructed with a P-channel MOSFET. With the gate input voltage (V_i) at zero, the transistor does not conduct and the output voltage (V_O) is the drain supply voltage (V_{DD}) as seen through the drain resistor (R_D). When the input voltage is made sufficiently negative beyond the threshold value, the transistor conducts and acts virtually as a short circuit. The output voltage at this time is near zero volts. An inverter using an N-channel device would be similar, but with positive logic levels and supply voltage.

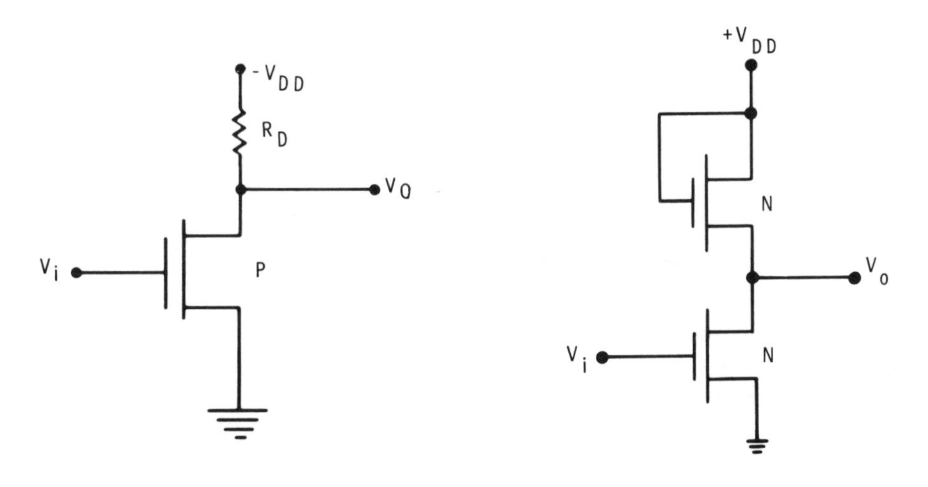

Figure 2-14
P-channel MOSFET inverter.

Figure 2-15
Using a biased MOSFET as a load resister.

In practical MOS circuits, the drain resistor (R_D) is not used. Because it occupies a substantial amount of space in an integrated circuit, it is generally eliminated and replaced by another MOSFET, biased to act as a resistance. The transistor itself is smaller than a diffused resistor. This circuit is illustrated in Figure 2-15.

A very popular type of MOS digital circuit combines both P-channel and N-channel devices to form what is known as a complementary MOS (CMOS) logic circuit. You will learn more about these devices in a later unit.

12. The MOSFET is also known as a ______________________ .

13. To cause an N-channel enhancement mode MOSFET to conduct the gate-source voltage must be:

    a. zero.
    b. negative.
    c. positive.
    d. above the threshold level.

14. The gate-source appears to external circuits primarily as a:

    a. short circuit.
    b. low impedance.
    c. capacitor.
    d. high impedance.

15. The switching time of a MOSFET compared to that of a bipolar transistor is:

    a. less.
    b. more.
    c. about the same.

16. To cause a P-channel MOSFET to conduct, the gate-source voltage must be higher than the ____________ and the drain must be ______________ with respect to the source.

Summary

The most common element in binary logic circuits is the switch. Since a mechanical switch is too slow for most computer operations, the electronic switch is normally used. Electronic transistor switches are either bipolar transistors or metal oxide semiconductor field effect transistors (MOSFETs).

In addition to performing a switching function, the transistor can amplify and invert the digital signal. Inversion means shifting the input signal by 180 degrees. In digital signals, inversion causes logic ones to become zeros and zeros to become ones.

Bipolar transistor switches operate in three basic modes—cut-off, linear, and saturation. The transistor is said to be operating in cut-off when it is nonconducting. A transistor in cut-off acts as an open circuit. The linear mode of operation is when the transistor is active and current is flowing. A transistor is in saturation when it is conducting so heavily that it acts as a short circuit.

Bipolar transistor switches can be classified as saturating or non-saturating devices. A saturated switching circuit switches between cut-off and saturation to represent ones and zeros. Due to saturation, turn-off delay time limits the switching speed of the circuit. Non-saturating switching circuits are designed to overcome the relatively long turn-off delay time of a saturated circuit and increase the switching speed. Non-saturating switching circuits switch between the cut-off and linear regions to represent ones and zeros.

MOSFETs can be either P-type or N-type devices. They are smaller and consume less power than bipolar transistors. Because of this, they are preferred in digital integrated circuitry.

The only advantages discrete bipolar transistors have over MOSFETs is their power handling capabilities and speed of operation. In digital computers, high power handling capability is not normally a requirement, or considered an advantage.

Unit 3
Digital Logic Circuits

Contents

Introduction 3-3

Unit Objectives 3-5

Types of Logic Circuits 3-6

The Inverter 3-10

Decision-Making Logic Elements 3-14

The Dual Nature of Logic Gates 3-24

NAND/NOR Gates 3-27

Practical Logic Circuits 3-35

Summary 3-41

Appendix — Positive and Negative Logic
Equivalent Circuits 3-43

Introduction

All digital equipment, simple or complex, is constructed from just a few basic circuits. These circuits are called logic elements. A logic element performs some specific logic function on binary data.

There are two basic types of digital logic elements: decision-making and memory. Decision-making logic elements monitor binary inputs and produce outputs based on the input states, and the operational characteristics of the logic element. Memory elements store binary data.

Whether the digital equipment is a simple piece of test equipment or a large scale digital computer, this equipment is made up entirely of such logic circuits. Once you learn the basic logic elements and the most commonly used forms, you will be able to understand and determine the operation of any piece of digital equipment. By understanding how to apply these basic logic elements, you will be capable of designing and troubleshooting digital equipment.

In this unit you are going to study the basic types of digital logic circuits. You will learn the operation of decision-making and memory circuits. You will also discover several special classes of logic circuits. We will also discuss the practical implementation of these logic circuits using switches and relays, discrete electronic components and integrated circuits. This unit provides the base upon which all of the remaining units in this program are built. The study of digital techniques is, in effect, a study of digital logic circuits and how they are applied. As a result, this is an extremely important background lesson.

Unit Objectives

When you complete Unit 3 you will have the following knowledge and capabilities.

1. You will be able to list the three basic types of logic elements.

2. You will be able to write a definition for combinational logic circuits.

3. You will be able to write a definition for sequential logic circuits.

4. You will be able to draw the schematic and explain the operation of both diode and switch contact AND gates.

5. You will be able to draw the schematic and explain the operation of both diode and switch contact OR gates.

6. You will be able to draw the schematic and explain the operation of a transistor and switch contact inverter.

7. Given a list of symbols, you will be able to identify the industry standard symbols for inverters, AND, OR, NAND, and NOR gates.

8. From a list of truth tables, you will be able to identify the logic functions being performed.

9. You will be able to write a truth table for any of the basic logic functions: AND, OR, NOT, NAND, NOR.

10. Given a list of logic equations you will be able to identify the logic function expressed by each.

11. You will be able to write the logic equation for any of the basic logic functions AND, OR, NAND, NOR, NOT.

Types of Logic Circuits

The two basic types of logic circuits are decision-making and memory. Both types accept binary inputs and produce binary outputs. The nature of the output is a function of the state of the inputs and the characteristics of the particular logic circuit.

Decision-making logic circuits do exactly what their name implies; make decisions. The basic decision-making logic element is called a gate. A gate has two or more binary inputs and a single output. Figure 3-1 shows the generalized symbol used for representing a logic gate. More specific symbols are used to represent practical types of gates. There are several different types of logic gates, each performing a specific decision-making operation. The gate looks at its binary inputs, and based upon their states and its operation, it generates an appropriate output signal that reflects the decision it has made.

While many simple logic functions can be implemented with a gate, generally gates are combined to form more sophisticated and complex decision making logic networks called combinational circuits. A combinational circuit is made up of two or more gates and has two or more inputs and one or more outputs. Combinational circuits still perform a decision-making function but of a more sophisticated nature. Most combinational circuits perform some unique logic function such as decoding, encoding, multiplexing, comparison or an arithmetic operation with binary numbers. A generalized block diagram of a combinational logic circuit is shown in Figure 3-2.

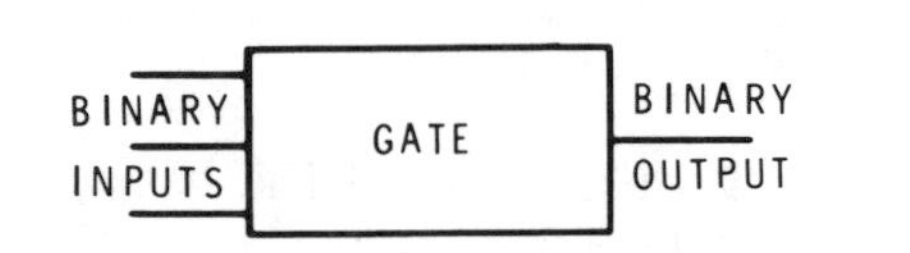

Figure 3-1
Basic symbol of a logic gate.

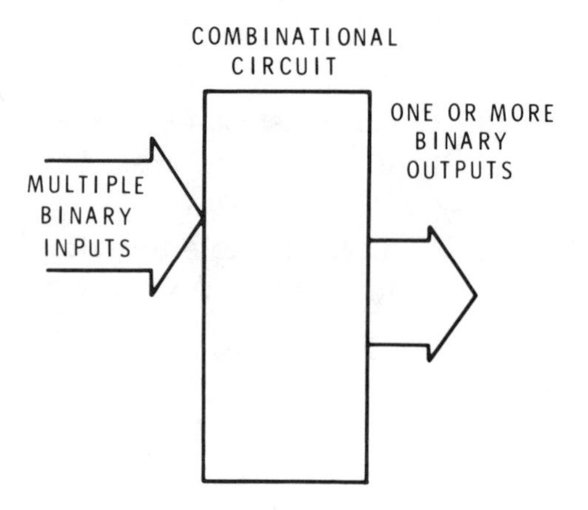

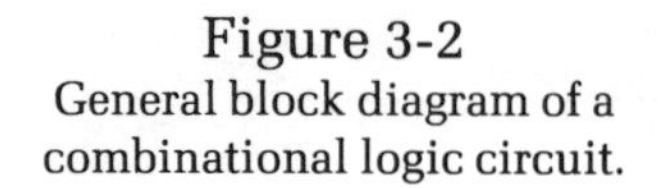

Figure 3-2
General block diagram of a combinational logic circuit.

The other type of logic element is a memory circuit. The basic memory element is a bistable storage device known as a flip-flop. This circuit has two stable states which can represent the two binary numbers 0 and 1. The circuit can be placed into either state so that it retains that state or remembers the bit stored there. Most memory circuits store a single binary bit. Many of these elements can be combined to store complete binary numbers or words.

Most memory elements are interconnected with combinational circuits to form another more sophisticated form of memory element known as a sequential circuit. A general block diagram of a sequential circuit is shown in Figure 3-3. The inputs to the sequential circuit consists of external binary data and feedback signals developed within the sequential circuit itself. The outputs of a sequential circuit are binary signals that are used to operate or control external circuits. The output of the sequential circuit is a function of the binary inputs, the binary data stored in the sequential circuit itself and the specific characteristics of this circuit.

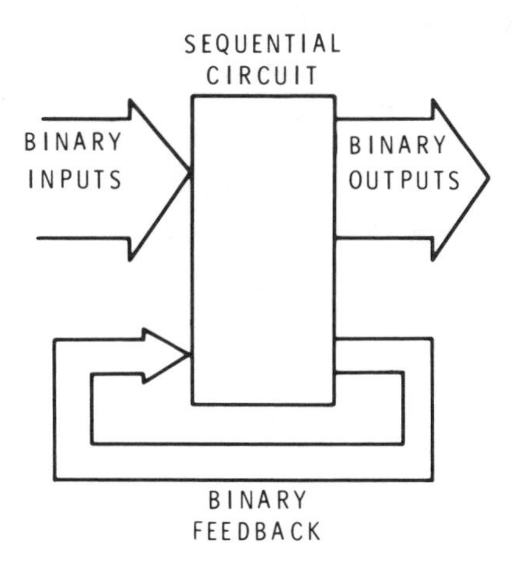

Figure 3-3
General block diagram
of a sequential logic circuit.

Sequential circuits are used for a variety of operations in digital equipment. Typical sequential circuits consist of counters, shift registers, timers, sequencers, and other circuits where binary data is stored and manipulated as a function of time. You will study these circuits in later units.

The three basic decision-making logic elements are the AND gate, the OR gate, and the inverter. All other digital logic elements and circuits are variations or combinations of just these three basic elements. Each of these elements receive one or more binary inputs and generates a single binary output.

In order to distinguish one binary input signal from another and in order to identify both binary inputs and outputs, each signal is generally assigned a name or label. In its simplest form the label consists of a letter, a small word or mnemonic (pronounced ne-mon-ik). This label or designation indicates a specific logic signal which can assume either of the two binary states 0 or 1. In the discussions of the logic circuits presented here all inputs and outputs will be given such names and labels. In most cases a simple letter designation will be used. However, keep in mind that these designations may be words or letter and number combinations. Some typical examples are A, X D3, CLR, JMPZ, etc.

Self-Test Review

1. The two basic classifications of logic circuits are ______________ and ____.

2. When multiple gates are interconnected to perform a specific function, the resulting circuit is called a ________________ circuit.

3. The basic logic memory element is called a ________________ and is capable of storing one ______________________ of data.

4. Combining memory elements with a combinational logic circuit produces a _______________________ logic circuit.

5. The three basic logic elements are the ____________________, _______________, and ______________________________________.

6. A point in a logic circuit labeled STB3 can assume which of the following states:

   a. binary 0.
   b. binary 1.
   c. either binary 1 or 0.

The Inverter

The simplest form of a digital logic circuit is the inverter or NOT circuit. The inverter is a logic element whose output state is always opposite of its input state. If the input is a binary 0 the output is a binary 1. If the input is a binary 1, the output is a binary 0. We say that the inverter has an output that is the complement of the input. The binary states 1 and 0 are considered to be complementary.

The operation of the inverter is clearly summarized by a simple chart known as a truth table. The truth table shows all possible input states and the resulting outputs. Figure 3-4 is the truth table for an inverter. The input to the inverter is designated A while the output is labeled $\overline{A}$ (pronounced A NOT or NOT A). The bar over the letter A indicates the complement of A. Note that the truth table shows all possible input combinations and the corresponding output for each. Since the inverter has a single input, there are only two possible input combinations: 0 and 1. The output in each case is the complement or opposite of the input.

INPUT	OUTPUT
A	$\overline{A}$
0	1
1	0

Figure 3-4
Truth Table for logic inverter.

The symbols used to represent a logic inverter are shown in Figure 3-5. The triangle portion of the symbol represents the circuit itself while the circle designates the inversion or complementary nature of the circuit. Either of the two symbols may be used. Note the input and output labeling. Such simplified symbols are used instead of the actual electronic schematic in order to simplify the drawing and application of a logic circuit. It is the logic function and not the circuit that is the most important.

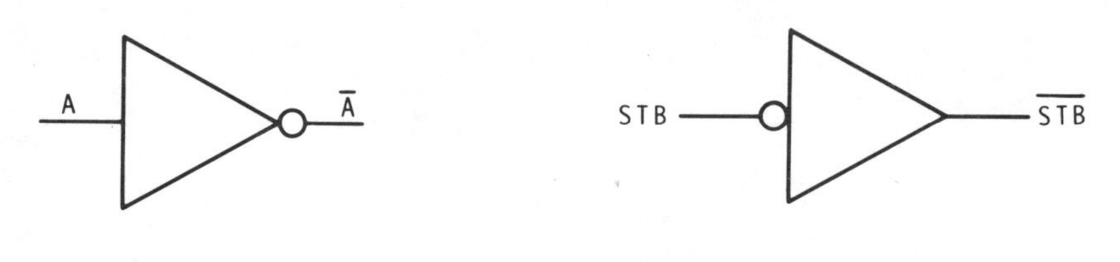

Figure 3-5
Symbols for a logic inverter.

The simplest and most widely used form of logic inverter is the transistor switching circuit shown in Figure 3-6. This inverter circuit operates with a binary input signal whose logic levels are 0 volts (or ground) and some positive voltage approximately equal to the supply voltage $+V_{CC}$. When the input B to the transistor is 0 volts, or ground, the emitter-base junction of the transistor is not forward biased. Therefore, the transistor does not conduct. With the transistor cut-off, the output $\overline{B}$ is at the supply voltage potential $+V_{CC}$. As you can see, with positive logic level assignments, the binary 0 input produces a binary 1 output.

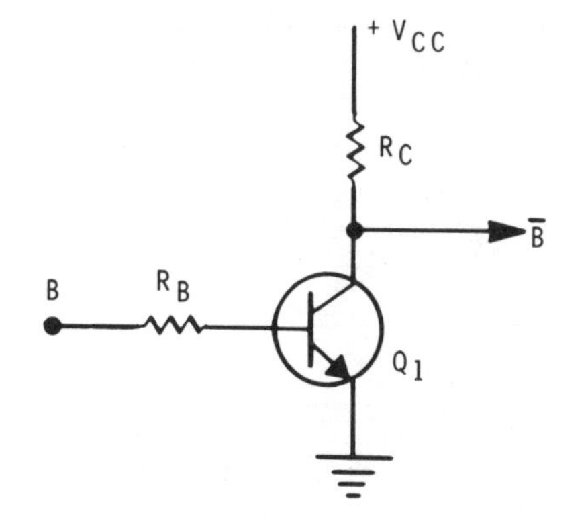

Figure 3-6
A transistor logic inverter.

Whenever a binary 1 or positive voltage level approximately equal to $+V_{CC}$ is applied to the input, the emitter-base junction of the transistor becomes forward-biased. Sufficient base current flows through the circuit to cause the transistor to saturate. When the transistor is saturated, both the emitter-base and base-collector junctions of the transistor are forward-biased and it acts as a very low impedance. At this time, the complement output $\overline{B}$ is approximately equal to zero volts or ground as seen through the conducting transistor. The actual voltage will be equal to the saturation voltage of the transistor V_{CE} (sat). For most good high speed switching transistors this voltage is several tenths of a volt or less and for most practical purposes can be considered to be zero. With a positive voltage binary 1 input the output is a binary 0. This circuit obviously performs logic inversion. The input and output voltage waveforms representing the operation of this circuit are shown in Figure 3-7. Most modern switching transistors are capable of turning off and on at nanosecond speeds, therefore very high frequency operation with this circuit is possible.

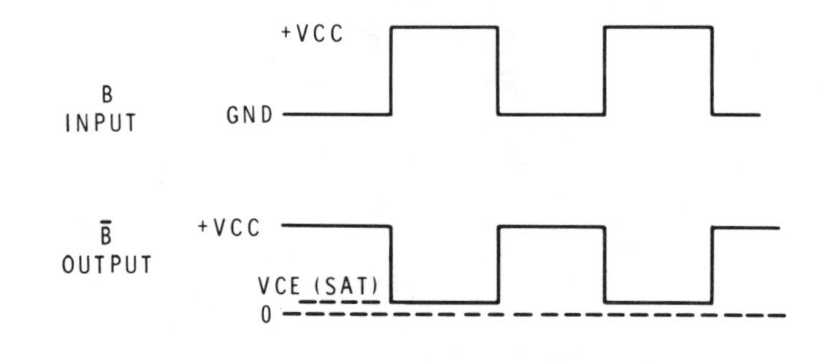

Figure 3-7
Input and output waveforms
of a transistor logic inverter.

7. If the input to a logic inverter is labeled PLS, the output will be:

   a. PLS.
   b. SLP.
   c. $\overline{\text{PLS}}$.
   d. binary 0.

8. The inverter input PLS is a voltage level that represents:

   a. binary 0.
   b. binary 1.
   c. either binary 0 or binary 1.
   d. Cannot be determined with information given.

9. If the input to the inverter in Figure 3-6 is simply left open the transistor will not conduct. What will the output be if negative logic level assignments are assumed?

   a. binary 0.
   b. binary 1.
   c. Cannot be determined with information given.

10. Saturation means:

    a. both emitter-base and base-collector junctions reverse biased.
    b. both emitter-base and base-collector junctions forward-biased.
    c. emitter-base junction forward-biased, base-collector junction reverse-biased.
    d. emitter-base junction reverse-biased, base-collector junction forward-biased.

11. The output of inverter 2 in Figure 3-8 with a binary 1 input will be:

    a. binary 0.
    b. binary 1.
    c. Cannot be determined with information given.

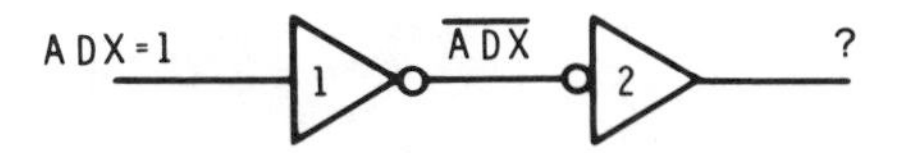

Figure 3-8
Circuit for Self-Test Review Question 11.

Decision-Making Logic Elements

The two basic types of decision-making logic elements are the AND gate and the OR gate. These are logic circuits with two or more inputs and a single output. The output state is a function of the input states and how the particular gate operates. The gate makes its decision based upon the input states and its particular function, then generates the appropriate binary output. Let's consider each of these basic gates in detail.

The AND Gate

The AND gate is a logic circuit that has two or more inputs and a single output. The operation of the gate is such that the output of the gate is a binary 1 if and only if all inputs are binary 1. If any one or more inputs are a binary 0 the output will be binary 0. The AND gate is a control circuit whose output is a binary 1 only when all inputs to the gate are in the binary 1 state at the same time.

The operation of a two input AND gate is indicated by the truth table in Figure 3-9. The inputs are designated A and B. The output is designated C. The output for all possible input combinations is indicated in the truth table. The total number of input combinations is determined by raising 2 to a power equal to the number of inputs. With two inputs, each capable of assuming either of the two binary states, the total possible number of combination inputs is $2^2=4$. Note that the output is binary 0 for any set of inputs where either, or both, of the inputs are binary 0. The output is binary 1 only when both inputs are binary 1.

The basic symbol used to represent an AND gate is shown in Figure 3-10. Note that the inputs and outputs are labeled to correspond to the truth table in Figure 3-9. Keep in mind that the AND gate may have any number of logical inputs.

INPUTS		OUTPUT
A	B	C
0	0	0
0	1	0
1	0	0
1	1	1

Figure 3-9
Truth Table for an AND gate.

An important point to note about the AND symbol in Figure 3-10 is the equation at the output, $C = A \cdot B$ or $C = AB$. This equation is a form of algebraic expression that is used to designate the logical function being performed. The equation expresses the output C in terms of the input variables A and B and is read "C equals A AND B". Here the AND function is designated by the dot between the two input variables A and B. The AND function is designated by an expression similar to the product of algebraic variables.

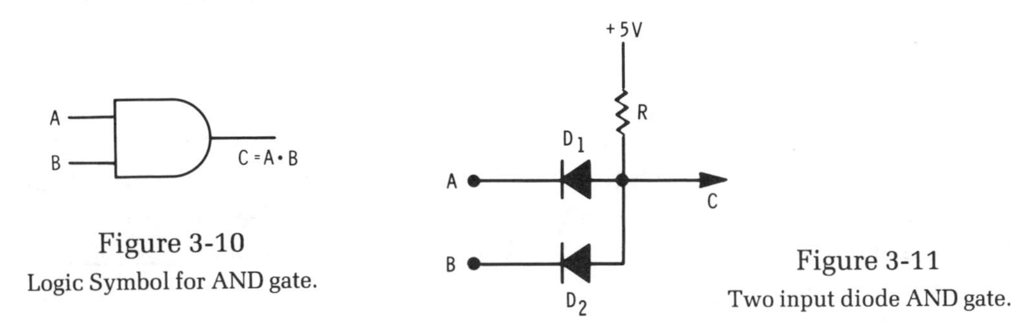

Figure 3-10
Logic Symbol for AND gate.

Figure 3-11
Two input diode AND gate.

As you will see, the operation of all logic elements and gates can expressed in the form of an algebraic equation. These expressions permit circuits to be analyzed, designed and optimized by using standard algebraic operations and special algebraic manipulations designated by rules of Boolean algebra. Boolean algebra is a special form of two state algebra that is useful in working with binary variables. You will learn more about this in a later unit.

The circuit in Figure 3-11 shows one electrical implementation of a logic AND gate. Here two diodes and a resistor form an electronic circuit that produces the AND function using binary signals. To analyze this circuit, assume the use of binary input signals using positive logic designations of zero volts (ground) and +5 volts. Let's also assume that perfect diodes are used. Keep in mind that in a practical circuit real diodes have a threshold voltage level before they conduct and a finite voltage drop across them during conduction.

Now let's analyze the operation of the AND circuit shown in Figure 3-11. If both inputs are a binary 0 (zero volts or ground) both diodes conduct. Assuming no forward voltage drop across the diode, the output will be zero volts. If either one of the inputs is a binary 0, while the other is at the binary 1 level (+5 volts), the diode associated with the input whose state is binary 0 will be forward-biased and will conduct thereby clamping the output at the binary 0 level. (The diode associated with the input at the binary 1 level will be reverse-biased and cut off.)

If both inputs are at the binary 1 level, neither diode will conduct and the output will be +5 volts. As you can see, the only time the output is at the binary 1 level is when both inputs are binary 1.

The operation of the AND gate shown in Figure 3-11 is fully illustrated by the voltage truth table in Figure 3-12 and the waveform timing diagram in Figure 3-13. Note that if positive logic is assumed, the voltage truth table corresponds to the logic truth table given in Figure 3-9. In the wave form diagram, both inputs A and B are shown switching at various times between the binary 0 and binary 1 levels of ground and +5 volts. The output C corresponding to this particular combination of inputs is also illustrated. Note that the only time that the output is binary 1 is when the inputs are both in the binary 1 state. The output is a binary 1 for a period of time during which the two inputs are coincidentally at the binary 1 level. The AND gate is sometimes referred to as a coincident gate.

INPUTS		OUTPUT
A	B	C
0V	0V	0V
0V	+5V	0V
+5V	0V	0V
+5V	+5V	+5V

Figure 3-12

Voltage truth table for diode AND gate.

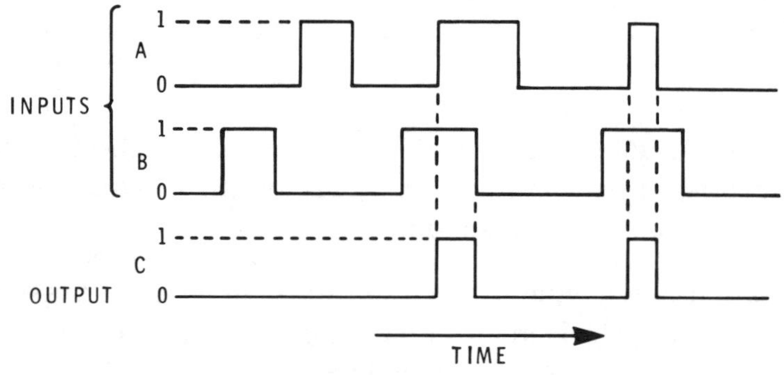

Figure 3-13
Input and output waveforms of the diode AND gate.

Figure 3-14 shows one of the most common applications of the AND gate in digital circuits. Here one input of the AND gate is used to control the passage of the other input signal to the output. The input control signal CTL enables or inhibits the passage of the other logic signal which is a train of square waves designated SQW. The output is identical to SQW during the time the CTL input is binary 1. Note the input and output waveforms as well as the logic expression for this function indicated in Figure 3-14.

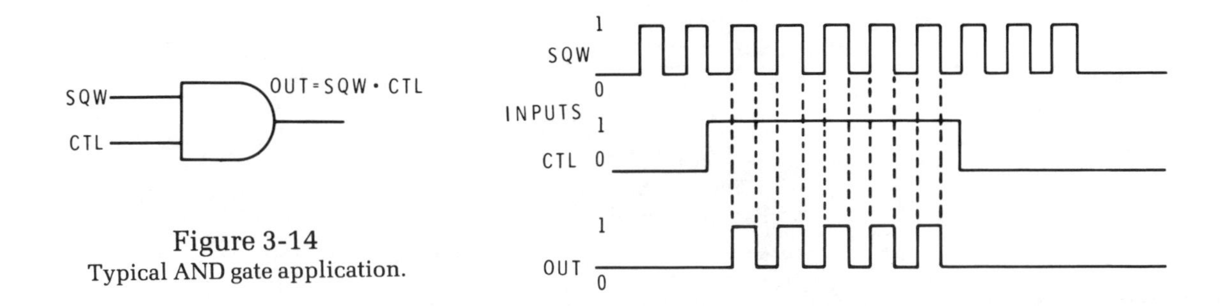

Figure 3-14
Typical AND gate application.

Remember that an AND gate may have more than two inputs, the exact number being dictated by the application. In addition, there are many other ways of implementing the logical AND function with hardware. Later in this unit and in the program you will learn about some of these circuits.

Self-Test Review

12. Draw the logic symbol for an AND gate with inputs J7, K6, L4, and output F3.

13. Write the logic equation for an AND gate with inputs XLT, ZMO, KMD, A3 and output TF. ______________________.

14. The logic gate in Figure 3-15 will have how many different input combinations?

    a. 4.
    b. 8.
    c. 16.
    d. 32.

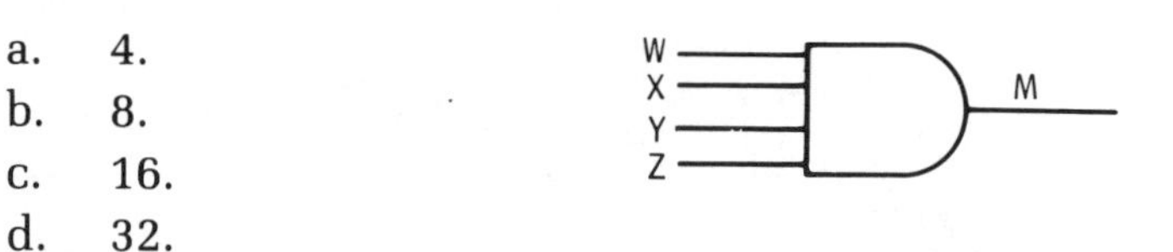

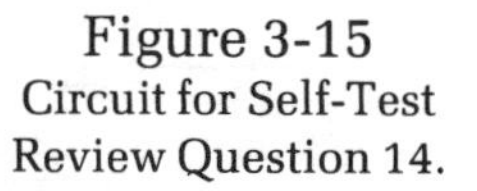

Figure 3-15
Circuit for Self-Test
Review Question 14.

15. Write the truth table for a three-input AND gate with inputs A, B, C, and D as the output.

16. What is the algebraic output equation for the circuit in Figure 3-16?

    a. $P = \overline{MN}$.
    b. $P = M\overline{N}$.
    c. $P = \overline{M}N$.
    d. $P = MN$.

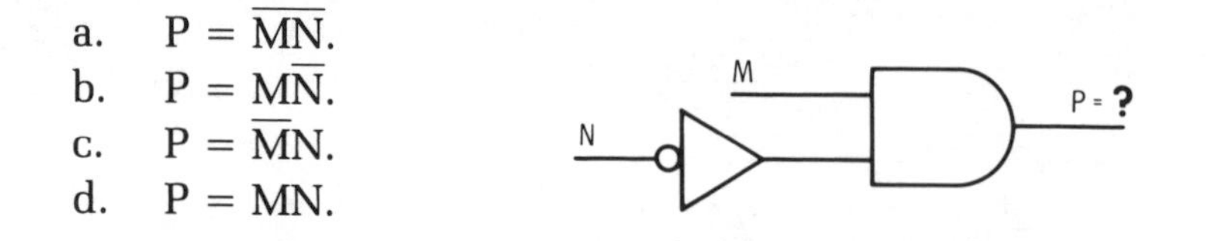

Figure 3-16
Circuit for Self-Test
Review Question 16.

The OR Gate

The other basic logic element is called an OR gate. Like the AND gate it can have two or more inputs and a single output. Its operation is such that the output is a binary 1 if any one or all inputs are a binary 1. The output is binary 0 only when both inputs are binary 0.

The logical operation of an OR gate is expressed by the truth table in Figure 3-17. With two inputs there are $2^2 = 4$ possible input combinations as explained earlier. The truth table designates all four possible input combinations and the corresponding output. Note that the output is binary 1 when either or both of the inputs are binary 1. The output is binary 1 if the D input, OR the E input, OR both are present.

INPUTS		OUTPUT
D	E	F
0	0	0
0	1	1
1	0	1
1	1	1

Figure 3-17
Truth Table for OR gate.

The logical symbol for an OR gate is shown in Figure 3-18. The inputs are labeled according to the truth table in Figure 3-17. Note the output algebraic expression for the OR gate F = D + E. The plus sign is used to designate the logic OR function. The output F is expressed in terms of the input logic variables D and E.

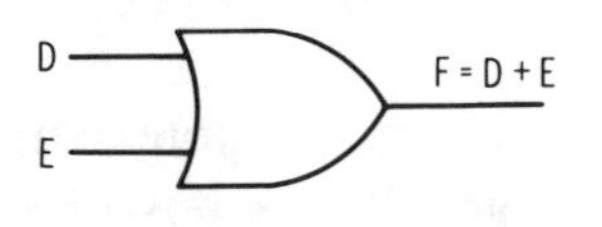

Figure 3-18
Logic symbol for OR gate.

The circuit in Figure 3-19 illustrates the implementation of the logic OR function using semiconductor diodes. This gate is similar to the AND circuit considered earlier except that the diodes are reversed, and the output is referenced to ground. This circuit operates with logic input levels of zero and +5 volts, as did the AND gate considered previously. Using positive logic designations, let's evaluate the operation of this circuit.

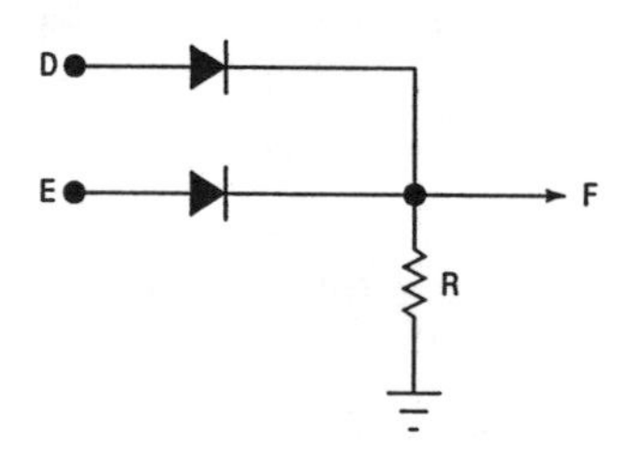

Figure 3-19
Diode OR gate.

When both inputs D and E are at binary 0 (zero volts or ground) neither diode conducts. The output will be binary 0. If either one of the logical inputs is a binary 0, while the other is a binary 1 (+5 volts), the diode associated with the input at the binary 1 state will conduct causing the output to be +5 volts, or a binary 1, assuming no losses through the diode/resistor series circuit. The diode associated with the input at the binary 0 state will not affect the circuit. When both inputs are at the binary 1 or +5 volt level, both diodes conduct and the output is a +5 volts or binary 1 level. The voltage truth table for this circuit is shown in Figure 3-20. Using positive logic, it corresponds to the table in Figure 3-17.

INPUTS		OUTPUT
D	E	F
0V	0V	0V
0V	+5V	+5V
+5V	0V	+5V
+5V	+5V	+5V

Figure 3-20
Voltage Truth Table
for the diode OR gate.

The operation of the OR gate is illustrated more fully by the waveforms shown in Figure 3-21. These diagrams show the output state for various combinations of the input voltages D and E as a function of time. Note that if one of the inputs switches to the binary 1 level the output switches to binary 1. The output is binary 1 when either or both inputs are binary 1. Study the waveforms in Figure 3-21 carefully at each point to be sure that you understand the OR function.

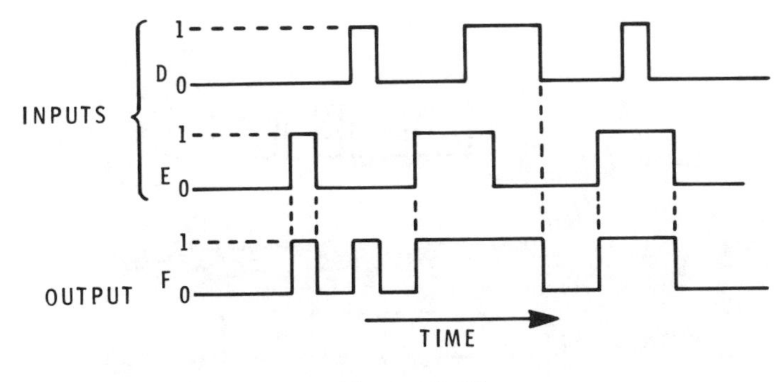

Figure 3-21
Input and output waveforms
of the diode OR gate.

Figure 3-22 illustrates a typical application for the OR gate in a digital circuit. There are two inputs to the OR gate in this application: a push button switch SW2 and a train of pulses designated PLS. The output OPR will be binary 1 when either SW2 or PLS is at the binary 1 (+5 volts) level. Switch SW2 is a normally closed pushbutton. The SW2 input to the OR gate is normally ground or binary 0. When the switch is depressed, the contacts open and the SW2 input becomes +5 volts or binary 1 level as seen through the resistor. The other input PLS is a series of pulse trains that switch momentarily between the binary 0 and binary 1 levels. Note the algebraic expression for the output, OPR = SW2 + PLS. The accompanying waveforms in Figure 3-22 illustrate the operation of the circuit. The OR gate permits either of the two inputs to control the output.

When considering the operation and application of an OR gate you should remember that this logic element can have two or more inputs as called for by the application. At the same time we have only illustrated one method of implementing the OR gate with electronic hardware. Many other circuit variations are used and these will be discussed later in the text.

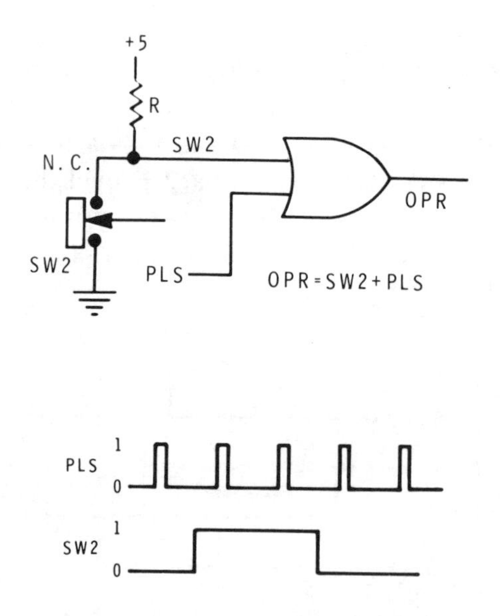

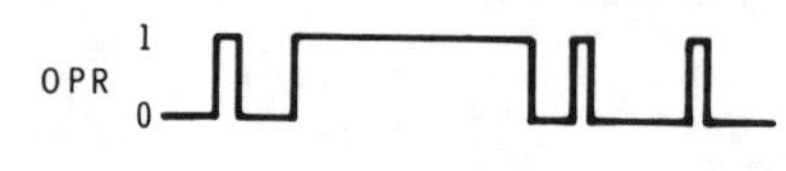

Figure 3-22
Typical OR gate application.

17. Draw the logic symbol for an OR gate with inputs GB, PH, CD, SH, and output FF.

18. Write the output equation of the gate in Figure 3-23.

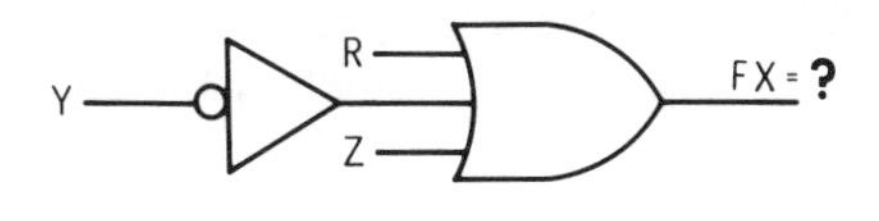

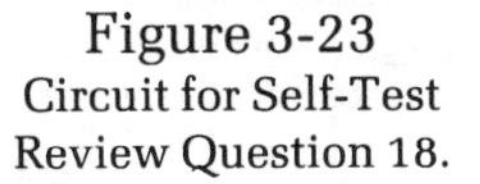
Figure 3-23
Circuit for Self-Test
Review Question 18.

19. Write the truth table for a 4-input OR gate with inputs W, X, Y, Z, and output J.

20. The output of an OR gate is binary 0 when:

    a. all inputs are binary 0.
    b. any one or more inputs are binary 0.
    c. all inputs are binary 1.
    d. any one or all inputs are binary 1.

21. The logic OR function when expressed in algebraic terms is analogous to the:

    a. product.
    b. sum.
    c. difference.
    d. quotient.

The Dual Nature of Logic Gates

When we explained the operation of the diode gate circuit in Figure 3-11, we indicated that it performs the logic AND function. We proved this by considering the output voltage level for each of the four possible combinations of input voltage levels. The voltage truth table for this gate is repeated here in Figure 3-24A. In considering the operation of this circuit, we assumed the use of positive logic level assignments. By doing this we were able to translate the voltage levels given in the truth table into the table shown in Figure 3-24B. Naturally this table clearly indicates that the AND function is being performed. The output is a binary 1 only when both inputs are binary 1.

INPUTS		OUTPUT
D	E	F
0V	0V	0V
0V	+5V	0V
+5V	0V	0V
+5V	+5V	+5V

A

INPUTS		OUTPUT
D	E	F
0	0	0
0	1	0
1	0	0
1	1	1

B

INPUTS		OUTPUT
D	E	F
1	1	1
1	0	1
0	1	1
0	0	0

C

Figure 3-24
Truth Tables for diode gate in Figure 3-11.

Now let's consider the function of this circuit when we assume negative logic level assignments. In this case the 0 volt level would represent a binary 1 and +5 volt level would represent a binary 0. Using the original data as developed in Figure 3-24A and translating it into a truth table using binary 1's and 0's with negative logic level assignments, we obtain the truth table shown in Figure 3-24C. By studying this truth table, you will see that the circuit no longer appears to be performing the AND function. Close inspection of the truth table will reveal that the circuit is now performing the OR function, since the output is a binary 1, when either one or both of the inputs is a binary 1. (The order sequence of the inputs is not the same as that for the AND gate, but this is not important. It is the function that counts.) Our only conclusion can be that with positive logic the circuit in Figure 3-11 performs the AND function, but with negative logic the circuit performs the OR function. This clearly indicates that the diode gate circuit is capable of performing either of the two basic logical functions. Refer to the Appendix for comparison of positive and negative logic equivalent circuits.

This dual nature of logic gates applies to any logic circuit. The diode gate that you considered in Figure 3-19 is also dual in nature. With positive logic level assignments it performs the OR function as indicated previously. However, if you analyze the circuit by using negative logic level assignments you will find that the circuit performs the AND function. Keep this important fact in mind as it will help you in analyzing, troubleshooting and designing digital circuits. You must not only know how the circuit operates electrically, but also what logic level assignments are being used.

Figure 3-25 shows the logic symbols normally used to represent gates that perform the logic AND and OR functions with negative logic level assignments. The circles at the inputs represent the effect of reversing the logic level assignments from positive to negative.

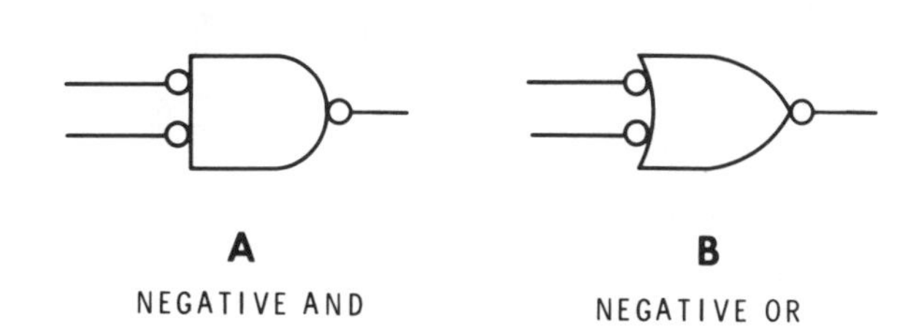

Figure 3-25
Negative logic gates.

22. Any logic gate can perform both AND and OR operations.

    a. True.
    b. False.

23. A given logic circuit performs the AND function when binary 0 = 0 volts and binary 1 = −6 volts. Reversing the logic level assignments makes the gate perform as a ______________ gate.

NAND/NOR Gates

While many digital circuits can be constructed with just the three basic digital logic elements—AND, OR, and NOT—most digital equipment is implemented with special versions of these circuits known as NAND and NOR gates. Such circuits are basically AND and OR gates combined with an inverter. NAND/NOR gates are the most widely used types of digital logic elements because they offer numerous advantages over the simple diode gates considered earlier. In large, complex, digital logic networks, it is difficult to cascade more than just a few of the simple diode logic gates. Because there is no buffering between the gates, loading problems occur and the speed of operation suffers. For that reason, it is generally desirable to combine a simple diode logic gate with some type of transistor buffer to permit more flexible interconnection of circuits. This transistor buffer is most often an inverter.

NAND Gate

The term NAND is a contraction of the expression NOT-AND. A NAND gate, therefore, is an AND gate followed by an inverter. Figure 3-26A shows the basic diagram of a NAND gate. Note the algebraic output expression for the AND gate and the inverter. The entire AND output expression is inverted as indicated by the bar over it.

Figure 3-26B shows the standard symbol used for a NAND gate. It is similar to the AND symbol, but a circle has been added at the output to represent the inversion that takes place.

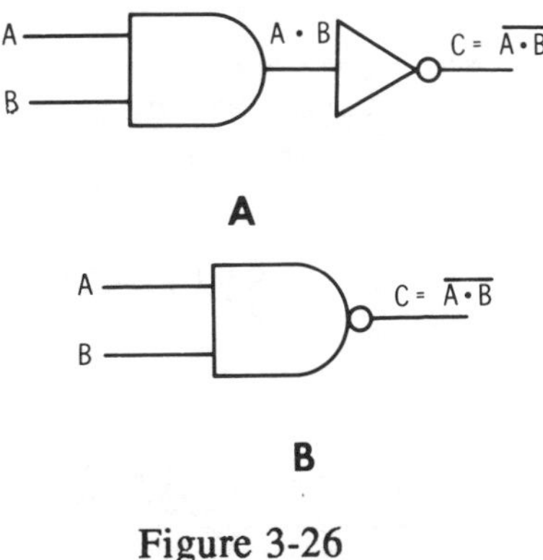

Figure 3-26
NAND gate.

INPUTS		OUTPUT	
A	B	AND $A \cdot B$	NAND $\overline{A \cdot B} = C$
0	0	0	1
0	1	0	1
1	0	0	1
1	1	1	0

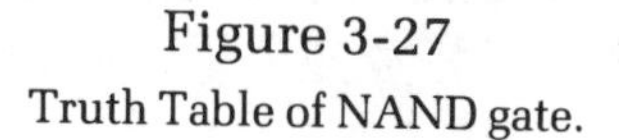

Figure 3-27
Truth Table of NAND gate.

The logic operation of the NAND gate is easy to infer from the circuit in Figure 3-26. This operation is indicated by the truth table in Figure 3-27. The NAND output is simply the complement of the AND output.

NOR Gate

Like the NAND gate, the NOR gate is an improved logic element used for implementing decision-making logic functions. The term NOR is a contraction for the expression NOT-OR. Therefore, the NOR gate is essentially a circuit combining the logic functions of an OR gate and an inverter.

Figure 3-28A is a logical representation of a NOR gate. Figure 3-28B shows the standard symbol used to represent a NOR gate. Note that the output expression is the inverted OR function.

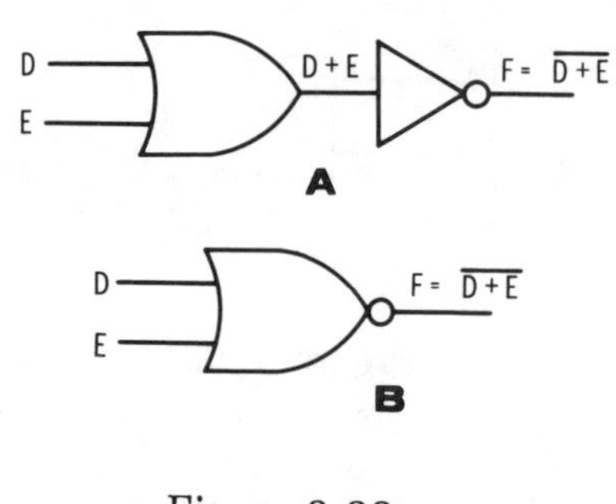

Figure 3-28
NOR gate.

The logic operation of a NOR gate is illustrated by the truth table in Figure 3-29. The NOR output is simply the complement of the OR function. Like any other logic gate, NAND and NOR gates may have two or more inputs as required by the application.

INPUTS		OUTPUT	
D	E	OR $D+E$	NOR $\overline{D+E}=F$
0	0	0	1
0	1	1	0
1	0	1	0
1	1	1	0

Figure 3-29
Truth Table of NOR gate.

NAND and NOR gates can be used to implement any of three basic logic functions. For example, by tying all inputs together, either the NAND or NOR gate performs inversion. By combining the NAND or NOR gates with external inverters, the AND and OR operations can be performed.

24. NAND/NOR gates are more widely used than simple AND/OR circuits because:

    a. NAND/NORs can also perform AND/OR operations.
    b. NAND/NORs are less expensive and smaller.
    c. NAND/NORs are self-buffering – this permits higher speed and reasonable loading.
    d. AND/ORs can't perform the NOT function.

25. A 3-input NAND gate has inputs of 0, 1 and 1. The output is:

    a. binary 0.
    b. binary 1.

26. A 4-input NOR gate has inputs of 1, 0, 0 and 0. The output is:

    a. binary 0.
    b. binary 1.

27. The output equation of a NAND is:

    a. $C = A \bullet B$.
    b. $C = A + B$.
    c. $C = \overline{A \bullet B}$.
    d. $C = \overline{A + B}$.

28. The output equation for a NOR is:

    a. $F = D + E$.
    b. $F = D \bullet E$.
    c. $F = \overline{D \bullet E}$.
    d. $F = \overline{D + E}$.

How NAND/NOR Gates Are Used.

The AND and OR logic functions can be performed by connecting inverters on the outputs of NAND and NOR gates respectively. Since the NAND and NOR functions are simply complementary logic functions of basic AND and OR operations, then it is logical to assume that the AND and OR operations can be obtained from NAND and NOR gates simply by adding an additional inversion. As stated in the previous section on inverters, the effect of one inversion is canceled by adding a second. Cascading an even number of inverters removes the inversion function.

Figure 3-30 shows how the AND and OR operations are performed with NAND and NOR gates. But now, how is the OR function performed with a NAND gate and the AND function performed with a NOR gate?

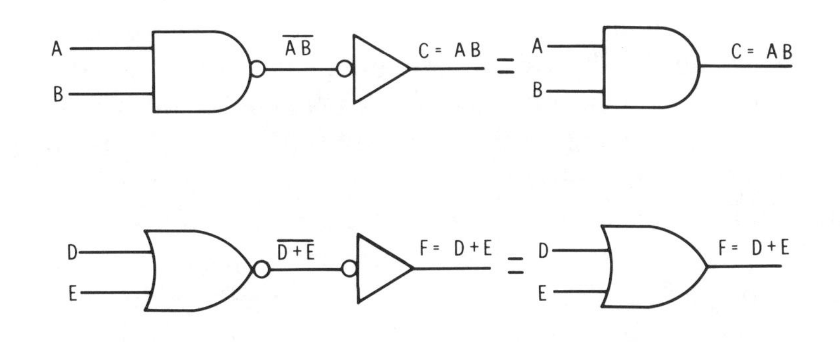

Figure 3-30
Performing AND and OR
operations with NAND and NOR gates.

As mentioned earlier, any of the three basic logic functions—AND, OR, and NOT—can be performed by either a NAND gate or a NOR gate. You have already seen how the AND and OR functions can be obtained with NAND and NOR gates by simply inverting the output. To obtain the other logic functions with each type of gate, inverters are used on the inputs.

INVERTED INPUTS		NAND INPUTS		OUTPUT
X	Y	A	B	C
1	1	0	0	1
1	0	0	1	1
0	1	1	0	1
0	0	1	1	0

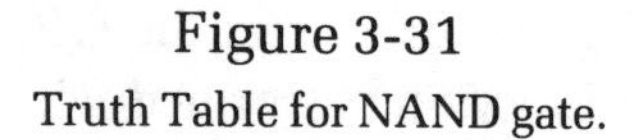

Figure 3-31
Truth Table for NAND gate.

Figure 3-31 shows the truth table for a NAND gate. The inputs are A and B and the output is C. Now consider the effect of adding an inverter to each input as shown in Figure 3-32. These inverters simply complement the input signals. The effect is illustrated in the truth table of Figure 3-31. The input signals to the inverters are labeled X and Y. Note that they are the complements of the signals A and B respectively. Considering the two inverters and the NAND gate as forming a single composite circuit, our inputs become X and Y instead of A and B. Output C remains the same. By observing the truth table in Figure 3-31 with this change in mind, you can now evaluate the logic function of the circuit. Disregarding the sequence of the X and Y input combinations and the A and B inputs, note the output state for each of the input states. You can see that the circuit produces a binary 1 output any time a binary 1 is applied to either one or both of the inputs. By definition this is the logic OR function. The OR function can be performed with a NAND gate by simply placing inverters ahead of each input.

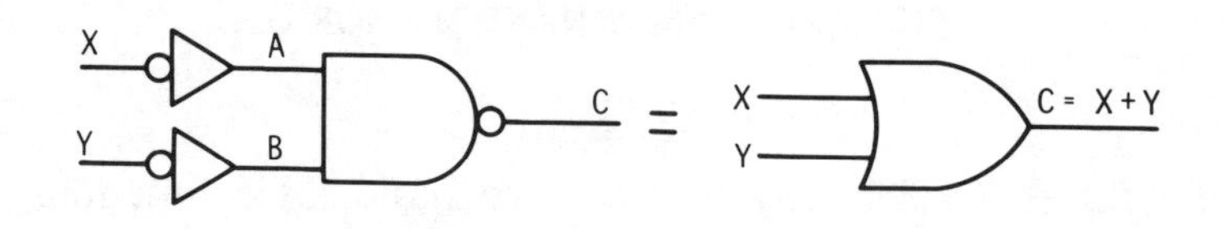

Figure 3-32
Performing the OR function
with a NAND gate.

INVERTED INPUTS		NOR INPUTS		OUTPUT
L	M	D	E	F
1	1	0	0	1
1	0	0	1	0
0	1	1	0	0
0	0	1	1	0

Figure 3-33
Truth Table for NOR gate.

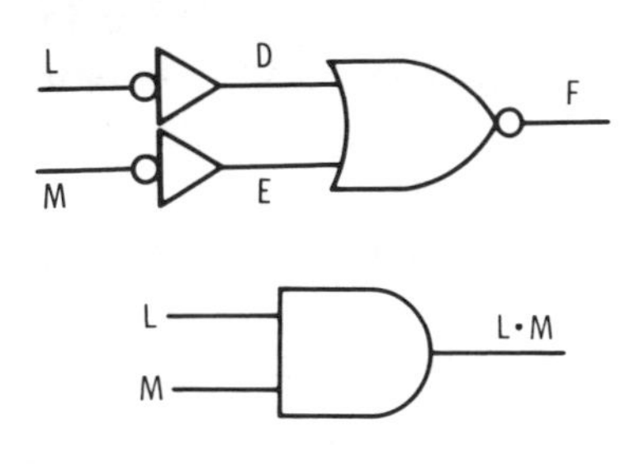

Figure 3-34
Using a NOR gate to perform the AND function.

By using inverters at the input of a NOR, the AND function can be performed. Figure 3-33 shows the truth table for a NOR gate. The inputs are D and E and the output is F. Now assume that inverters are connected ahead of the NOR gate and the new inputs are labeled L and M as shown in Figure 3-34. The inverter or complementary input states would be as indicated in the truth table of Figure 3-33. If we interpret the logic function of the composite circuit where the inputs are L and M and the output is F, then you can see by studying the truth table that the AND function is being performed. Note that the only time that the output F is a binary 1 is when both inputs L and M are at the binary 1 level. By definition this is the AND logic function. As Figure 3-34 indicates, a NOR gate with inverters at its input performs the AND function.

As you can see any of the three basic logic functions can be performed with either a NAND gate or a NOR gate. For that reason entire digital circuits can be constructed with just one type of gate. The choice is arbitrary and strictly up to the designer. There are some cases where both NANDs and NORs are mixed within a circuit. As you will see later, some circuit economies result when NAND and NORs are combined. However, just remember that any logic function can be implemented with NAND gates or NOR gates alone.

Self-Test Review

29. A NAND or NOR gate can perform any of the three basic logic functions AND, OR, and NOT.

    a. True.
    b. False.

30. When inverters are used at the inputs to a NOR gate, the resulting circuit performs what logic function?

    a. AND.
    b. OR.
    c. NAND.
    d. NOR.
    e. NOT.

31. When inverters are used at the input to a NAND gate, the circuit performs what logic function?

    a. AND.
    b. OR.
    c. NAND.
    d. NOR.
    e. NOT.

32. A NOR or NAND can be used as a NOT circuit by:

    a. inverting the output.
    b. inverting the inputs.
    c. connecting all inputs together.
    d. cascading an even number of circuits.

33. Which circuit is preferred in implementing an entire circuit with one type of gate?

    a. NAND.
    b. NOR.
    c. Either.

Practical Logic Circuits

Now that you have completed this overview of the types of logic circuits in common use in digital equipment, let's take a look at several typical ways those logic elements are implemented. There are many different ways of electrically or mechanically obtaining the particular characteristics specified by the various types of logic elements. Here we will consider several popular ways of realizing digital logic elements with hardware.

Relays and Switches

The three basic logic functions – AND, OR, and NOT – can be readily implemented with relay contacts and switches. For example, Figure 3-35 shows an AND gate made with relays. Here the normally open (N.O.) contacts of two relays labeled A and B are connected in series with a battery and a lamp. In this circuit, a closed relay contact and an ON lamp represent a binary 1. An open contact and an OFF lamp reprsent a binary 0. A zero voltage level represents binary 0 and a positive voltage level represents a binary 1 on the relay coil. You can see, for any of the four possible input combinations there is only one where the lamp will light. If either one or both of the relays are de-energized, their contacts will be open and current will not be supplied to the lamp. However, if voltage is applied to both relay coils, both contacts will be closed and a binary 1 (ON lamp) output will occur. Contacts A and B must be closed to light the lamp. Series connected switches usually perform the AND function.

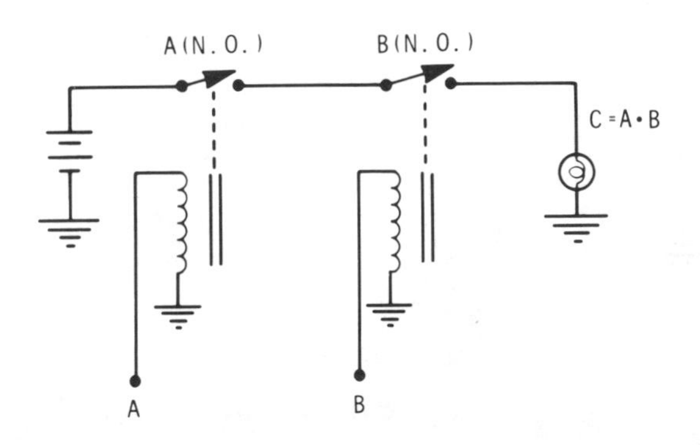

Figure 3-35
Relay AND gate.

Figure 3-36 shows an OR gate made with relays. The normally open relay contacts are connected in parallel. Here you can see that when a binary 1 voltage level is applied to either or both relay coils the D or E contacts will close, thereby supplying voltage to the lamp. An input to either relay D or E will close the circuit and turn on the lamp, representing a binary 1. Parallel connected contacts usually perform the OR operation.

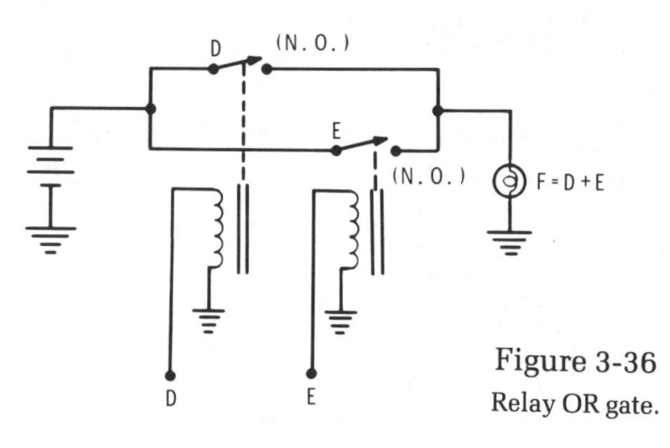

Figure 3-36
Relay OR gate.

A relay logic inverter circuit is shown in Figure 3-37. Here a relay with normally closed (N. C.) contacts is used. With a binary 0 (zero volts) applied to the relay coil, the relay is de-energized and the contact is closed representing a binary 1. This connects the battery to the lamp causing it to light. Therefore, with a binary 0 input the output is binary 1. Applying a binary 1 voltage level to the relay coil will energize the relay and open the contacts. This will cause the lamp to go off indicating a binary 0.

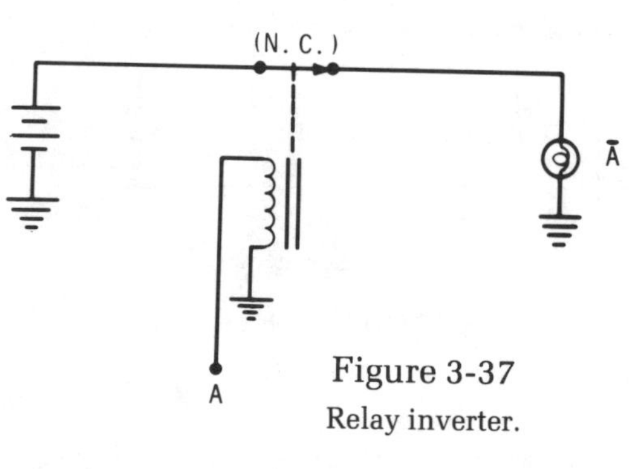

Figure 3-37
Relay inverter.

Practical Logic Circuits

Now that you have completed this overview of the types of logic circuits in common use in digital equipment, let's take a look at several typical ways these logic elements are implemented. There are many different ways of electrically or mechanically obtaining the particular characteristics specified by the various types of logic elements. Here we will consider several popular ways of realizing digital logic elements with hardware.

Relays and Switches

The three basic logic functions – AND, OR, and NOT – can be readily implemented with relay contacts and switches. For example, Figure 3-35 shows an AND gate made with relays. Here the normally open (N.O.) contacts of two relays labeled A and B are connected in series with a battery and a lamp. In this circuit, a closed relay contact and an ON lamp represent a binary 1. An open contact and an OFF lamp reprsent a binary 0. A zero voltage level represents binary 0 and a positive voltage level represents a binary 1 on the relay coil. You can see, for any of the four possible input combinations there is only one where the lamp will light. If either one or both of the relays are de-energized, their contacts will be open and current will not be supplied to the lamp. However, if voltage is applied to both relay coils, both contacts will be closed and a binary 1 (ON lamp) output will occur. Contacts A and B must be closed to light the lamp. Series connected switches usually perform the AND function.

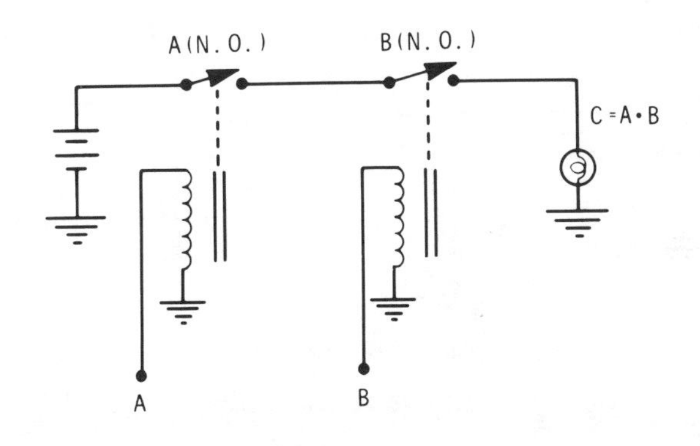

Figure 3-35
Relay AND gate.

Figure 3-36 shows an OR gate made with relays. The normally open relay contacts are connected in parallel. Here you can see that when a binary 1 voltage level is applied to either or both relay coils the D or E contacts will close, thereby supplying voltage to the lamp. An input to either relay D or E will close the circuit and turn on the lamp, representing a binary 1. Parallel connected contacts usually perform the OR operation.

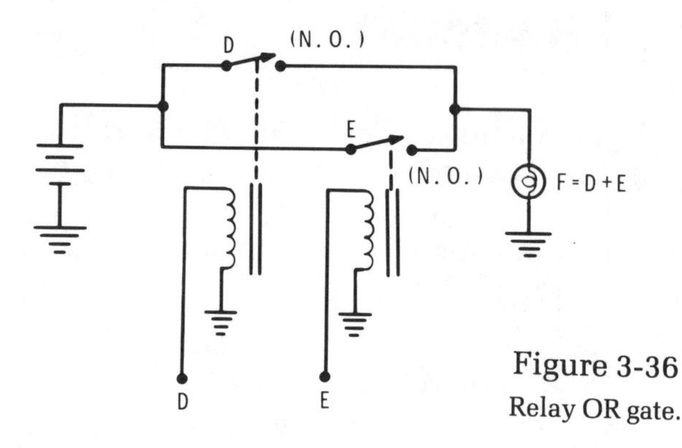

Figure 3-36
Relay OR gate.

A relay logic inverter circuit is shown in Figure 3-37. Here a relay with normally closed (N. C.) contacts is used. With a binary 0 (zero volts) applied to the relay coil, the relay is de-energized and the contact is closed representing a binary 1. This connects the battery to the lamp causing it to light. Therefore, with a binary 0 input the output is binary 1. Applying a binary 1 voltage level to the relay coil will energize the relay and open the contacts. This will cause the lamp to go off indicating a binary 0.

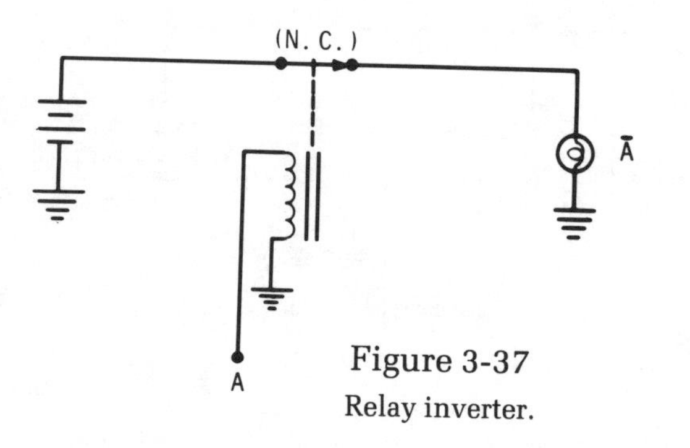

Figure 3-37
Relay inverter.

These relay switching circuits can be combined in many ways to form any logic function. In addition, manually operated switches can also be substituted for the relay contacts in some applications. Such relay or switch logic circuits are not often used today. Such circuits are large, slow in operation, and consume a significant amount of power. For most applications they are not practical. The very earliest of digital equipment, including some computers, were implemented with relays. However, many other different types of logic circuits are available now and these have many significant advantages over relays. There are still a few practical uses for relay and switch logic circuits. In some heavy industrial control systems where speed and power consumption is of little importance, relay logic circuits can handle high power applications and are very reliable. There are some applications where a mechanical means of operating the switches is available, thereby making mechanical or manual switching logic necessary or desirable.

Discrete Component Logic Circuits

A discrete component logic circuit is a logic element made up of individual electronic components such as transistors, diodes, resistors, capacitors, and other devices. These are assembled to form a complete circuit like the diode gates and inverter described earlier. For many years digital logic circuits were implemented with discrete components. They offered small sized, high performance, and reasonable power consumption. However, today such discrete component circuits are rarely used. Like relay and mechanical switching logic circuits they have essentially been replaced by logic elements with greater performance, lower cost, and improved features. You may still encounter discrete component logic circuits in some high power applications or in older digital equipment. Today, however, most digital logic functions are implemented with integrated circuits.

Integrated Circuits

An integrated circuit (IC) is a semiconductor device which combines transistors, diodes, resistors, and capacitors in ultra-miniature form on a single silicon chip. The advances in semiconductor technology have permitted the semiconductor manufacturers to design, develop, and produce entire electronic circuits on a single silicon wafer that is generally less than one-tenth of an inch square. these circuits are not only significantly smaller in size than discrete component logic circuits, but also offer many other benefits as well. Because they are mass produced, their cost is substantially less than discrete component circuits. Many offer significant savings in power consumption. Perhaps even more important is the elimination of the need for circuit wiring. When discrete components are used, the components must be interconnected physically on a printed circuit board and then tested. With an integrated circuit the entire circuitry, all components included, are manufactured simultaneously. Manufacturing costs are reduced and reliability is improved.

Integrated circuits have been in existence since the late 1950's. During this time significant advances have been made. The complexity and sophistication of the circuits have increased significantly while the prices have continued to decline. Today, with integrated circuit techniques, it is not only possible to implement the basic logic elements, but also it is possible to fully integrate complete combinational and sequential circuits. Integrated circuits implementing the basic logic functions such as NAND, NOR, and flip-flops are known as small-scale integrated circuits (SSI). Complete functional circuits of either the combinational or sequential type such as counters and decoders are generally designated as medium-scale integrated circuits (MSI). Complete circuits and systems, an entire computer memory for example, can also be constructed on a single chip and are known as large-scale integrated circuits (LSI), and even higher density circuits are also available. An entire microcomputer with CPU, memory, I/O, and related circuits can be obtained as a single integrated circuit. A complex device such as this is usually referred to as a very large-scale integrated circuit (VLSI).

Today most digital equipment is implemented with integrated circuits. This course emphasizes digital integrated circuits, their operations and application.

Self-Test Review

34. Write the logic equation of the relay logic circuit shown in Figure 3-38.

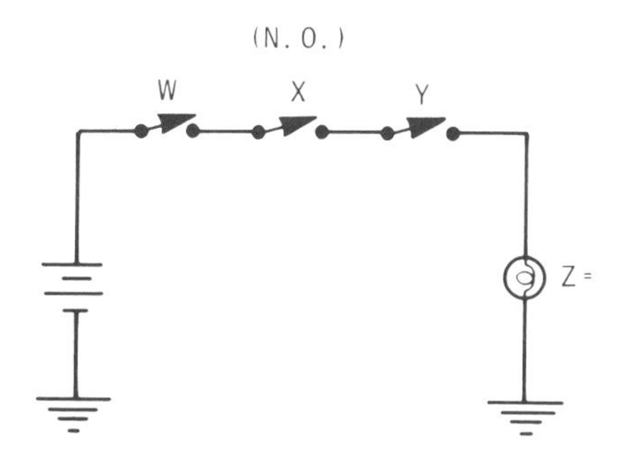

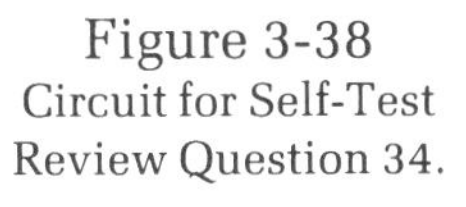

Figure 3-38
Circuit for Self-Test
Review Question 34.

35. Write the logic equation of the relay logic circuit shown in Figure 3-39.

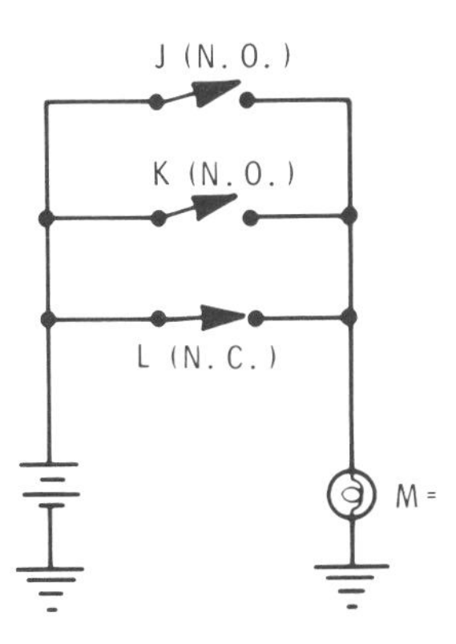

Figure 3-39
Circuit for Self-Test
Review Question 35.

36. Draw a relay logic diagram for the function $J = L\overline{K}$.

37. Draw a relay logic circuit for the function $D = A \bullet B + \overline{C}$

38. Some relay and discrete component logic circuits are still used in applications requiring:

a. high speed.
b. low cost.
c. small size.
d. high power.

39. The basic logic functions NAND, NOR, etc., in IC form are known as:

a. SSI.
b. MSI.
c. LSI.
d. discrete.

Summary

The three basic logic gates are the AND, OR, and NOT. The AND gate provides a binary 1 output only when all of the inputs are binary ones. The OR gate provides a binary 1 output when any, or all, of the inputs are binary ones. The NOT gate or inverter, provides an output that is the complement of its input. A zero input results in a 1 output, and a 1 input results in a 0 output.

The logic equation that describes a 2-input AND gate is AB = 1. This means that when both A and B = 1 the output will be 1. In a schematic, the AND gate can be represented as switches in series. A + B describes the 2-input OR gate and means that when A or B or both = 1 the output will be 1. In a schematic, the OR gate could be represented as switches in parallel.

The NOT gate's logic equation is $A = \overline{A}$, meaning its output state is always opposite its input state. When A = 1, $\overline{A} = 0$. Remember, that a digital bit has only 2 values, either zero or one. The circuit configuration would be a common emitter amplifier with the input applied to the base and the output taken from the collector. Remember it takes a 3 element device to invert and only the common emitter circuit configuration has inverter capability.

The three basic gates can be used in combination, (referred to as combinational logic circuits), to form a variety of other logic gates. Functions such as decision-making, can be performed by these gates. The various logic gates can be described by equations that can be extracted from truth tables. A truth table is a plot of all the possible combinations of a logic gate. For example, if a logic gate has 3 inputs there is a possibility of 2^3 or 8 distinct outputs. This is because each input can be either zero or one and there are 3 separate inputs. Therefore the truth table will contain 8 steps from binary 000 to 111. Eight separate numbers from zero to decimal 7. If the logic gate is an AND circuit, the input will provide a 1 in the output for step 8 only. Therefore, 111 describes the input that results in a 1 in the output and the logic equation will be ABC.

When a NOT gate is combined with the output of an AND or OR gate, the combinational logic gate is called a NAND or NOR gate respectively. In this case, all of the outputs will be inverted. All the zeros will become ones and the ones will become zeros.

Logic gates can represent two different types of logic (dual logic). A positive logic AND gate is also a negative logic OR gate. This means that they both perform the same function. The only difference is in what you define as binary 1 and 0.

If positive and negative logic seems confusing, study the examples shown in the Appendix at the end of this unit.

Appendix
Positive and Negative Logic Equivalent Circuits

POSITIVE LOGIC

INPUTS		OUTPUT
0V	0V	0V=0
0V	+5V	0V=0
+5V	0V	0V=0
+5V	+5V	+5V=1

TRUTH TABLE FOR POSITIVE LOGIC **AND**

INPUTS		OUTPUT
0	0	0
0	1	0
1	0	0
1	1	1

TRUTH TABLE FOR **AND** GATE

NEGATIVE LOGIC

INPUTS		OUTPUT
+5V	+5V	+5V=0
+5V	0V	+5V=0
0V	+5V	+5V=0
0V	0V	0V=1

TRUTH TABLE FOR NEGATIVE LOGIC **OR**

POSITIVE **AND**

← EQUIVALENT CIRCUITS →

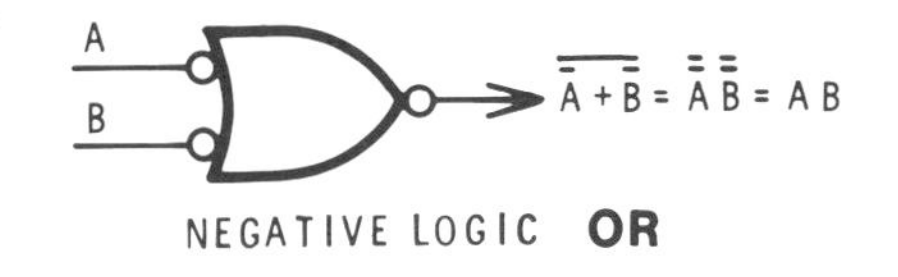

NEGATIVE LOGIC **OR**

Both gates provide a 1 output only when all inputs are 1.

EXAMPLE 1.

To convert to negative logic, invert all inputs and the output.

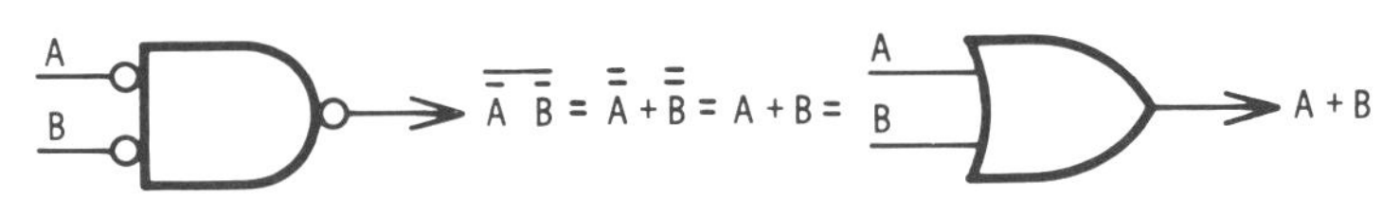

A negative logic AND is a positive logic OR.

EXAMPLE 2.

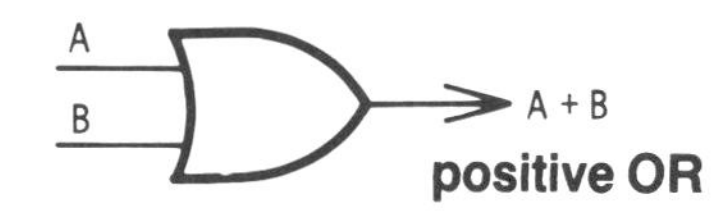

positive OR

To convert to negative logic, invert all inputs and the output.

A negative logic OR is a positive logic AND.

EXAMPLE 3.

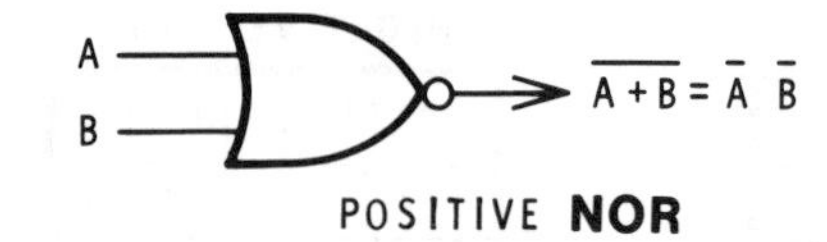

POSITIVE **NOR**

To convert to negative logic, invert all inputs and the output.

The two output inverters cancel each other. Thus, the symbol becomes:

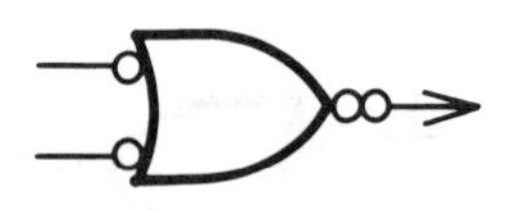

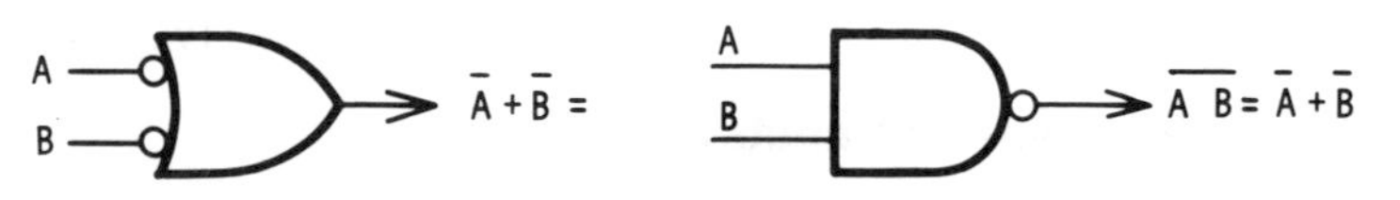

A negative NOR is a positive NAND.

EXAMPLE 4.

POSITIVE **NAND**

To convert to negative logic, invert all inputs and the output.

Again, the two output inverters cancel and the symbol becomes:

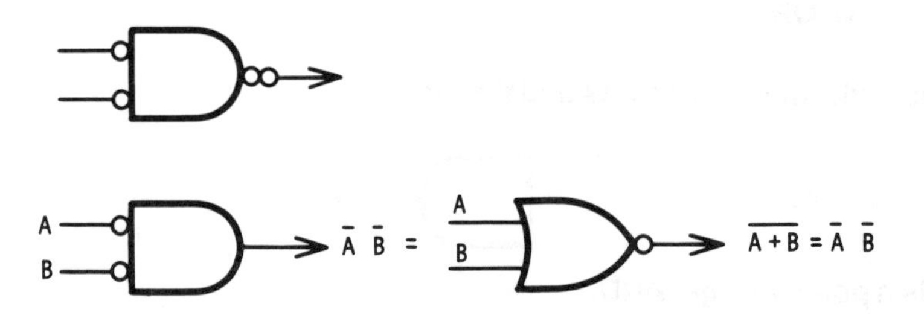

A negative NAND is a positive NOR.

EXAMPLE 5.

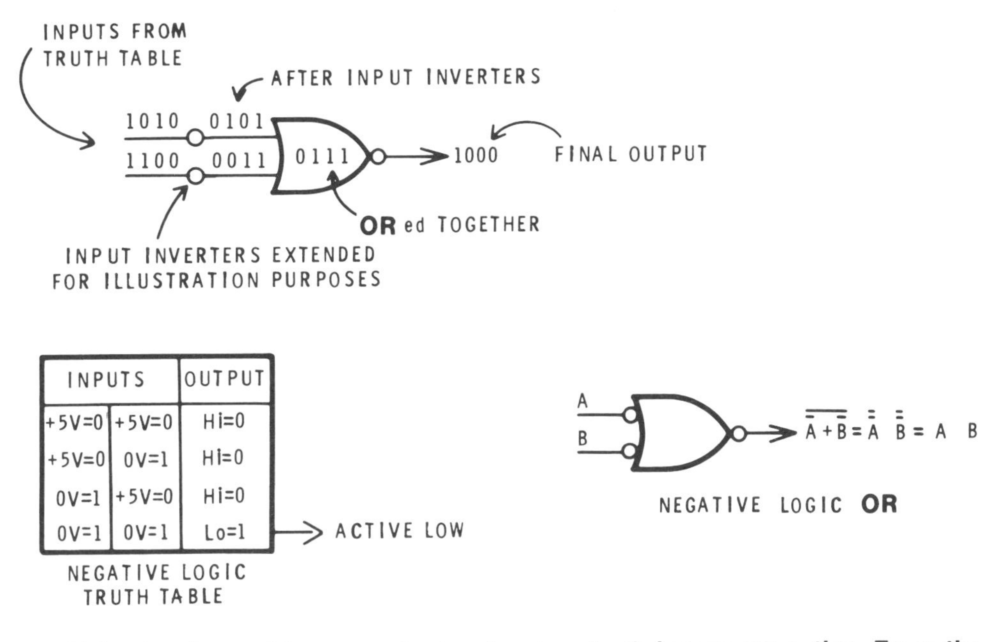

INPUTS		OUTPUT
+5V=0	+5V=0	Hi=0
+5V=0	0V=1	Hi=0
0V=1	+5V=0	Hi=0
0V=1	0V=1	Lo=1

NEGATIVE LOGIC
TRUTH TABLE

This circuit provides an output only when both inputs are active. From the truth table, you can see that the inputs are active low. Thus, the term negative logic means active low.

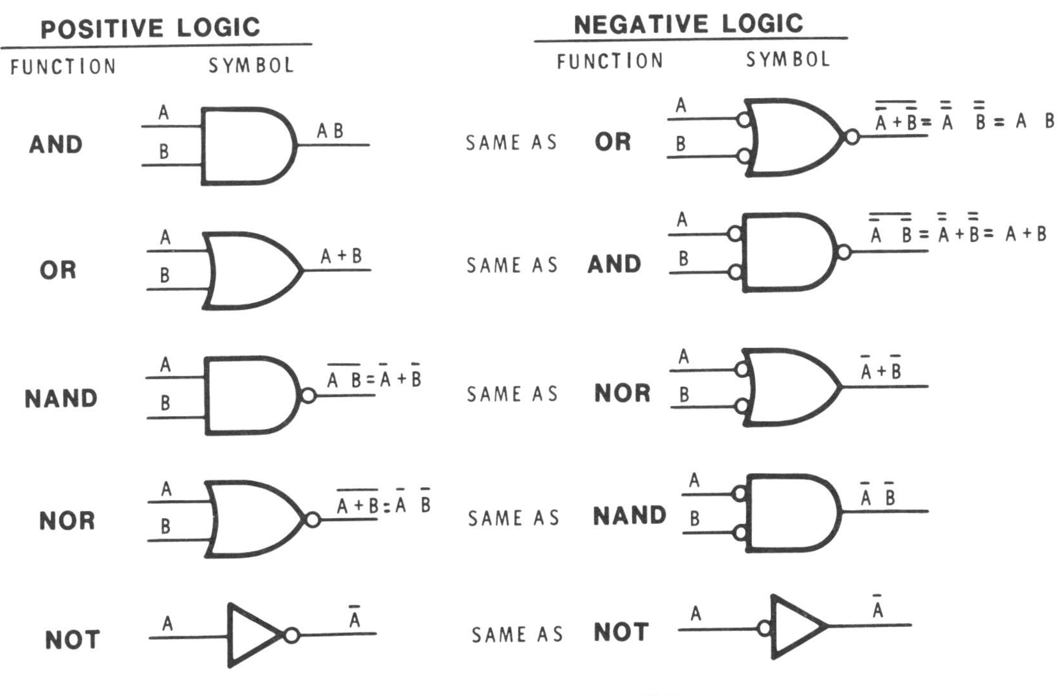

DE MORGAN EQUIVALENT CIRCUITS

Unit 4
Digital Integrated Circuits

Contents

Introduction. 4-3

Unit Objectives 4-5

Logic Circuit Characteristics 4-6

Integrated Circuits. 4-13

Transistor-Transistor Logic. 4-21

Emitter-Coupled Logic 4-35

Metal Oxide Semiconductor Integrated Circuits. 4-39

Integrated Injection Logic. 4-47

Selecting a Digital Integrated Circuit For A Specific Application 4-54

Summary. 4-59

Introduction

All modern digital equipment is constructed with integrated circuits. A study of digital techniques, therefore, is a study of digital integrated circuits and their application. Because of integrated circuits, digital equipment can be analyzed and designed almost entirely at a conceptual logic or systems level as opposed to an electronics or circuits level. Digital integrated circuits are, in the true sense of the word, building blocks used to construct digital equipment. Previously, the designer of digital equipment had to design not only the logic involved, but also the electronic circuits necessary to implement that logic. With integrated circuits, the designers job is primarily that of selecting commercially available devices and applying them to his specific application. No knowledge of electronic circuit design is necessary to the understanding and use of most digital techniques. However, by understanding techniques your understanding of the basic components and circuits will increase your ability to work with integrated circuits.

In this unit you will study the basic components and circuits used in the most common types of digital integrated circuits. The information in this unit will help you to analyze the operation of digital circuits and to select a type of integrated circuit for a specific application. Look closely at the Unit Objectives that follow to determine the specific knowledge and skills you will have when you complete this unit.

Unit Objectives

When you complete this unit, you will have the knowledge and skills indicated below. You will be able to:

1. Name the two basic types of semiconductor switching elements used in digital circuits.

2. Define the four basic logic circuit characteristics of propagation delay, power dissipation, noise immunity and fan out.

3. Name and visually identify the three basic types of digital IC packages.

4. Name four distinct families of digital ICs.

5. Describe the detailed operation and capabilities of TTL, ECL, MOS, CMOS, and IIL integrated circuits given a schematic diagram of the circuit.

6. Select a type of digital IC to implement a given application for optimum performance and economy.

Logic Circuit Characteristics

There are many different types of digital integrated circuits available to implement digital equipment. Both saturated and nonsaturated bipolar transistors as well as MOSFETs are used to implement a variety of logic circuits. Each type or family of digital integrated circuits has its own special capabilities and limitations. Their characteristics vary widely and the optimum circuit to use in a given application depends upon the application's specific needs and requirements.

Some of the most important characteristics of digital integrated circuits are logic levels, propagation delay, power dissipation, noise immunity, and fan out. By understanding the meanings of these characteristics you can quickly compare, contrast and evaluate different IC logic families.

Logic Levels

Logic levels are the voltage values assigned to the binary 1 and binary 0 states for a given type of digital integrated circuit. Nominal values for the two levels are generally given, but in practice, the actual voltage levels may vary somewhat because of internal component tolerances, power supply variations, temperature, and other factors. Generally, the manufacturer will list maximum and minimum acceptable voltage values for the binary 0 and binary 1 levels.

It is important to know the logic levels for a given type of integrated circuit so that when you are working with the equipment you can readily identify input and output logic states by measuring the logic levels with a voltmeter or an oscilloscope. A knowledge of the logic levels will permit you to analyze the operation of a circuit or determine whether it is functioning properly.

Propagation Delay

The propagation delay is a measure of the speed of operation of a logic circuit. Speed of operation is one of the most important characteristic of a digital circuit. For most digital applications high speed operation is beneficial.

Propagation delay is the amount of time that it takes the output of a digital circuit to respond to the input level change. It is the accumulation of all of the rise times, delay times, and storage times associated with any logic circuit. When the input voltage changes from the binary 0 to binary 1 or from the binary 1 to binary 0 levels, the output of the logic circuit will respond at some finite time later.

Figure 4-1 illustrates propagation delay. Shown here is the input to a digital circuit and the corresponding output. The circuit could be an inverter, a NAND gate, or a NOR gate. A binary 0 to binary 1 transition causes a binary 1 to binary 0 transition at the output. Note that the output transition occurs a specific time after the input transition. This is the propagation delay. The propagation delay (t_p) is generally measured between the 50 percent amplitude points on the corresponding leading and trailing edges of the input and output pulses. Note also that there are two types of propagation delay, the propagation delay occurring when the output changes from high to low (t_{pHL}) and the propagation delay that occurs on the low to high output transition (t_{pLH}). Because of the characteristics of the logic circuit, the propagation delays for the two types of level changes are generally different. They are of the same order of magnitude and close in value but nevertheless unequal.

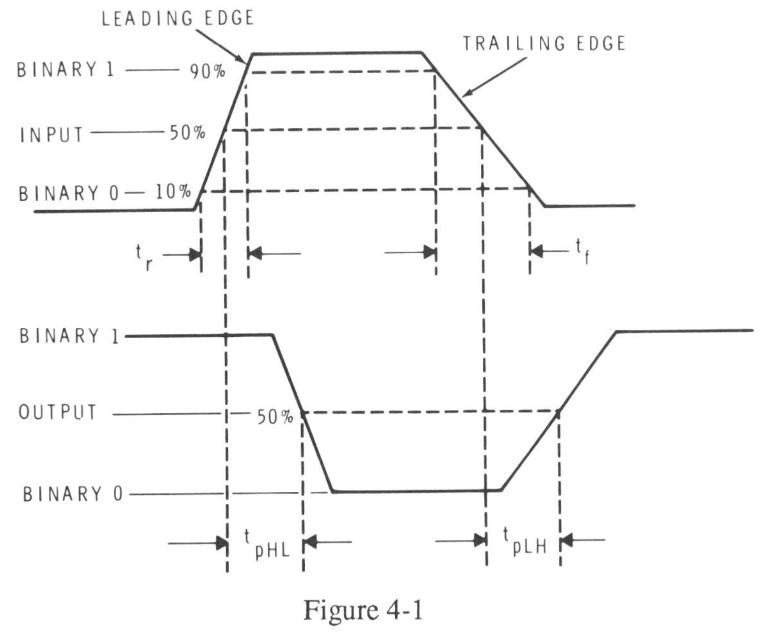

Figure 4-1
Propagation Delay.

The rise and fall times of the input and output pulses are another important consideration. The rise time (t_r) is the time it takes the pulse to rise from 10 percent to 90 percent of its maximum value. The fall time (t_f) is the time it takes for the pulse voltage to fall from 90 percent to 10 percent of its maximum value.

For most modern digital integrated circuits propagation delays are very short but finite. Propagation delays as low as 500 picoseconds are achievable. Some types of modern logic circuits have propagation delays as high as several hundred nanoseconds. Rise and fall times are usually less than the propagation delays. Because of manufacturing tolerances, circuit wiring and other factors, propagation delays can vary considerably from their nominal indicated value. In addition propagation delays are additive. When gates and other combinational logic circuits are cascaded, the propagation delays accumulate. If there is more than one level of logic, the total propagation delay from input to output is simply the sum of the individual gate propagation delays.

Power Dissipation

Another important characteristic of digital logic circuits is power dissipation. This is a measure of the amount of power consumed by the components in a typical logic gate or other circuit. Power dissipation, in milliwatts per logic gate, is an average value since the power consumption is usually different for the binary 1 and binary 0 output states.

The amount of power dissipated by a logic circuit is a very important consideration in the design of any digital equipment. A high power dissipation will mean high electrical energy consumption. Naturally, it is desirable to conserve as much electrical power as possible since the cost of operation of the equipment is an important consideration. This is particularly true of large scale digital systems such as computers.

The total power dissipation of the digital circuitry will also determine the size and cost of the power supply. In addition, high power dissipations mean high heat levels. In some instances special cooling requirements may be necessary to ensure proper operation of the equipment. Power dissipation is particularly important in portable or battery operated equipment. In order to reduce the cost of the battery and ensure long battery life, low power dissipation is desirable.

Gate power dissipation runs all the way from microwatts for certain types of MOS circuits to as high as 60 to 100 milliwatts per gate for certain types of high speed non-saturated logic.

The Speed-Power Trade-Off

Two of the characteristics that we have considered so far, namely, speed and power dissipation are directly dependent upon one another in all types of digital logic circuits. The relationship between these two characteristics is such that speed is proportional to power dissipation. The faster a logic circuit switches the higher its power dissipation. In order to get high speed operation you must accept the penalty of high power dissipation. This trade-off or compromise between speed and power, is one of the most important considerations that a digital designer must make in the selection of a type of logic circuit for a given application. High speed digital logic circuits use non-saturating bipolar transistors. Because the transistors do not saturate, their emitter-collector voltage drops are higher. Combine this with the very low circuit resistance values to minimize charge and discharge times of stray capacitances and the result is high power consumption.

MOS integrated circuits consume a very small amount of power. Their high impedance nature is partially responsible for this, however, this characteristic plus the built-in capacitances make for very slow switching speeds. The result is that the frequency of operation is severely limited. Nevertheless, the extremely low power consumption (on the order of nanowatts) makes MOS circuitry extremely desirable for portable and battery operation where high speed is not required. Other types of logic circuits fall between these two extremes. The speed-power trade-off is an inherent compromise.

You will sometimes see the speed-power relationship expressed with a number called the "speed-power product." It is obtained by multiplying the propagation delay in nanoseconds by the power dissipation in milliwatts. The result is the speed-power product in picojoule. Joule is the unit of energy (power per unit of time) while pico means 10^{-12}. For example, a logic gate with a propagation delay of 5 nanoseconds and power dissipation of 3 milliwatts has a speed-power product of $5 \times 3 = 15$ picojoules. The **lower** the speed power product, the higher the quality of the circuit.

Noise Immunity

Noise immunity is a measure of the susceptibility of a logic circuit to noise pulses on the inputs and output of a logic circuit. Noise is considered to be any extraneous and undesired signal generated within the equipment itself or externally that is added to and appears superimposed upon, the standard system logic levels. This noise can be a slowly varying DC level or very high frequency, short duration voltage or current spikes. The noise may be either randomly occurring or repetitive. In any case, noise signals can cause the logic circuit to switch to an undesirable state at an improper time.

All digital logic circuits have built-in noise immunity. Because of the voltage thresholds associated with the components and the circuit, most logic circuits are capable of rejecting noise spikes of a relatively high amplitude. The noise immunity of most logic circuits is from approximately 10 to 50 percent of the supply voltage. This means that a noise spike occurring on a binary 0 or binary 1 level will be rejected if its amplitude is below a level that is 10 percent to 50 percent of the supply voltage. A circuit with a noise immunity of one volt, for example, would reject noise pulses that are one volt or less different from the nominal binary 0 or binary 1 logic levels. In some cases, noise is rejected by the logic circuit by virtue of its slow response. Some noise is high frequency in nature and noise pulses are of such short duration, that the logic circuits cannot respond fast enough to cause a logic state change.

Noise immunity is an important consideration of digital logic circuits, since most digital systems generate a substantial amount of noise during high speed switching. In addition, much digital equipment is used in noisy industrial environments where transients from the power line and other electrical equipment can cause false triggering of the logic circuitry. When selecting a particular digital integrated circuit for a logic application, noise immunity is an important consideration.

Fan Out

Fan out is generally expressed in terms of the number of standard size loads that a logic gate output can drive and still maintain proper operation. Because of the component limitations and circuit configuration, there is a limit to the number of loads that can be connected to a logic circuit. A standard logic gate, for example, may have a fan out of ten, indicating that ten standard gate inputs can be attached to the output of this logic circuit and still maintain proper operation according to the manufacturer's specifications.

Self-Test Review

1. The most important logic circuit characteristics are:

   a. ____ .
   b. ____ .
   c. ____ .
   d. ____ .
   e. ____ .

2. The accumulation of all the rise times, delay times, and storage times of a logic circuit is referred to as its:

   a. Fan out.
   b. Logic levels.
   c. Propagation delay.
   d. Power dissipation.

3. Decreasing the propagation delay of a logic circuit generally results in an increase in:

   a. power dissipation.
   b. fan out.
   c. noise immunity.
   d. package size.

4. The ability of a logic circuit to reject noise spikes of a relatively high amplitude is its:

   a. power dissipation.
   b. fan out.
   c. noise immunity.
   d. propagation delay.

5. A standard logic gate having a fan out of 3 can drive how many standard gate inputs?

   a. 1
   b. 3
   c. 6
   d. 10

6. A logic circuit with a noise immunity of 40 percent is better in rejecting noise than one with 10 percent.

   a. True.
   b. False.

Integrated Circuits

Since all modern digital equipment is made up of integrated circuits, you should be familiar with the various types. In this section you are going to learn how integrated circuits are classified and something about their physical characteristics. You will also learn of the most popular families of integrated circuits used in digital equipment today.

Integrated circuits are classified in three basic ways: by method of manufacturing, by application and by function. Let's briefly consider each of these types of classifications.

Manufacturing Methods

There are four basic ways of making integrated circuits. The most widely used method is called monolithic. Other types of manufacturing methods include thin film, thick film, and hybrid.

Monolithic

A monolithic integrated circuit is one that is constructed entirely on a single chip of silicon semiconductor material. Semiconductor materials are diffused into the basic substrate or base material to form the various junctions making up components such as diodes, transistors and resistors. The semiconductor materials to be diffused into the substrate are in gaseous form, and are deposited on the substrate through a series of masking operations under very high temperature. The result is that the entire circuit, all components and interconnections are on a single base, thus the term monolithic. Most integrated circuits are constructed using this monolithic technique.

There are two basic forms of monolithic integrated circuits: bipolar and MOS. Here, the difference is primarily that of the type of transistors used in constructing the circuits. The MOS circuitry is easier to make and takes up less space; therefore, much more circuitry can be placed on a silicon chip of a given size. The simplicity of the components also makes the manufacturing yield much higher. The result is that MOS circuits can be constructed with higher density and at lower costs. In some applications, however, MOS circuits are not appropriate. Therefore, bipolar circuitry must be used.

Thin and Thick Film Techniques

Thin and thick film integrated circuits are manufactured by depositing certain materials on a non-conducting base such as ceramic. Through a series of masking procedures, various resistive and conducting materials are deposited on the base or substrate to form resistors, capacitors, and inductors. Semiconductors are not usually manufactured in this way. Thin and thick film techniques are primarily used for manufacturing passive networks such as attenuators, filters, phase shift networks and the like. Because such networks can be made extremely small, they offer the same advantages over discrete component circuits as do monolithic integrated circuits. Another advantage is that component tolerances can be closer than equivalent components made by monolithic techniques. For high quality precision circuits, thin and thick film techniques are preferred.

Hybrid Circuits

A hybrid integrated circuit is made up of a combination of monolithic, thin film or thick film circuits. Any number of combinations are considered to by hybrid. A hybrid integrated circuit may consist of multiple monolithic chips interconnected in a single package. Another example of a hybrid is a monolithic circuit combined with a thin or thick film circuit. Thin film or thick film circuits are also combined with individual semiconductor component chips to form a special high grade circuit for an unusual application.

Hybrids offer the advantage that a variety of different integrated circuits and components can be combined to offer special advantages not available in individual types of integrated circuits alone. For example, because of the ultra small size of a monolithic circuit, power dissipation is limited. In order to handle high power requirements, it may be necessary to combine a low power monolithic circuit with a power transistor mounted on a separate chip, but physically interconnected within the same package. High precision circuit requirements might be met by a combination of a monolithic circuit and a highly accurate thin film network. Because more than one type of technique is involved, and the complication of the interconnections that are necessary, hybrid circuits are more complex and expensive than other types. However, they do offer the designer a wide range of capabilities while still maintaining the ultra small size, and other benefits generally associated with the integrated circuits. Hybrids are often used where it is necessary to combine analog (linear) and digital circuits.

Application

Another method of classifying integrated circuits is by their application. Primarily, this is a means of distinguishing between linear and digital circuits. Digital integrated circuits, of course, work with logic levels, pulses and binary data. Such switching circuits use either bipolar transistors or MOSFETs. Linear integrated circuits usually involve amplifiers of some kind and work with analog signals. They are constructed with bipolar transistors.

The chart in Figure 4-3 shows the basic integrated circuit hierarchy.

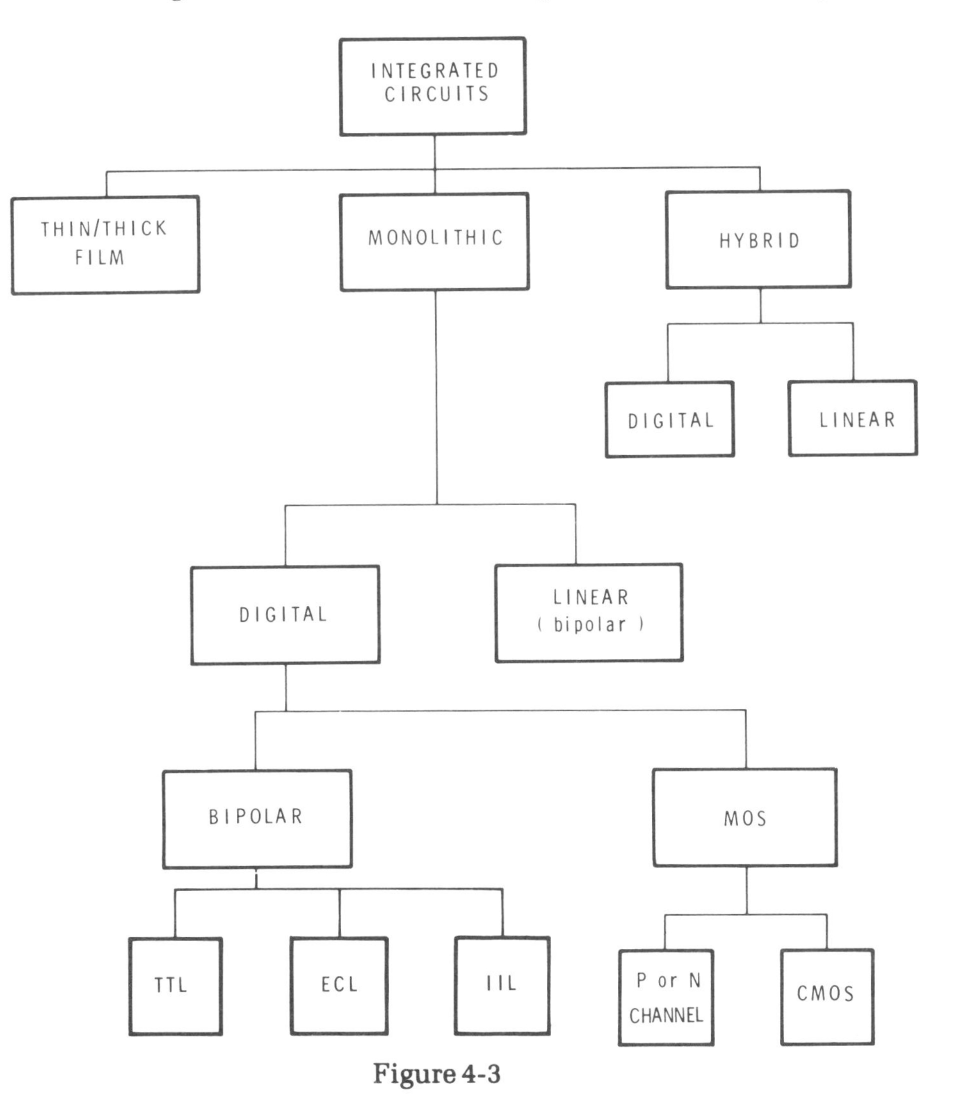

Figure 4-3

Hierarchy of integrated circuits.

Function

There are four basic classifications that identify the function of a digital integrated circuit: small-scale integration (SSI), medium-scale integration (MSI), large-scale integration (LSI), and very large-scale integration (VLSI).

SSI circuits are the simplest and most basic form of integrated circuits. These are amplifier or gate circuits that perform a single basic function. They must be interconnected externally in order to form complete functional or operational circuits. A typical SSI digital integrated circuit might consist of several multiple input gates or a flip-flop.

Medium scale integrated circuits are more complex. MSI circuits involve multiple gates which are interconnected to form a complete functional circuit. Most MSI circuits contain twelve or more equivalent gates or circuitry of similar complexity. An MSI circuit is usually a complete functional operating network such as a decoder, a counter or multiplexer. Such circuitry eliminates the need of having to interconnect individual gates in SSI packages to form the same function. MSI circuits greatly reduce the number of integrated circuits in a system and thereby reduce cost, assembly time, and in some cases, power consumption.

LSI circuits contain 100 or more equivalent gate circuits or networks of a similar complexity. LSI circuits are larger functional circuits or are the equivalent of multiple MSI circuits. An LSI circuit often forms a complete system or instrument. The major application of LSI circuits is in semiconductor memories which store binary data. However, there are many different types of complex LSI circuits including electronic calculators, computers and certain types of test instruments.

VLSI circuits usually contain a thousand or more equivalent gate circuits. Chips with this much circuitry can form complete systems. Extraordinarily large logic networks like those in super mainframe computers can be implemented with VLSI circuits.

Integrated Circuit Packaging

A primary consideration to the integrated circuit user is the packaging and physical characteristics of integrated circuits. There are three basic methods of packaging the silicon chip. These are the TO5 can, the flat pack, and the dual in-line package. These three basic types of packages are illustrated in Figure 4-4.

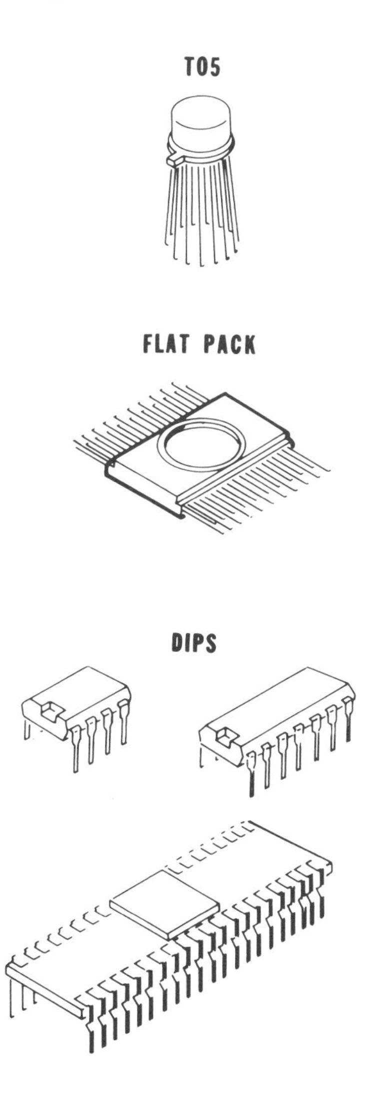

Figure 4-4
Illustrations of typical TO5, flat pack and DIP ICs.

TO5

The earliest form of package used for integrated circuits was the TO5 can. This is a standard configuration for packaging transistors. This same package was modified by including additional leads. This type of package is still available for some integrated circuits today, but it is not the most popular form. Its advantage is that it can dissipate a substantial amount of heat. For that reason, this package is used mostly with linear integrated circuits.

Flat Pack

The flat pack was another type of housing used in the early development stages of integrated circuits. It is the smallest of all available integrated circuit packages and is designed for high density packaging. The packages are flat and are designed to be soldered or spot welded to a circuit board. Circuits can be placed close together and, therefore, a considerable amount of circuitry can be packaged in an extremely small area. Because of their ability to be packed so densely, these integrated circuits are generally made of a ceramic material that can withstand high temperatures. Closely packaged circuits cause heating and cooling problems. Therefore, the circuitry must be able to withstand such an environment. Flat pack circuits are used primarily in critical-size applications such as avionics, high reliability military systems and special industrial equipment.

DIP

The most widely used form of integrated circuit packaging is the dual in-line package (DIP). It is slightly larger than the other types available, but it offers many advantages. Such circuits are easy to mount and use. They are designed to be adaptable to machine insertion on printed circuit boards. They are available in various sizes, all the way from an 8-pin package (mini DIP) to a 64-pin package. Most SSI circuits are housed in 8, 14, or 16-pin dual in-line packages. MSI circuits are found in 14, 16, 18, 20, 22, and 24-pin dual in-line packages. LSI circuits, because of their greater size complexity, require a greater number of input and output leads and, therefore, are usually housed in 24, 28, 40 and 64-pin packages.

Several different types of dual in-line package materials are used. The most commonly used and least expensive is a plastic package. In this type of package, the integrated circuit chip is spot welded to a metal lead frame. The entire circuit is then encapsulated by an injection molded plastic technique.

For some critical integrated circuits, several types of ceramic packages are used. These are capable of withstanding higher temperatures and are generally hermetically sealed to provide an extra clean and safe environment for the circuit.

Temperature Ranges

Most integrated circuits are rated according to the range of temperatures over which they can operate satisfactorily. Most manufacturers generally specify both a military grade and a commercial or industrial grade circuit. The military grade circuits can be packaged in TO5 cans, ceramic flat packs, or ceramic dual in-line packages. These devices are capable of operating over a wide temperature range, usually from −55°C to +125°C. Circuits that perform properly over this wide temperature range are generally much more expensive. Such circuits are used only in high quality military equipment or in industrial equipment that is to be operated in severe environments.

For most general applications the commercial or industrial grade integrated circuits can be used. These are generally housed in plastic packages and are capable of operating over the 0°C to 70°C temperature range. Other temperature ranges are sometimes specified for different types of integrated circuits. Check the manufacturer's data sheet for specific information on temperature ranges.

7. Most digital ICs are:

   a. Thin film.
   b. Thick film.
   c. Hybrid.
   d. Monolithic.

8. The IC containing the most gates is:

   a. SSI.
   b. MSI.
   c. LSI.
   d. VLSI.

9. A functional digital IC containing 50 gates is classified as:

   a. SSI.
   b. MSI.
   c. LSI.
   d. VLSI.

10. The most popular IC package is the:

    a. TO5 can.
    b. flat pack.
    c. DIP.

11. The two types of DIP packaging materials are ____________ and ____________.

12. List the two temperature ranges of most digital ICs.

    Military ____________.
    Commercial/Industrial ____________.

Transistor-Transistor Logic

There are many different types of integrated circuit logic elements used in implementing digital equipment. All of them perform the basic logic functions but have different characteristics, capabilities and limitations. Different types of digital logic circuits have been developed to meet special needs. Over the years a variety of circuits have emerged.

One of the biggest and most important design decisions made by an engineer designing digital equipment is in the selection of a type of digital logic circuit. In this section we are going to discuss the most popular form of bipolar integrated circuit logic elements, transistor-transistor logic. Non-saturating bipolar circuits and MOS digital integrated circuits will be considered in following sections.

The most popular and most widely used type of digital bipolar IC is transistor-transistor logic (TTL or T^2L pronounced T squared L). Its popularity is primarily the result of its extremely low cost and the availability of a wide variety of SSI logic elements and MSI functional circuits. Its ease of use, high performance characteristics and interfacing capability are other features that make it desirable. A number of special types of TTL circuits are available to match special needs. Even though TTL integrated circuits have been available since the early 1960's, this type of logic circuit continues to remain popular for use in new equipment designs. Most of the experiments you will perform in this program use TTL integrated circuits.

Circuit Operation

Figure 4-5 shows the circuit of a typical TTL logic gate. It operates from a single +5-volt power supply and has typical logic levels of .4 volts for binary 0 (low) and 3.6-volts for a binary 1 (high). The circuit consists of three basic sections: a multiple emitter input transistor (Q_1), a phase splitter transistor (Q_2), and a totem-pole output circuit consisting of transistors Q_3 and Q_4. The multiple emitter-base junctions of transistor Q_1, along with R_1, form a diode gate. The primary advantage of this arrangement over individual diodes is that higher speed operation can be obtained.

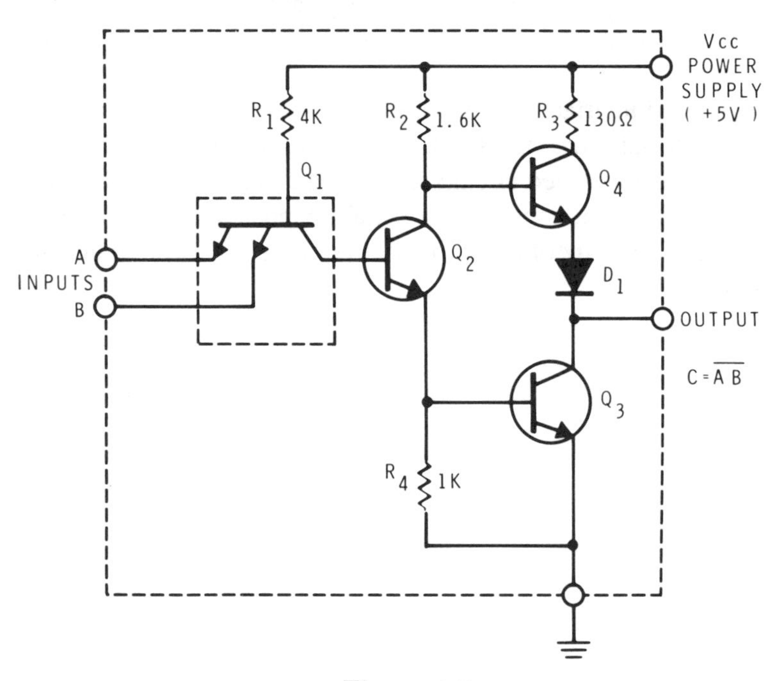

Figure 4-5
A typical transistor-transistor logic gate.

The phase splitter transistor (Q_2) is a circuit that provides complementary drive signals for the two output transistors. The output circuit consists of transistors Q_3 and Q_4. These transistors are stacked one upon the other. Thus, this arrangement is given the name totem-pole. Transistor Q_3 is simply a shunt transistor switch. Q_4 in this circuit essentially serves as an active load resistor for Q_3. In some logic circuits, the collector of the output transistor is returned through a collector resistor to the supply voltage. This collector resistor is known as a pull-up resistor because it causes the output to be pulled up to the supply voltage when the output transistor cuts off. In the TTL gate, Q_4 serves as an active *pull-up* resistor. Current to any shunt load on the output is supplied by this transistor. This arrangement provides a much lower output impedance in the high output state; and, therefore, higher speed operation can be obtained. In logic circuits using a pull-up resistor, any shunt output capacitance must be charged through the collector pull-up resistor. This charging time can be long depending on the amount of shunt capacitance and the value of the collector resistor. With the active pull-up arrangement in the TTL gate, any output capacitance can be charged more quickly through the very low impedance represented by Q_4.

To simplify the discussion of the TTL logic circuit, it is convenient to show a diode equivalent of the key parts to this circuit. This diode equivalent arrangement is shown in Figure 4-6. Diodes D_1 and D_2 in this circuit represent the emitter-base input junctions of transistor Q_1. Diode D_3 represents the base-collector junction of transistor Q_1. Diode D_4 represents the emitter-base junction Q_2, and D_5 is the emitter-base junction of Q_3. Study the diode equivalent in Figure 4-6 and relate it to Figure 4-5. Keep in mind that a PN junction silicon diode requires approximately 0.7 volts across it before it conducts. The forward voltage drop across this diode is also approximately 0.7 volts. Since diodes D_3, D_4 and D_5 are connected in series, the voltage at point X will be the sum of the individual voltage drops or in this case approximately $3 \times 0.7 = 2.1$ volts. A voltage less than 2.1 volts at point X will mean that all three diodes will be cut off.

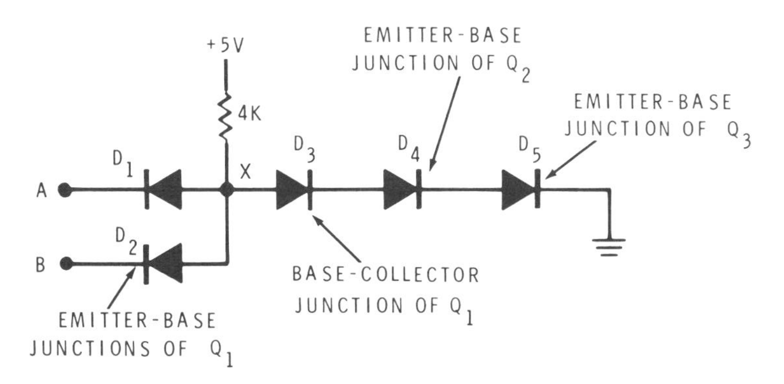

Figure 4-6
Diode equivalent circuit of TTL gate.

Now consider the operation of the circuit. If either one or both of the logic inputs are at their binary 0 level, 0.4 volts or less, the associated input emitter junction will conduct. The voltage at the base of Q_1, (point X in Figure 4-6) will be the input logic level voltage plus the drop across the input emitter-base diode, in this case approximately 0.4 + 0.7 = 1.1 volts. Current will flow through the input diode whose input is low and through the 4K pull-up resistor. Since the voltage at the base of Q_1 (point X in Figure 4-6) is less than that required to cause the three diode string to conduct, the base-collector junction of Q_1 will not conduct. The emitter-base junctions of Q_2 and Q_3 will not conduct therefore these transistors will be cut off. With Q_2 off, base current will be supplied to transistor Q_4 through resistor R_2. Q_4 will conduct if an output load is connected to ground. The output voltage at this time will be the supply voltage $+V_{CC}$ less the drop across diode D_1, Q_4 and the 130 ohm collector resistor. A typical TTL binary 1 output voltage level is approximately +2.4 to +3.6 volts. A binary 0 voltage level at either or both of the inputs will produce a binary 1 output.

Now assume binary 1 logic levels applied to both inputs. A typical binary 1 logic level input will be +2.4 volts or higher. Most of the inputs will be driven from other TTL output circuits and, therefore, the output voltage will, in most practical situations, approach +3.6 volts. The diode equivalent string D_3, D_4, and D_5 in Figure 4-6 will conduct through the 4K resistor. The voltage at point X in Figure 4-6 will be about +2.1 volts. Therefore, with +3.6 volt inputs, D_1 and D_2 will be reverse-biased, thus cut off.

The emitter-base junctions of Q_2 and Q_3 will be forward-biased as well as the base-collector junction of Q_1. With Q_2 conducting, its collector voltage is lower than that required to turn Q_4 on. Base current normally supplied to Q_4 through R_2 is shunted away by the conduction of Q_2. With Q_2 conducting Q_3 will saturate. At this time the output voltage is the emitter-collector saturation voltage of Q_3 which will be +0.4 volts or less. As you can see, with binary 1's on both inputs, the output will be binary 0. From this circuit description you can see that the circuit performs the NAND function for positive logic and the NOR function for negative logic. The truth tables in Figure 4-7 sum up the operation of the basic TTL gate. Notice that figures B and C are **NOT** equivalent circuits, but complements. Typical TTL characteristics are summarized in Table I.

INPUTS		OUTPUT
A	B	C
+.4V	+.4V	+3.6V
+.4V	+3.6V	+3.6V
+3.6V	+.4V	+3.6V
+3.6V	+3.6V	+.4V

A

INPUTS		OUTPUT
A	B	C
0	0	1
0	1	1
1	0	1
1	1	0

B

INPUTS		OUTPUT
A	B	C
1	1	0
1	0	0
0	1	0
0	0	1

C

Figure 4-7
Truth tables for typical TTL logic gate (A) electrical, (B) positive logic NAND, (C) negative logic NOR.

Table I

TTL Characteristics
Type of logic: Current sinking
Propagation delay: 1-40 nanoseconds
Power dissipation: 1-25 milliwatts
Fan out: 10-30
Noise immunity: high
Logic levels: binary 0 = + .4 volts
binary 1 = +3.6 volts
Basic gate form: positive NAND/negative NOR
Supply Voltage V_{CC} + 5 volts ±10 percent

TTL integrated circuits continue to be one of the most popular and widely used forms of logic elements. Many new equipment designs continue to use this type of circuit. Many manufacturers supply TTL circuits and new circuits are developed regularly. The wide range of SSI and MSI types make TTL circuitry perhaps the most versatile line of digital integrated circuits available. The most common type of TTL circuits are the 7400 series originally developed by Texas Instruments. Almost all other integrated circuit manufacturers second source this series of TTL circuits. Other TTL circuits are also available. These include the 9300 series made by Fairchild and the 8000 series manufactured by Signetics. All of these types of TTL circuits are compatible with one another. In this program you will use many different types of the 7400 series of TTL ICs.

Special TTL Variations

All TTL integrated circuits whether SSI or MSI, combinational or sequential use the basic TTL gate circuit shown in Figure 4-5. In addition, there are several other versions of this TTL circuit made for special applications. These include gates for low power operation, higher speed operation or special logic functions.

Low Power TTL

Low power TTL circuits are similar to the basic TTL circuit described earlier. The only difference is that the resistor values in the circuit are approximately ten times higher, meaning that the power consumption of the circuit is one-tenth of that of the standard circuit. Low power TTL circuits are excellent for applications requiring a relatively high speed logic line with minimum power consumption. Increasing the values of the internal resistances, causes the propagation delay of the circuit to be increased. The propagation delay in a typical low power gate is approximately 30 to 40 nanoseconds. High speed is sacrificed for low power consumption.

High Speed TTL

The high speed TTL circuit is basically the same as the standard circuit considered earlier. In this circuit resistor values are decreased significantly in order to improve operating speed. Typically, the gate propagation delay is reduced to approximately 6 nanoseconds. This increase in speed is accompanied by a power dissipation approximately twice that of a standard gate. This is approximately 22 milliwatts average power dissipation per gate. High speed TTL circuits have for the most part been replaced by the newer Schottky TTL circuits, which are not only faster but also consume less power.

Schottky TTL

The transistors in a TTL logic circuit operate in the saturation mode. To achieve higher speed operation than that obtainable with a standard or high power TTL gate, non-saturating transistors must be used. This is what is done to improve the speed of operation of Schottky TTL circuits.

The circuit of a Schottky TTL gate is basically the same as the standard TTL gate circuit we discussed earlier. The primary difference is that a diode is connected between the base and collector of each transistor in order to prevent those transistors from saturating. See Figure 4-8A.

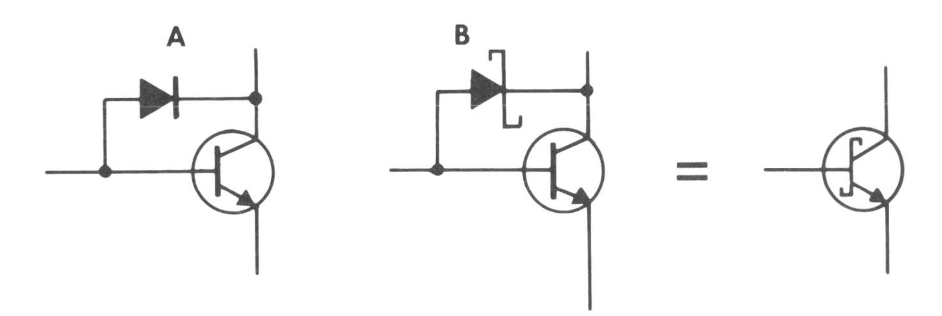

Figure 4-8
Hot carrier diode clamped transistors used in Schottky TTL circuits to prevent saturation, and increase switching speed.

When the transistor begins to turn on, its collector voltage will drop quickly to some low value. When it drops beyond a certain point, the diode will conduct and shunt current away from the collector-base junction that would normally conduct during saturation. The diode effectively clamps the collector to a voltage sufficiently high to keep the base-collector junction reverse-biased. This circuit permits the condition of saturation to be closely approached but still avoided.

The diode used to provide the clamping that prevents saturation is a hot carrier or Schottky diode. This type of diode, unlike other semiconductor diodes, is not a PN junction type. Instead, a Schottky diode is the junction of a metal such as gold or aluminum, and N-type semiconductor material. These diodes are not separate units. Instead, they are part of the complex integrated circuit diffusion on the silicon chip. These diodes are high speed in operation because they do not have the normal charged storage normally associated with PN junction diodes. The forward voltage drop or voltage required for the diode to conduct, is also much less than a standard PN junction.

The Schottky clamp diode as it is used on the transistors in a TTL gate is illustrated in Figure 4-8B. Note the special symbol used to represent the Schottky diode. The special symbol on the right in this figure is a Schottky diode clamped transistor. You will see this symbol used in schematic diagrams of Schottky TTL logic circuits.

The primary advantage of the Schottky TTL gate is its higher speed of operation. Since the transistors do not saturate, no charge storage problems occur. Gate propagation times as low as 3 nanoseconds are possible with this type of circuit. At the same time, Schottky TTL gates achieve this rate of switching at a power dissipation of approximately 19 milliwatts, something less than the high power TTL circuit. Advanced Schottky TTL circuits with propagation delays as low as 1 nanosecond with a power dissipation of 2 milliwatts are now being made. Special low power Schottky TTL circuits with a propagation delay of 10 nanoseconds and a power dissipation of 2 milliwatts are also available. This form of TTL has one of the most favorable speed-power trade-offs of any digital integrated circuit.

Three-State TTL and Data Busses

Three-state TTL integrated circuits are a special version of TTL circuits whose output can assume three states instead of the normal two. Besides the binary 0 and binary 1 logic levels normally associated with a TTL gate output, the three-state circuit has a third *open* state. This open state represents a very high impedance and is essentially equivalent to disconnecting the TTL totem pole output circuit from the output pin on the integrated circuit. This particular type of circuit is useful in digital systems using multiplexed or bussed data transmission.

A data bus is a group of wires, transmission lines or cables over which digital information or binary numbers are transferred in parallel from one point to another. There are basically two types of data busses, unidirectional and bi-directional. On a unidirectional bus, data is transferred in only one direction. On a bi-directional bus, data can move in either direction. Most digital busses are bi-directional in nature.

Instead of having multiple parallel paths for the transmission of digital data in two directions, a common bus is used and the information is transferred from one place to another on a time shared basis. While data from one particular source is being transferred, other data waits until the current transfer is complete. The concept of having one bus serve as a carrier for multiple signals is known as multiplexing. Circuits not currently in use are disabled, while those sending and receiving data on the bus are activated.

Figure 4-9 shows a simplified diagram of a typical bi-directional digital data bus. Only one of several identical bus lines is shown. This bus line is generally responsible for transmitting one-bit of data of a multiple-bit binary word. The bus itself may be simply a cable several feet long or a transmission line several hundred feet long. Gates 1, 2, or 3 can transmit one-bit of information down the bus line to be received by gate 8. Only one of the three gates will be enabled at a time to transmit the desired data. Note that the same bus can be used to transmit binary information from either gate 6 or gate 7, down the transmission line, to be received by gates 4 or 5. Just keep in mind that only a single data transmission may take place at any given time. It may, however, be in either direction from any one of several sources or to several destinations.

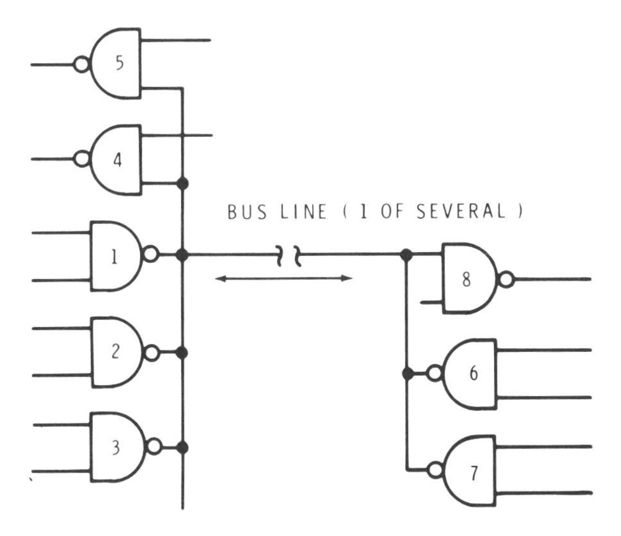

Figure 4-9
Bi-directional digital data bus.

The digital bus is relatively easy to implement with logic circuits using collector pull-up resistors. The outputs of the gates from which the digital data comes are simply connected in parallel as illustrated in Figure 4-10. By connecting their outputs directly together, we effectively parallel the collector resistors, thereby reducing the total resistance to one-half the value of an individual resistor. The two output transistors then share a common collector resistance. With this arrangement either transistor Q_1 or Q_2 can bring the output to the binary 0 condition. If Q_1 conducts and Q_2 is cut-off or if Q_2 conducts and Q_1 is cut-off, the output will be binary 0. The only time that the output will rise to $+V_{CC}$ is when both Q_1 and Q_2 are cut-off. The way digital data is transmitted by one gate then, is to disable the gates not responsible for transmitting data. This is done by applying the appropriate input to the gate so that its output transistor is cut-off. This permits the other transistor to control the state of the output.

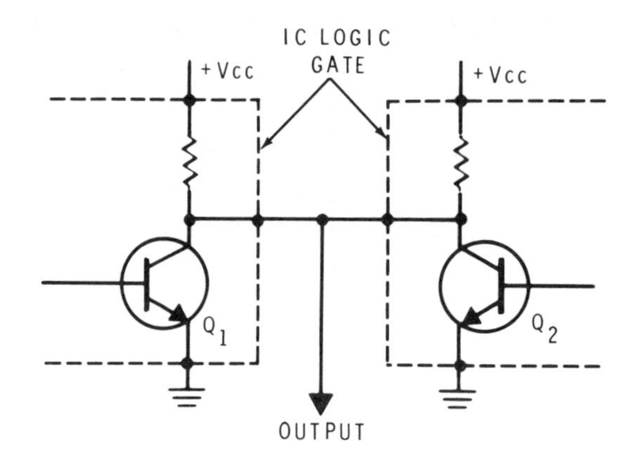

Figure 4-10
Paralleling gate outputs to share
a common output line.

Parallel gate outputs can form what is known as the wired–AND connection. It is given this name simply because either transistor Q_1 OR Q_2 can bring the output to the binary 0 level. This connection is frequently used to implement the logical AND function without the need of an additional gate.

Because of the active pull-up circuit in the totem pole output of a TTL gate, TTL circuits cannot be wired in the AND arrangement. Improper operation or damage can occur. For this reason TTL ICs cannot be used in bussing operations. To overcome this problem, open collector TTL circuits can be used. In these circuits, the active pull-up stage is eliminated and the collector of the shunt output transistor is made available at an output pin. An external collector pull-up resistor, is connected to this output. The wired-AND arrangement can then be used. However, because the active pull-up transistor is removed, one of the primary advantages of a TTL gate is eliminated. The active pull-up produces higher speed operation and lower output impedance, both of which are desirable not only from a speed standpoint but from one of improving noise immunity.

The disadvantage of not being able to use TTL circuits in bus applications was overcome by the development of three-state logic. This type of logic was originally introduced by National Semiconductor Corporation. Three-state logic is a special form of TTL that retains the basic TTL circuit configuration including the totem pole active pull-up output circuit. However, additional circuitry has been added to produce an optional high impedance third state. This then, effectively removes from any common bus line those circuits not transmitting data.

A typical three-state TTL circuit is shown in Figure 4-11A. The circuit arrangement is basically identical to the TTL gate circuit we discussed earlier (see Figure 4-5). Q_1 is the multiple emitter input transistor, Q_2 is the phase splitter while Q_4 and Q_5 form the totem pole output circuit. Transistor Q_3 has been added in order to provide better control of output transistor Q_4. Together, Q_3 and Q_4 form a compound or Darlington transistor with high gain. Components D_1, Q_6, Q_7 and Q_8 have been added to control the third state.

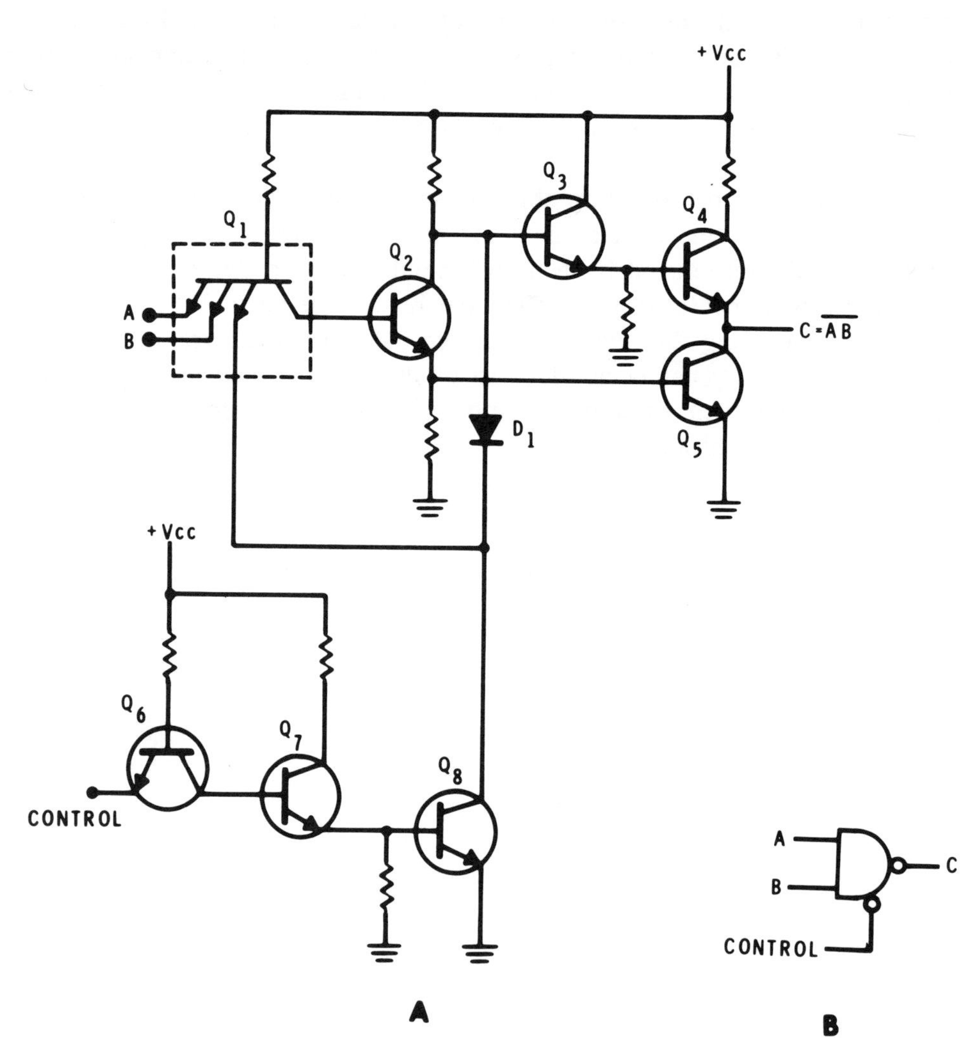

Figure 4-11
Three-state TTL gate schematic (A) and the logic symbol (B).

Whenever the control input is low, transistor Q_6 saturates. When it saturates it causes the collector of Q_6 and hence the base of Q_7 to be nearly the same low input value. This means that Q_7 and Q_8 are cut-off. The TTL gate then functions normally. Here the standard TTL output logic levels for binary 0 and binary 1 are achieved according to the input states.

When the control input is made a binary 1, Q_6 cuts off. The emitter-base junctions of Q_7 and Q_8 become forward-biased through the base-collector junction of Q_6 and the associated base resistor. With Q_8 saturated, the third input to Q_1 is brought to ground along with the cathode of diode D_1. As you recall, when any one or more of the inputs of a TTL gate are brought to a binary 0 level, the output is forced high. This is done by turning on the active pull-up transistor Q_4 and turning off the shunt output transistor Q_5. But in this case, both output transistors Q_4 and Q_5 are cut-off. When Q_8 saturates, the cathode end of D_1 is grounded. All the base current for Q_3 is shunted away. This causes Q_3 and Q_4 to cut-off. With both output transistors Q_4 and Q_5 cut-off, the output is effectively an open circuit. Looking from the output of the gate back into the circuit, any load sees an extremely high impedance. Because of the high quality of the circuit and the low leakage, any load sees essentially an open circuit. With this arrangement, any number of three-state TTL outputs may be paralleled to form a common bus line. When data is to be transmitted, all of those gates not transmitting data will have their control lines at binary 1 so that their outputs represent an open circuit. Only the gate designated to transmit data will be enabled.

Figure 4-11B shows the logic symbol normally used to represent a three-state TTL gate.

Self-Test Review

13. A standard TTL gate performs what logic function for positive logic?

    a. AND.
    b. OR.
    c. NAND.
    d. NOR.

14. If all inputs of a TTL gate are binary 1, the output will be:

    a. binary 0.
    b. binary 1.
    c. indeterminate.

15. The typical TTL logic levels are:

    binary 0. ______________ volts
    binary 1. ______________ volts

16. Two features that make the TTL gate faster than other types of gates are: ______________ and ______________ .

17. Schottky TTL is faster than standard TTL because:

    a. smaller resistor values are used.
    b. it consumes more power.
    c. hot carrier diodes are faster than regular diodes.
    d. non-saturating transistors are used.

18. Three-state TTL has three possible output states. These are: ______________ , ______________ and ______________ .

19. The type of TTL gate that can be wire-ANDed is ______________ .

20. What type of circuitry is used to effectively remove non-transmitting circuits from a common bus line?

    a. Schottky TTL
    b. Low power TTL
    c. High speed TTL
    d. Three-state TTL

Emitter-Coupled Logic

The major switching speed limitation of bipolar logic circuits is the charge storage that occurs in the base region when both the emitter-base and base-collector junctions of a bipolar transistor are forward-biased to achieve saturation. The time required for this charge to be eliminated delays the turn-off of the transistor. Switching speeds can be greatly increased if this delay time is minimized or eliminated. In Schottky TTL circuits this storage problem is eliminated by preventing the transistors from saturating. This significantly increases the switching speed. Non-saturating transistor circuits offer the best potential for fast logic.

Another major form of logic circuits using non-saturating bipolar transistors is called emitter-coupled logic (ECL). Also known as current mode logic, this circuitry is essentially a differential amplifier configuration which effectively prevents transistor saturation. ECL ICs are the highest speed logic circuits available today.

Circuit Operation

Figure 4-12 shows the schematic diagram of a typical ECL logic gate.

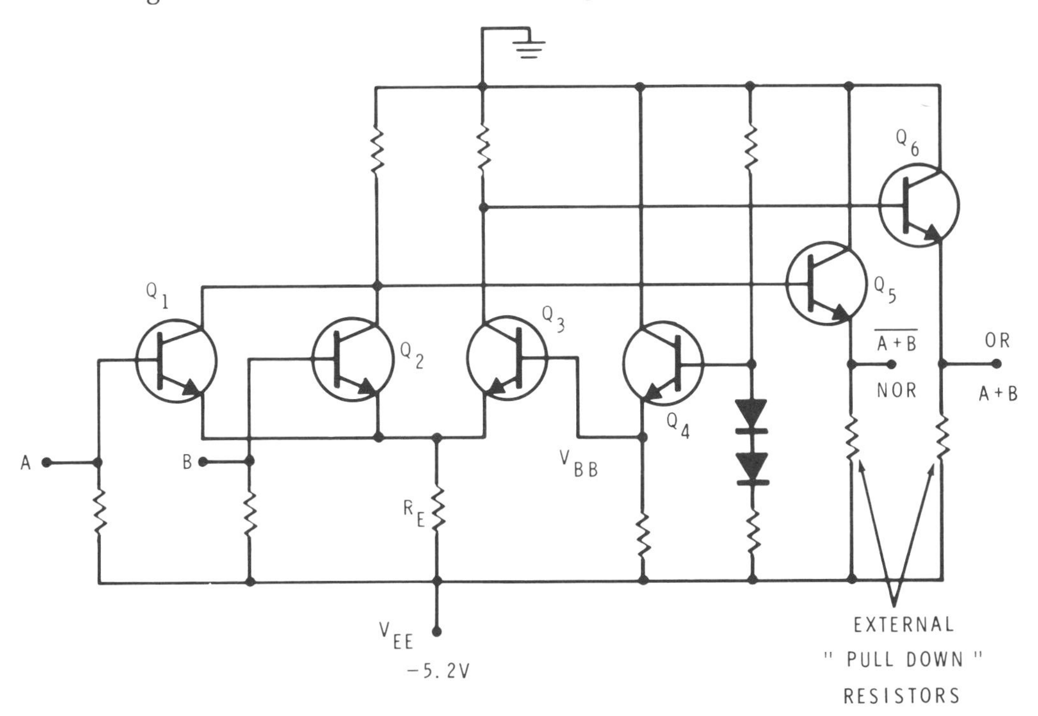

Figure 4-12
Typical emitter-coupled logic gate.

Transistors Q_1 and Q_2 along with Q_3 form a differential amplifier. The inputs (A and B) are applied to transistors Q_1 and Q_2 whose emitter and collector connections are in parallel to form one side of the differential amplifier circuit. If additional inputs are required, more transistors are paralleled. Q_3 is the other side of the differential amplifier. Input logic levels are typically -1.75 volts (binary 0) and $-.9$ volts (binary 1). The output and input voltage swing is typically the difference between these two voltage levels or $(1.75 - .9) = .85$ volts. The supply voltage V_{EE} is -5.2 volts. The supply voltage V_{EE} and R_E form a current source that supplies a fixed current whose level is below the point that permits saturation.

In Figure 4-12, transistor Q_4 and the associated components form a temperature stabilized voltage source that biases the base of Q_3 to approximately -1.3 volts. The emitter of Q_3 will be approximately .8 volts more negative than its base because of its emitter base voltage drop. Therefore, the voltage at the emitters of Q_1, Q_2, and Q_3 will be approximately $(-1.3-.8) = -2.1$ volts.

Assume that both logic inputs A and B are at the binary 0 logic level of -1.75 volts. With this condition, transistors, Q_1 and Q_2 will not conduct because the emitter-base bias is insufficient. At this time the collectors of Q_1 and Q_2 are high while the collector of Q_3 is low. These two output levels are buffered by output emitter followers Q_5 and Q_6 and produce the proper binary 0 and binary 1 logic levels. Note that both the normal and complement outputs are available simultaneously.

If any one or both of these logic inputs rise to the binary 1 state $(-.9$ volts), the associated input transistor will conduct. The emitter of Q_1, Q_2, and Q_3 will then be one emitter-base junction drop more negative than the input voltage or approximately -1.7 volts. This means that when one or more of the inputs rises to the binary 1 level, the common emitter point will rise from -2.1 volts to -1.7 volts. This voltage will cause transistor Q_3 to cut-off. As you can see the current supplied by the emitter supply voltage and the common emitter resistor R_E switches from Q_3 to the conducting input transistor or transistors. With this arrangement the collectors of Q_1 and Q_2 will be low while the collector of Q_3 will be high. These logic output levels are buffered by the emitter followers Q_5 and Q_6. The circuit performs the OR and NOR functions for positive logic level assignments.

One of the major advantages of most commercial ECL IC logic circuits is the availability of both the normal and complement outputs simultaneously. This permits both OR and NOR functions to be obtained at the same time. No external inverters are required. Note that the emitter follower "pulldown" resistors are usually external to the integrated circuit itself. This permits the resistors to be located remotely at the end of a transmission line or in another desirable location depending upon the exact circuit configuration and application. It is also possible to tie together the OR or NOR outputs of ECL logic circuits to permit the wired OR function.

Circuit Characteristics

ECL logic circuits are extremely versatile, easy to use and produce high quality results. However, these circuits are normally higher in cost and of course consume significantly more power than other types of logic circuits. Their only real advantage is their high speed. Naturally, this high speed capability should be used only where absolutely necessary. Other types of logic are preferred for slower speed applications. The most widely used form of ECL is Motorola's MECL and 10K series.

Table II

ECL Characteristics
Type of logic: unsaturated, current sourcing
Propagation delay: .5–3 nanoseconds
Power Dissipation: 40–60 milliwatts
Fan Out: 10–25
Noise Immunity: High
Logic levels: binary 0 = −1.75 volts
binary 1 = −.9 volts
Basic gate form: OR/NOR
Supply voltage V_{EE}: −5.2 volts

21. The basic ECL circuit is a(n):

    a. inverter.
    b. differential amplifier.
    c. saturated switch.
    d. emitter follower.

22. ECL gate outputs can be wire ORed.

    a. True.
    b. False.

23. For positive logic in an ECL gate:

    binary 0 = ____________ volts.
    binary 1 = ____________ volts.

24. An ECL gate performs what functions in negative logic.

    a. AND.
    b. OR.
    c. NAND.
    d. NOR.

25. With ECL loads, ECL gates are:

    a. current sources.
    b. current sinks.

Metal Oxide Semiconductor Integrated Circuits

Metal oxide semiconductor field-effect transistors (MOSFETs) or insulated gate field-effect transistors offer numerous advantages over bipolar transistors in digital circuits. First, these devices are simpler in construction and therefore can be made much smaller. Because they occupy less space, higher density logic networks can be placed on a given silicon chip. This permits large scale digital integrated circuits to be readily constructed. Another advantage of the MOSFET is its high impedance and therefore, low power consumption. MOS digital integrated circuits consume only a fraction of the power of equivalent bipolar circuits.

The big disadvantage of MOS digital integrated circuits is their lower speed. The high impedance and capacitive nature of these circuits, produce switching speeds that are several orders of magnitude slower than bipolar digital integrated circuits. Despite their low speed nature, these circuits have nevertheless found wide application in those areas not requiring high speed operation. Recent technological advances in the manufacturing of MOSFET circuitry have also helped their switching speed approach that of some bipolar circuits.

There are two basic types of MOSFETs used in MOS digital ICs: the P-channel and the N-channel. As indicated earlier, the MOSFETs used in digital ICs operate in the enhancement mode. In this mode of operation, the transistor is normally cut-off. When the appropriate voltage level is applied between the source and the gate, the transistor suddenly switches on. These devices are near perfect switches in that they have an extremely high impedance when not conducting, and an extremely low impedance when conducting.

The earliest MOS devices in use in digital circuits were PMOS circuits. P-type MOSFETs are the simplest and easiest to manufacture. N-channel MOS devices are more difficult to make, however, recent technological advances have simplified their construction. N-channel MOSFETs are smaller in size and switch at higher speeds. Their switching threshold is also much lower making them more compatible with bipolar digital integrated circuits. Another class of MOS logic circuits combines both P- and N-channel devices in a single circuit. These digital circuits are known as complementary MOS or CMOS.

MOS digital integrated circuits are clearly the digital ICs of the future. Their small size, low power consumption and simplicity make them attractive for many medium and large scale applications. Most MOS ICs are LSI. Entire test instruments and computers can be made on a single silicon chip with MOS techniques.

PMOS and NMOS Circuits

When a digital IC circuit is constructed only with P-channel MOSFETs, it is known as PMOS. If the circuitry uses only N-channel enhancement mode MOSFETs, the circuits are referred to as NMOS. The basic circuit configurations are the same for either type of transistor.

Figure 4-13 shows the circuit for an N-channel MOS logic inverter. Q_2 is the standard shunt inverter switch. Transistor Q_1 is connected to form a drain or load resistance. A standard integrated resistance occupies substantially more space than the MOSFET and therefore, if used in any quantity, greatly reduces the amount of digital circuitry that can be placed on a given size silicon chip. The gate and drain of Q_1 are connected together which biases the transistor into conduction. It acts as a resistor.

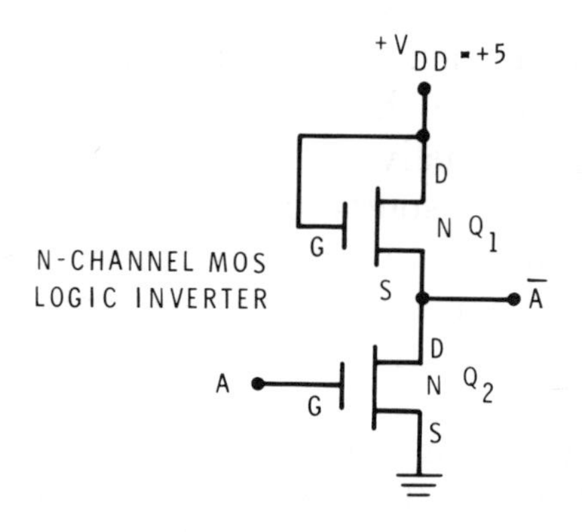

Figure 4-13
N-channel MOS logic inverter.

In operation, this circuit performs like any other inverter. When the logic input voltage is less than the gate-source threshold voltage, Q_2 is cut off. Since the gate and drain of Q_1 are connected together, Q_1 conducts and the output voltage is the supply voltage V_{DD} less the source-drain voltage. When the input voltage exceeds the gate-source threshold of Q_2 (usually about 1.5 volts for most NMOS), Q_2 conducts. Its output voltage drops to a very low level. The on resistance of transistor Q_2 is made significantly less than the resistance of Q_1 by a ratio of at least 20 to 1.

A logic inverter circuit using P-channel MOSFETs is shown in Figure 4-14. This circuit is similar to the N-channel inverter discussed earlier, however, a different means is used to bias the load transistor into conduction. In this circuit, the gate voltage is made more negative than the source voltage by the use of another power supply designated $-V_{GG}$. This voltage causes Q_1 to conduct and act as a resistor. Q_2 in this circuit is the shunt inverter switch. Note the power supply polarity difference in this circuit due to the use of P-channel rather than N-channel transistors. The circuit operation is as described before. When the gate-source threshold voltage is exceeded (4 to 6 volts in most PMOS), transistor Q_2 will conduct and the output voltage will drop to a value near ground. When the gate-source voltage is less than the threshold value, Q_2 will cut off and act as an open circuit. At this time the output voltage is some negative voltage less than $-V_{DD}$. This particular circuit arrangement produces somewhat faster switching speeds than the circuit in Figure 4-13 but the disadvantage is that it requires the additional power supply.

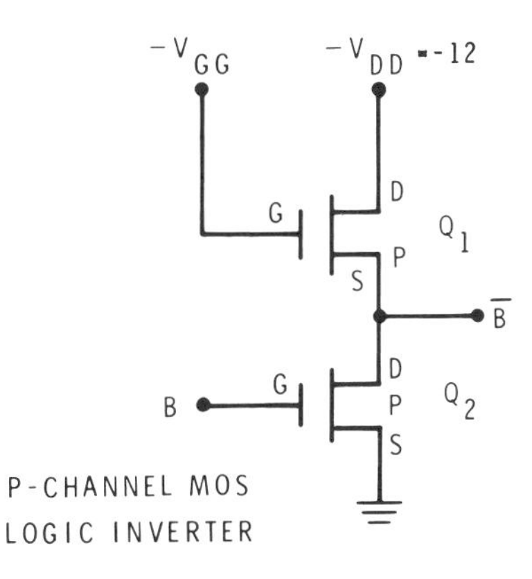

Figure 4-14
P-channel MOS logic inverter.

Figure 4-15 shows how the various logic functions are implemented using the MOSFETs. In Figure 4-15A, two N-channel devices are connected in parallel and share a common load (Q_3). If either one or both of the input devices is biased on, the output voltage will drop to a low value. When the input voltages are both less than the threshold voltage, Q_1 and Q_2 will be cut off, allowing the output to rise toward $+V_{DD}$. With this arrangement, the circuit performs a NOR function for positive logic.

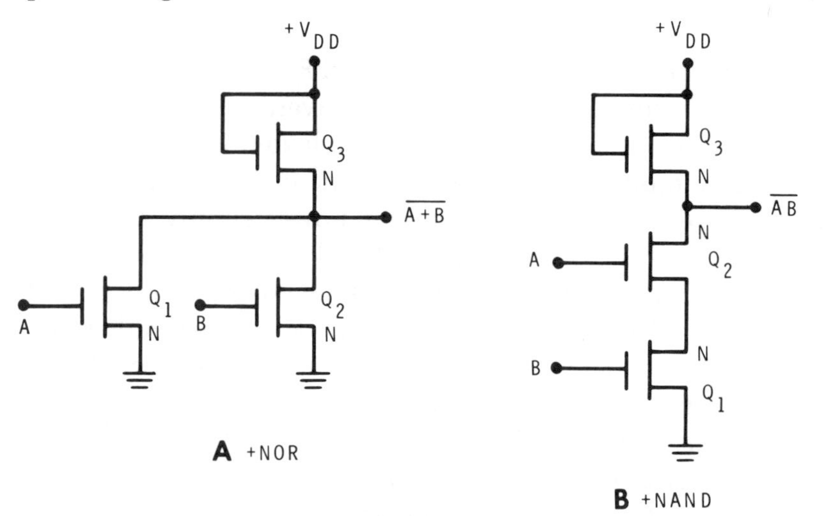

Figure 4-15
NMOS logic circuits.

The circuit in Figure 4-15B performs the NAND function for positive logic. Here transistors Q_1 and Q_2 are connected in series. In order for the output line to be brought low, input signals must appear high at both the A and B inputs simultaneously. If either one or both of the inputs are low, the output will be high. This is the NAND function.

The type of MOS logic circuits that we have discussed here are known as static logic circuits in that they perform logic functions with voltage levels. Another type of MOS logic is also widely used. Known as dynamic logic this circuitry has the same basic configuration as we have discussed here. However, the difference lies in that the circuits take advantage of the capacitive nature of the input to the MOS devices. Here the input capacitors are used to store charges or logic levels temporarily. During operation, high speed clock signals are used to transfer stored charges from one circuit to the next. The advantage of this type of MOS circuitry is still lower power consumption than the static circuits just discussed and higher operating speeds.

Complementary MOS

Complementary MOS or CMOS logic circuits use both P-channel and N-channel enhancement mode MOSFETs. A logic inverter constructed using both types of devices is shown in Figure 4-16. Here the input signal drives the gates of both devices simultaneously. When the input voltage is low or near ground, the gate-source threshold level for Q_2 is less than that required for conduction. Therefore Q_2 is cut off. However with the input low, the gate-source voltage threshold of Q_1 is exceeded. Since the gate is more negative than the source, this P-channel device conducts and connects the supply voltage V_{DD} to the output.

If the input voltage is brought to a high logic level, normally the same as the supply voltage $+V_{DD}$, the gate-source threshold voltage of Q_2 will be exceeded. Q_2 will conduct and act as a very low resistance bringing the output to a low level. At this time with the gate and source of Q_1 approximately at the same levels, the threshold is not exceeded, therefore, Q_1 is cut off. The logic inversion function is performed. It is interesting to note that in this circuit both the current sink and current source modes are used. When Q_2 conducts it sinks current from external loads connected between the outputs and the supply voltage. When Q_1 conducts it supplies current to any load connected between the output and ground. Because of the very low on resistance of a conducting device and the extremely high input impedance of other MOS devices, the logic levels are very nearly equal to ground and the supply voltage $+V_{DD}$.

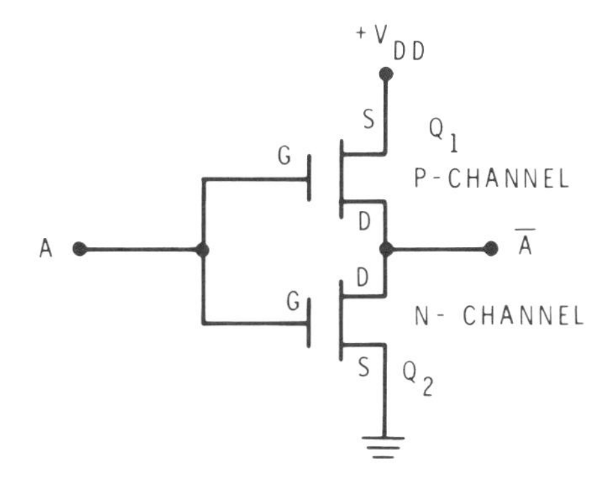

Figure 4-16
A complementary MOS logic inverter.

Figure 4-17 shows a diagram of a typical CMOS logic gate. It consists of two P-channel devices Q_1 and Q_2 connected in series and two N-channel devices Q_3 and Q_4 connected in parallel. When either one or both of the inputs go high to the positive binary 1 voltage level, the associated N-channel transistor Q_3 or Q_4 will conduct. This will cause the output to drop to a voltage level near zero volts indicating a binary 0 output. With either input high, either Q_1 or Q_2 will be cut-off. Since Q_1 and Q_2 are in series, the path between the supply voltage $+V_{DD}$ and the output is not completed unless both Q_1 and Q_2 conduct.

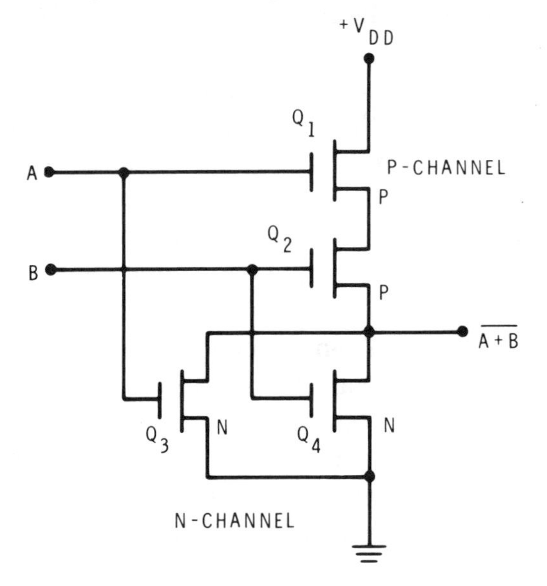

Figure 4-17
CMOS NOR logic gate.

When both inputs go low, Q_3 and Q_4 will become cut-off because their gate-source voltage is below the threshold level necessary to cause conduction. At this time the gate-source voltages of Q_1 and Q_2 will be approximately equal to $+V_{DD}$. Both devices conduct and form a low resistance path between the output and the supply voltage.

Summarizing the operation of this CMOS logic gate, you can see that the NOR logic function is being performed with positive logic. Any logic function including NAND, AND and OR can be performed by suitably arranging the P- and N-channel devices in the circuit.

If a digital designer were to specify the perfect logic circuit for all applications, this logic circuit would have characteristics very similar to those of CMOS. CMOS logic circuits offer a balanced combination of characteristics making it highly versatile and desirable. This type of logic circuit features very low power dissipation, excellent noise immunity, wide power supply voltage variations, high fan out and moderately high speed of operation.

Low power dissipation in CMOS circuits is achieved because there is never a continuous path through any of the devices in the circuit from the supply voltage to ground. A look at the inverter circuit in Figure 4-16 or the NOR gate in Figure 4-17 will indicate this. When the N-channel devices connected between the output and ground are conducting, the P-channel devices between the output and $+V_{DD}$ are cut off. Similarly, when the P-channel device between the supply voltage and the output is on, the N-channel devices from the output to ground are cut off. The current flow that does take place between the supply voltage and ground is that which flows when the output state switches. It is during this time that the P- and N-channel devices may be on together momentarily thereby causing a small current to flow. If the switching rate is high, the rate of occurrence of this current flow increases. The power consumption of a CMOS device increases with its operating frequency because of this effect.

Table III

CMOS Characteristics
Type of logic: Current sinking and current sourcing.
Propagation delay: 10–100 nanoseconds.
Power Dissipation: 10 microwatts (static) 1 milliwatt at 1 MHz
Fan out: 50+
Noise immunity: very high (45 percent V_{DD})
Logic levels: binary 0 = 0 volts binary 1 = $+V_{DD}$
Basic gate form: positive NOR/negative NAND
Supply voltage V_{DD}: +3 to +15 volts

The most popular forms of CMOS logic are the 4000 series circuits made by RCA, the 74C series made by National Semiconductor, and the 14000 series manufactured by Motorola. All offer a variety of SSI, MSI and LSI circuits.

26. P-channel MOS is faster than N-channel MOS.

    a. True.
    b. False.

27. MOS combining both P- and N-channel in series is called: ___________.

28. The primary disadvantage of MOS ICs is ___________.

29. The CMOS logic levels are:

    binary 0 = ___________ volts.
    binary 1 = ___________ volts.

30. Most MOS ICs are usually:

    a. SSI.
    b. MSI.
    c. LSI.

31. The input to a CMOS gate appears primarily as a:

    a. low resistance.
    b. high resistance.
    c. capacitor.
    d. inductor.

Integrated Injection Logic

One of the newest forms of integrated digital circuits is Integrated Injection Logic, usually abbreviated IIL or I^2L (I squared L). I^2L is a form of bipolar logic used primarily in LSI and VLSI applications. Its very small size permits very high density; and its ultra low power consumption eliminates heat problems and gives long battery life in portable applications. I^2L circuits are also more common than you think. In fact, if you are wearing a digital watch, you have an I^2L chip on you!

Circuit Description

The development of I^2L was an attempt to achieve the speed of operation of bipolar circuits while obtaining the packing density and low power consumption of MOS. The attempt was successful, as VLSI I^2L circuits are widely used today. I^2L designers created the smallest and simplest digital logic circuit available. A typical I^2L gate occupies only about half the space of even the smallest MOS circuit. The small size is the result of there being essentially only one transistor per gate.

A typical I^2L circuit is shown in Figure 4-18. It consists of Q_1 a multiple collector NPN shunt saturated switch and Q_2 a PNP current source. This circuit is used in various ways to produce the basic logic functions. Q_2 can also be used to supply current to other shunt switches like Q_1. As shown, the circuit in Figure 4-18 performs as a logic inverter.

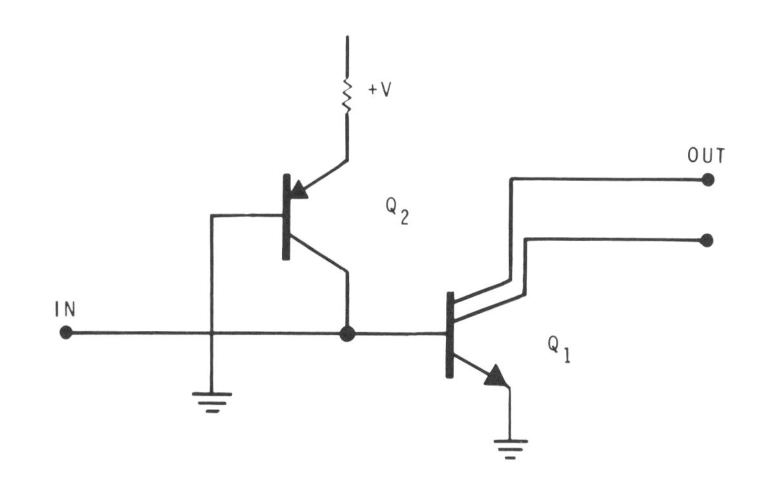

Figure 4-18
Basic I^2L Circuit.

To see how the circuit works, refer to Figure 4-19 where two basic I^2L inverters are cascaded. Normal logic levels are approximately +.1 volt for a binary 0 (or near ground) and +.7 volts for a binary 1. Current source Q_4 supplies current to the base of Q_3. This current is high enough to saturate Q_3. Therefore, Q_3 conducts and its output voltage V_{CE}(sat) is about +.1 volt or less (binary 0). This condition exists when the input to Q_3 is a binary 1, about +.7 volts. With Q_3 saturated, current from source Q_2 is shunted away from the base of Q_1. Therefore, Q_1 is cut-off. Its output will, therefore, be +.7 volts or the V_{BE} of the next transistor it drives.

Now assume that the input to Q_3 is brought low (+.1 volt or less). Current from Q_4 is shunted away from the base of Q_3 and Q_3 turns off. Q_2 can now supply base current to Q_1. Q_1 conducts. The voltage at the collector of Q_3 and base of Q_1 is now +.7 volts, the base-emitter voltage drop V_{BE} of Q_1. The collector voltage of Q_1 is now +.1 volts or less. As you can see, the two logic levels are derived from the V_{CE}(sat) of the driving transistor (binary 0) and the V_{BE} of the driven transistor (binary 1).

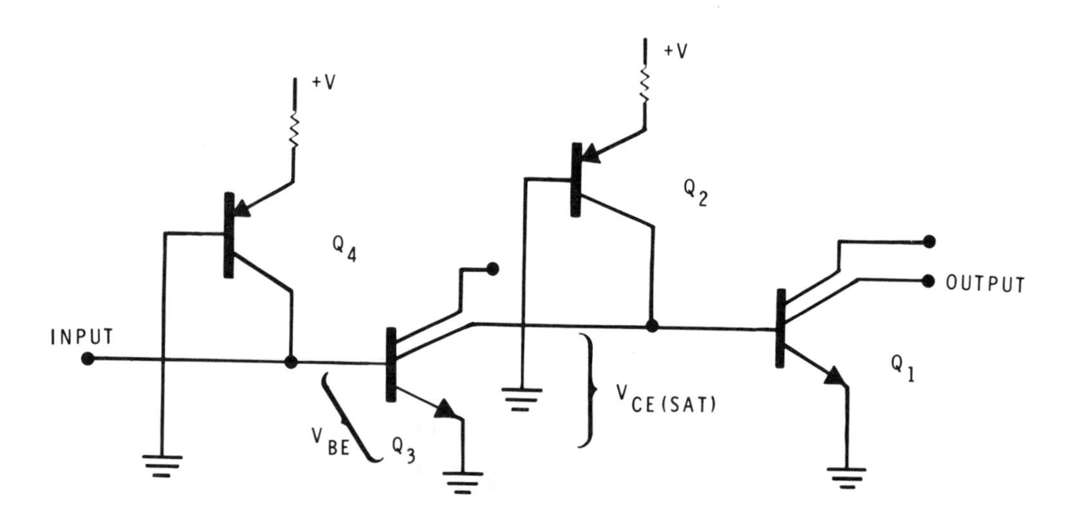

Figure 4-19
Cascaded I^2L Inverters.

The basic circuit can be combined in several ways to perform the various logic functions. An I^2L NAND gate is illustrated in Figure 4-20A. The only difference between this and the basic circuit is that multiple inputs A and B are connected to the base of Q_1. These inputs are driven by other I^2L circuits Q_3 and Q_4. If either one or both inputs are low (0), Q_1 is cut off and the output is high (1). If both inputs are high (1), Q_1 will conduct and its output will be low (0). This is the NAND function as the truth table in Figure 4-20B shows.

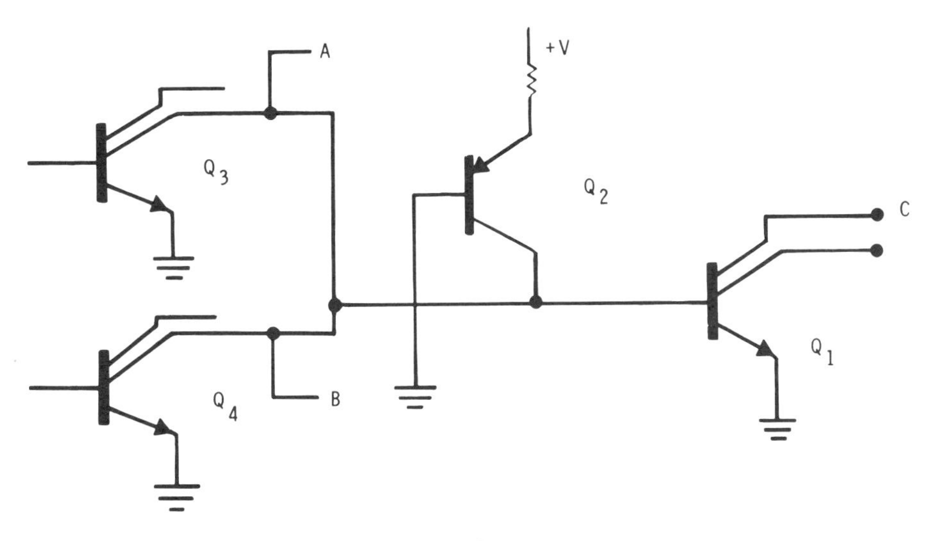

Figure 4-20A
I^2L NAND circuit.

A	B	C
0	0	1
0	1	1
1	0	1
1	1	0

Figure 4-20B
Truth Table.

An I^2L NOR gate is shown in Figure 4-21A. The NOR function is obtained by the wired OR connection. If either or both inputs are high (1), Q_1, Q_3, or both will conduct and the output F will be low (0). When both inputs are low (0), both Q_1 and Q_3 will be cut off and the output will go high (1). The operation is summarized in the truth table of Figure 4-21B. This is the NOR function.

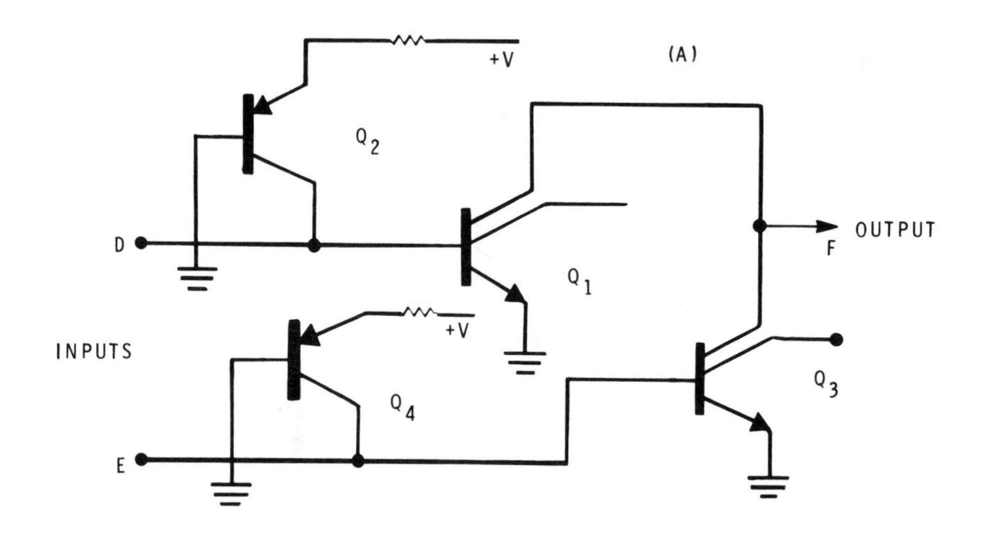

Figure 4-21B
Truth Table.

D	E	F
0	0	1
0	1	0
1	0	0
1	1	0

Figure 4-21A
I^2L NOR gate circuit.

Characteristics and Applications

We have already mentioned the very small size of I^2L circuits. Over 100 I^2L circuits can be constructed in about the same space that one TTL gate occupies. Literally thousands of gates can be made on a single silicon chip. I^2L circuits can achieve the same function of MOS in about one-half the space. And, the fewer diffusion and masking steps required in manufacturing I^2L makes for greater yields and lower cost.

As for speed, the typical I^2L gate has a propagation delay of 25 to 50 nanoseconds. Although, depending upon the application, delays can range from 20 to 250 nanoseconds. Keep in mind that this is accomplished with saturated bipolar transistors. Higher speeds are obtainable by using Schottky diodes as with TTL circuits. However, this does increase the gate area and cost.

The power consumption of a typical I^2L gate is in the 6 nanowatt to 70 microwatt range. The dissipation of an average 20 nanosecond gate is 50 microwatts. The power consumption of an I^2L gate is about the same as that of a CMOS gate; however, the I^2L gate is two or three times faster.

As it turns out, I^2L circuits have the most favorable speed-power product of any logic circuit. Typical circuits have a speed-power product of one picojoule or less, which beats even the best CMOS devices.

Finally, the noise margin is fair to good. The simple bipolar circuitry is also easy to interface to almost any other type of IC (TTL, CMOS, etc.). I^2L characteristics are summed up in Table IV.

Another major benefit of I^2L circuits is that the simplicity of their structure permits linear circuits to be easily fabricated on the same chip. With more complex standard digital circuits, it is difficult and not practical economically to put digital and linear circuits on the same chip. But with I^2L, it is easy to incorporate analog circuits such as op amps, comparators, LED/LCD drivers, memory sense amplifiers, and oscillators right on the chip with a complex digital circuit. Today, more and more designs incorporate both linear (analog) and digital functions. Plus, to create complete LSI or VLSI systems, it is desirable to put all circuitry on one chip.

Presently, I^2L circuits are used predominantly in digital watches. Their small size and ultra low power consumption make them perfect for the application. There are also I^2L memory circuits and microprocessors for special lower power uses. I^2L circuits are also used in 35 mm cameras for lighting, exposure, and timing control. Telephone dialing and electrical appliance control circuits have also been developed.

TABLE IV

I^2L Characteristics
Type of logic: Current sinking
Propagation delay: 25–50 nanoseconds
Power dissipation: .06 to 70 microwatts
Fan out: 2
Noise immunity: Fair to good
Logic levels: binary 0 = $< +.1$ volts
binary 1 = $+.7$ volts
Basic gate form: Positive NAND or NOR
Supply voltage: 1–15 volts

32. The logic levels of an I^2L circuit are:

    binary 0 ____________.
    binary 1 ____________.

33. I^2L gates are superior to all other types of ICs in:

    a. propagation delay.
    b. noise immunity.
    c. size.
    d. power dissipation.

34. I^2L circuits are used primarily in ______________________ and ____________ circuits.

35. The main element on an I^2L circuit is a:

    a. current source.
    b. multi-collector shunt switch.
    c. PNP saturated switch.
    d. Schottky diode.

Selecting a Digital Integrated Circuit For a Specific Application

The most important decision that you will make in designing a piece of digital equipment is in selecting the type of integrated circuit. The success or failure of your design from a performance and economic standpoint, will depend directly upon this choice. For this reason, you must carefully consider the requirements of your application.

The first step in selecting a digital integrated circuit is to completely define the system characteristics. Performance, economy, and reliability are the prime requirements. These are specifically stated in the terms of needed system speed, noise immunity, power dissipation and other factors. Once all of the specifications have been detailed, these can be matched against the capabilities and characteristics of the various types of integrated circuits available.

The three key factors in defining a digital system and selecting a type of integrated circuit are speed (propagation delay), power consumption and noise immunity. While these are the most important characteristics in terms of performance and economy, there are other considerations. These include: cost, availability, trends, and the need for complex functions. The cost and availability factors are obvious. Lowest cost circuits are best if they meet all the requirements of your application. And the circuits you choose must be readily available. It is desirable to select a circuit with several sources of supply.

Trends

The semiconductor industry is one of the most volatile in the field of electronics. New technological developments occur frequently and therefore some devices quickly become obsolete, while others with improved characteristics are added. These changes take place so quickly that it is difficult for any designer to select an integrated circuit with long life and a stable price. It is important for you to follow the trends by reading manufacturer's literature and technical publications. By staying abreast of the latest technology you will be better prepared to select a circuit, that not only meets your design requirements but also will have favorable life, cost and availability trends.

Complex Functions

A highly desirable characteristic of any integrated circuit type is the availability of medium scale integrated circuits (MSI). These are functional circuits either of the combinational or sequential type. Since most digital equipment is made up of only a few basic types of circuits (decoders, counters, etc.), a large portion of the equipment can be designed by simply interconnecting the functional circuits. It is much more economical to use MSI functions than to implement these same functions with SSI gate circuits. By using MSI functions the design time is reduced substantially. In addition the total package count and size is proportionally reduced. Savings in power consumption and in assembly labor can be significant. The more MSI functions available in a digital integrated circuit logic line, the more advantageous it is.

Trade-Offs

Keep in mind that all of these factors are somewhat inter-related. Your choice of a type of digital IC will be a compromise based on your application and the circuits available. The speed-power trade-off is one of the most critical trade-offs in selecting a circuit. Noise immunity is also a factor that may have to be traded off with some other characteristic depending upon the types of circuits available. You may have to juggle circuit specifications with cost and availability.

Figure 4-22 shows the primary characteristics of all of the types of digital logic circuits discussed in this section. It will permit you to compare the different types for your application. Only these types should be considered for new product design. TTL, ECL, and CMOS are available in a variety of SSI and MSI devices. MOS and IIL are used in LSI and VLSI only.

Comparison of IC Logic Family Characteristics

Characteristic	TTL	ECL	MOS	CMOS	IIL
Fan-out	10	25	20	50+	2
Cost	low	medium to high	medium to high	low to medium	low to medium
Power dissipation per gate (mW)	12 to 22	40 to 60	0.2 to 10	0.01 static 1 at 1 MHz	<.07
Noise generation	high	low to medium	medium	low medium	low
Immunity to external noise	good	good	good	very good	fair to good
Temperature range (°C)	−55 to +125 0 to 70	−55 to +125	−55 to +125 0 to 70	−55 to 125 −40 to 85	0 to 70
Typical supply voltage (V)	+5	−5.2	−12 (PMOS) +5 (NMOS)	+1.5 to 18	+1+.15
Avg. propagation delay per gate (ns)	1 to 40	.5 to 3	300 (PMOS) 50 (NMOS)	70	20-50
Avg. clock rate (MHz)	15 to 120	200 to 1000	2 (PMOS) 5 to 10 (NMOS)	5 to 10	1-10

Figure 4-22

Figure 4-23 shows a chart of speed vs. power consumption for the various types of integrated circuits. Here propagation delay is plotted as a function of power dissipation for all of the most popular types of digital logic circuits. Naturally, the best circuit is the one with the shortest propagation delay and the least amount of power dissipation.

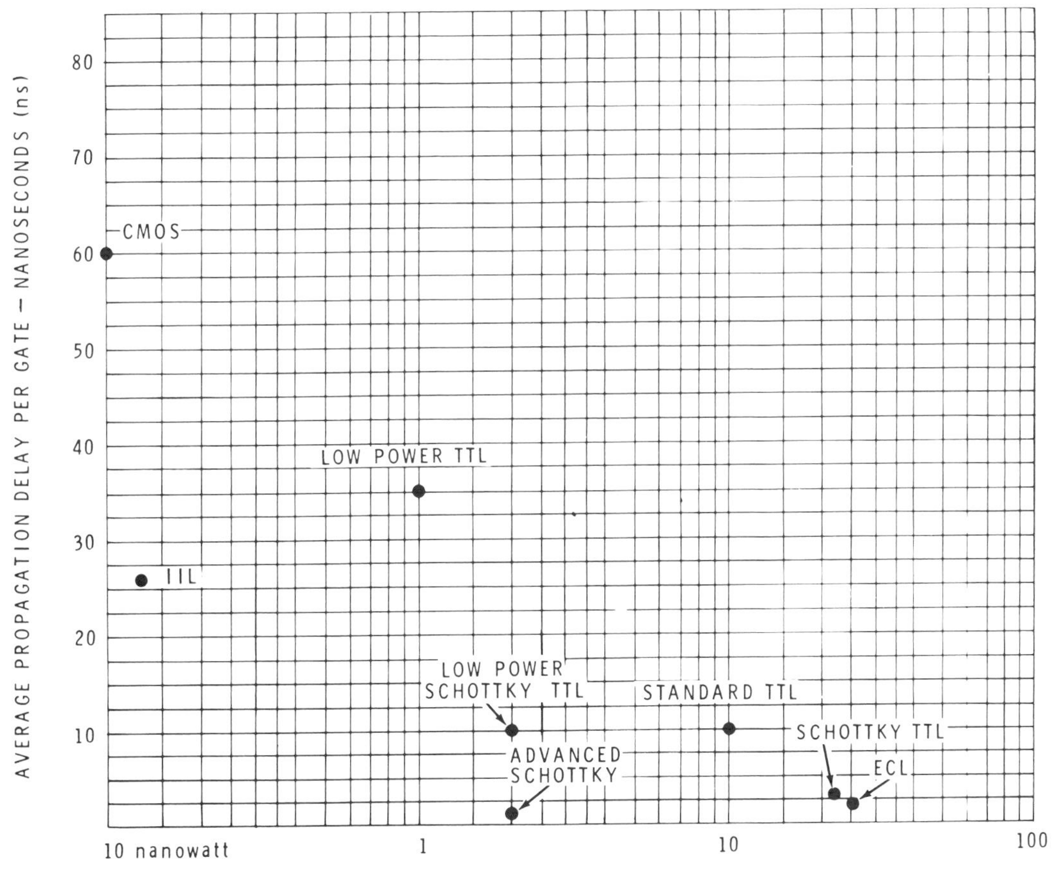

Figure 4-23
Speed (propagation delay) vs. Power dissipation
for popular digital integrated circuits.

Self-Test Review

36. The digital ICs primarily recommended for new equipment design are: ___________, ___________, ___________, ___________ and ___________.

37. Name three *non-technical* characteristics that affect a designer's choice of a digital IC.

    a. ___________.
    b. ___________.
    c. ___________.

38. The most important trade-off in selecting a digital IC is the one involving ___________ and ___________.

Summary

Logic levels are defined as either zero or one. They may be either positive or negative logic. The levels may be high or low. For example, in some equipment, below 1 volt may be defined as a binary zero and above 3.5 volts may be defined as a binary 1. In this case, the device would switch from a binary zero to a binary 1 when the voltage level reached 3.5 volts. It would switch back from a binary 1 to binary zero when the voltage level decreased below 1 volt.

Most digital logic circuitry is in the form of integrated packages commonly referred to as IC chips. There are a variety of integrated circuit families such as TTL, ECL, MOS, and CMOS. ECL logic represents the fastest speed of operation (using bipolar nonsaturating transistors). The speed of operation is important when discussing propagation delay. Propagation delay is defined as the time it takes the switching device to react to a change in data. This is the same thing that has been called transient time or time of energy transfer from input to output.

Another important consideration is power consumption. Power consumption generates heat as well as to load the power supply. This places a definite limit on how many devices can be driven by a given power supply. This is referred to as fan out (how many devices it can drive). Because TTL consumes the most power, fewer TTL devices can be driven than MOS devices from a given power supply. Therefore, the first trade-off is speed versus power.

The MOS devices consume little power because they have very high input impedance. However, they have an input gate capacitance that must be charged and discharged. As you know, charging and discharging a capacitor requires time and this slows the speed of operation of the MOSFET.

Another characteristic that logic devices must have is noise immunity. The ability to resist changes on the input line that are noise pulses instead of data pulses. This is partly compensated by having the devices only recognize specific logic levels like 3.5 and less than 1 volt.

Integrated circuits are manufactured using 3 techniques. The first is monolithic, which is the most common. In the monolithic method the integrated circuit is made by diffusing semiconductor material onto a single wafer. The two forms of monolithic ICs are bipolar and MOS.

Thick and thin film techniques are used to manufacture resistors, capacitors, and inductors on a nonconducting base material such as ceramic. Semiconductor devices are not normally manufactured using this method. Resistors, capacitors, and inductors are usually considered as passive components and semiconductor devices are considered to be active devices.

The hybrid method is combining the other methods to manufacture IC chips that contain combinations of the other components. A hybrid circuit offers the advantage of a variety of circuits and functions. Using this technique it is possible to get very fast circuits that don't consume much power. Their disadvantage is that this manufacturing process is the most expensive.

Integrated circuits are usually packaged in metal TO5 cans, flat pack, and the dual in-line package. The DIP (dual in-line package) is by far the most common. The TO5 is the most expensive. The flat pack is usually limited to applications where circuit board space is limited.

Integrated packages are also rated as SSI, MSI, and LSI chips. The SSI (small scale integration) is usually limited to circuits that perform only one function. The MSI (medium scale integration) usually contains a variety of gates to form a complete functional circuit, usually on the order of 10 or more gates. The LSI (large scale integration) is usually made up of 100 or more gates and forms a complete system or instrument.

TTL logic is also broken down into low-power, high-speed, Schottky, and three-state logic circuits. Low-power circuits are relatively fast with minimum power consumption. The Schottky type uses Schottky diodes and is very fast operating. A low-powered Schottky TTL logic circuit is fast operating with very low power consumption. A three-state logic circuit can be used in bussed transmission systems. Besides the binary zero and one states, it has an open-state that permits it to share a data line with other digital devices.

Another family of digital devices is the MOS chip. MOS chips can be manufactured easier and cheaper than bipolar components. They are also smaller and consume less power. Their main disadvantage is that they are much slower than bipolar components.

The most promising technique is called CMOS. CMOS is easy to manufacture, and by combining N-channel and P-channel MOS devices into complementary pairs during manufacturing, much more circuitry can be combined in the same space. This allows you to add more circuits in a given area or to reduce the size of your equipment. In these times, smaller means better and the fact that they consume even less power than MOS devices is another definite advantage. The disadvantage of CMOS is its slow speed of operation.

Unit 5
Boolean Algebra

Contents

Introduction 5-3

Unit Objectives 5-5

Relating Digital Logic Circuits and Boolean Equations 5-6

Truth Tables 5-18

Boolean Rules 5-27

DeMorgan's Theorem 5-40

DeMorgan's Theorem (Continued) 5-46

Minimizing Logic Circuits 5-50

Using NAND/NOR Gates 5-55

NOR Logic Equivalent Circuits 5-60

NAND Logic Equivalent Circuits 5-70

Rules of Boolean — Summary 5-79

Karnaugh Mapping 5-81

Summary 5-98

Introduction

Boolean algebra is the special language of digital logic circuits. It is a mathematical method of expressing, analyzing, and designing logic circuits. It is similar in many ways to conventional algebra. Boolean algebra is easy to learn and extremely useful. It is almost essential to the proper understanding and application of digital circuits. In this unit, you will learn how to use Boolean algebra. You will see how truth tables help you to design and understand logic circuits. You will learn how to implement practical digital circuits using integrated circuit logic elements. And, you will learn how to perform Karnaugh mapping.

The specific things you will learn in this unit are outlined in the Unit Objectives which follow.

Unit Objectives

When you complete this Unit on Boolean algebra, you will be able to:

1. Define Boolean algebra.
2. Write the Boolean expression corresponding to a given logic circuit.
3. Draw the symbolic logic circuit implementing or corresponding to a given Boolean expression.
4. Write the Boolean expression corresponding to a given truth table.
5. Give an example of each of the two basic types of Boolean expressions (sum-of-products and product-of-sums).
6. Minimize a given logic expression using the various rules of Boolean algebra.
7. Implement a given Boolean expression with either NAND or NOR gates.
8. Write the two versions of DeMorgan's theorem.
9. Write the Boolean expression of logic circuits using the wired–AND connection.
10. Perform Karnaugh mapping for problems with two, three, and four input variables.

Relating Digital Logic Circuits And Boolean Equations

Boolean algebra is a simplified mathematical system used to deal with binary or two value functions. It permits us to express all of the various logic functions, both simple and complex, in a convenient mathematical format. This system gives us a method of understanding and designing digital logic circuits.

The mathematical expression of logic functions permits a convenient means of analyzing and expressing operations in digital circuits. It also aids greatly in design. The proper application of Boolean algebra usually results in the simplest, least expensive, and most efficient logic circuit design.

Most digital equipment in use today is made with integrated circuits. Boolean algebra is used in designing these devices. The applications of integrated circuits in the design of modern electronic equipment, also involves Boolean algebra, but to a lesser extent. At one time, the engineer or technician designing a digital system had to design not only the logic functions but also the circuits to implement them. Boolean algebra was his primary design tool.

Today, the engineer and technician using and designing digital circuits, finds Boolean algebra most valuable in expressing and analyzing logic circuits. His design job is basically that of choosing and using existing integrated circuits to implement the functions required by the application. Occasionally, Boolean algebra will be used to minimize a function and achieve an efficient design.

Review of Basic Functions

A Boolean expression is an equation that expresses the output of a logic circuit in terms of its inputs. You were introduced to Boolean expressions when you studied basic logic gates. The binary inputs and outputs were expressed as letters of the alphabet, alpha-numeric combinations, abbreviations, or short words called mnemonics. For example, in the AND gate in Figure 5-1, the inputs are A and B and the output is C.

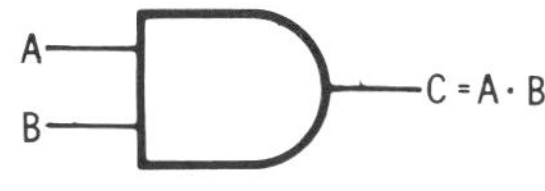

Figure 5-1

Note that the output C is expressed in terms of the inputs. The dot between the A and B indicates the AND function. The output expression $C = A \cdot B$ is read C equals A AND B. Remember that the inputs and outputs are binary signals which may assume either the binary 0 or binary 1 state.

As another example, the output expression of the AND gate in Figure 5-2 is $X = \overline{C} \cdot D \cdot E$. In most Boolean expressions for the AND function, the dot between each input variable can be eliminated and the expression written as a standard algebraic product like $X = \overline{C}DE$. The AND function is sometimes referred to as the logic product.

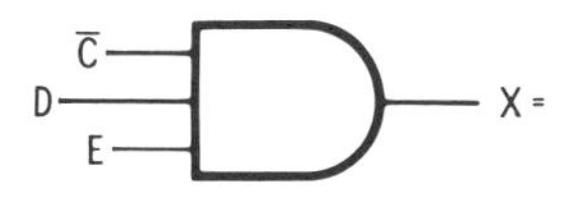

Figure 5-2

Consider the output expression for the AND gate in Figure 5-3, VL = JRF • LEF • KMD • CME. In this expression, each input is identified by a 3-letter combination called a mnemonic. The output is a 2-letter mnemonic. The dot between each input not only designates the AND function but also helps to separate or distinguish the inputs from one another. Occasionally you will see parenthesis used to separate the inputs and indicate the logic product or AND function.
VL = (JRF) (LEF) (KMD) (CME).

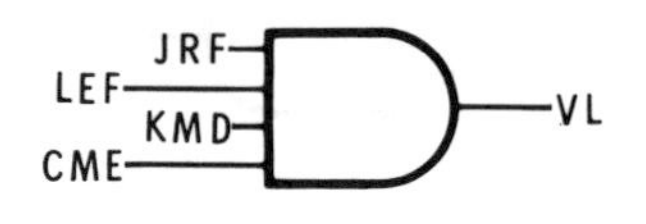

Figure 5-3

In the previous examples, you wrote the output equation of a given gate. Now, to be sure you understand the principles, let's translate from the equation to the gate. Consider the circuit that implements the function W = (F) (MX) ($\overline{G}$). See Figure 5-4.

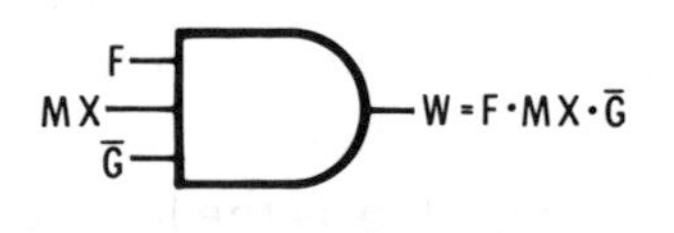

Figure 5-4

Other logic functions like inversion are also expressed with Boolean expressions. For example, if the input to an inverter is B and the output is designated Z, the output expression is $Z = \overline{B}$. The output of an inverter is the complement of the input. This is expressed by putting a bar over the input variable. The term $\overline{B}$ is expressed as NOT B or B NOT. The term NOT refers to logic inversion. See Figure 5-5.

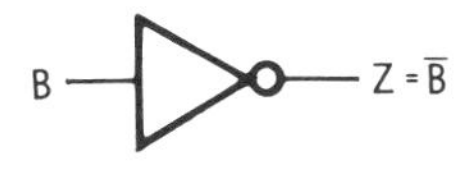

Figure 5-5

Another example is the logic circuit corresponding to the expression $CTL = \overline{INV}$ in Figure 5-6. The output CTL is the complement of the input INV. $CTL = \overline{INV}$.

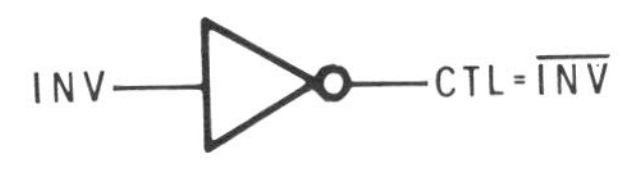

Figure 5-6

Another common logic function is the OR. In an OR gate, the output will be binary 1 if any one or more inputs are binary 1. A typical OR logic gate and its related output expression is shown in Figure 5-7. The plus sign between the input variables designates the OR function. It is sometimes referred to as the logic sum. Figure 5-8 further illustrates the OR function. The output expression of the logic gate in Figure 5-8 is $Y = ZT + \overline{K} + MA$. The plus sign or OR function separates the input variables.

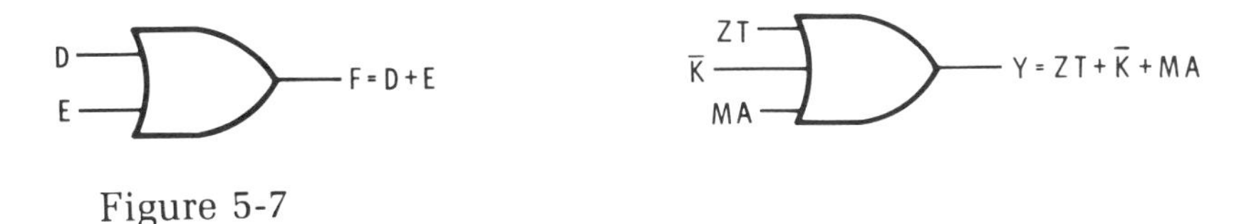

Figure 5-7

Figure 5-8

Now, consider the logic circuit for the expression FN = MAF + $\overline{DG}$ + BF + JS. See Figure 5-9.

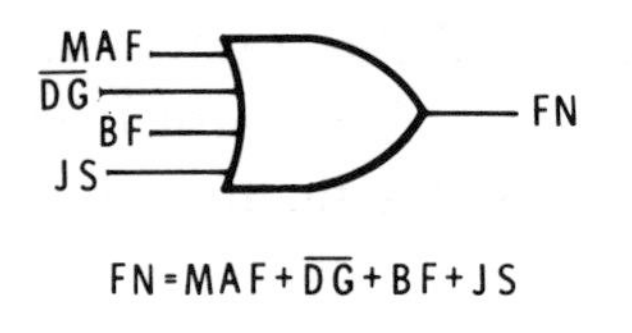

Figure 5-9

Boolean Formats

While there are some simple digital control operations that can be implemented with a single logic gate, more often it is necessary to use a number of logic gates to implement the desired decision-making function. When two or more logic elements are combined, the result is known as a combinational logic circuit. The circuit usually has multiple inputs and either a single output or multiple outputs depending upon its exact function. Any combination of multiple ANDs, ORs, and NOTs is called a combinational logic circuit. Such circuits are used for sophisticated decision-making functions.

There are many common combinational logic circuits used in digital equipment. They perform specific functions that tend to regularly reoccur in digital equipment. However, regardless of the type of combinational logic circuits there are two basic circuit forms. These are referred to as the sum-of-products and product-of-sums circuits. Here the term product refers to the AND function while the sum refers to the OR function.

The AND function is written in the same form as the algebraic product or the multiplication of two variables. (A AND B = AB) The OR function is written as the sum of two input variables. (D OR E = D + E). The sum-of-products or product-of-sums expressions combine the AND and OR functions in a variety of ways.

Sum-Of-Products

The most commonly used Boolean expression of complex decision-making functions is the sum-of-products. The expression $X = A \cdot B + C \cdot D \cdot E$ is an example.

Figure 5-10 shows the logic circuit implementing this sum-of-products logic function. Here AND gate 1 forms the logic product AB while gate 2 forms the product CDE. These products are summed or logically ORed in gate 3 to form the output expression. This is what is meant by the sum-of-products.

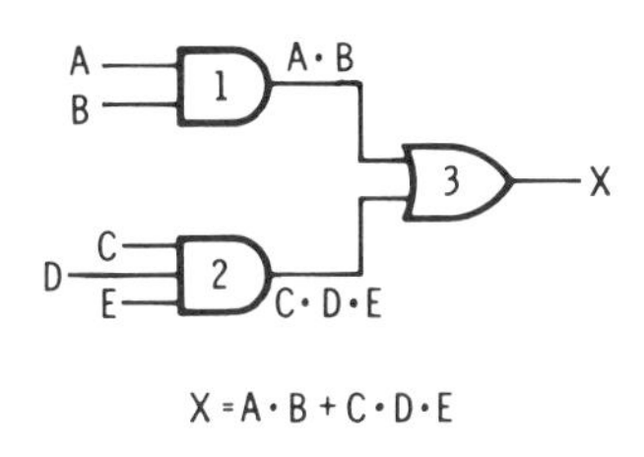

Figure 5-10

Another example of the sum-of-products format is the expression $QT = PJ \cdot \overline{W} + HV \cdot LM + GND \cdot \overline{C} \cdot F$. The various inputs are ANDed together in several combinations which are then ORed together. The circuit for this function is shown in Figure 5-11. The distinguishing feature of this circuit is that the inputs feed AND gates and the output is derived from an OR gate.

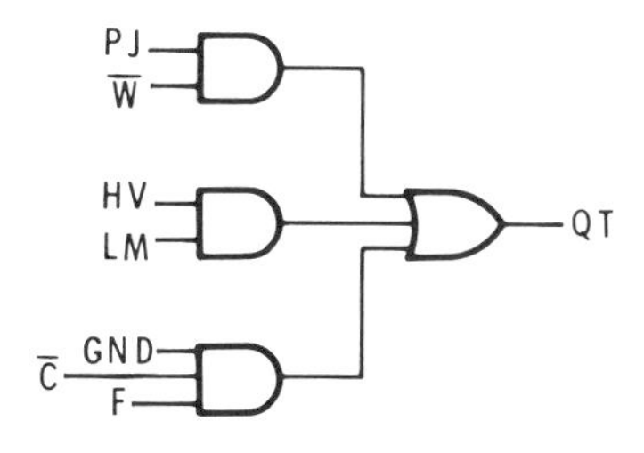

Figure 5-11

Product-Of-Sums

The other type of Boolean expression is the product-of-sums. An example is the expression $L = (M + N)(P + Q)$. The equivalent circuit is shown in Figure 5-12. Inputs M and N are ORed together in gate 1 while inputs P and Q are ORed in gate 2. The two logic sums are ANDed in gate 3 to produce the logic product. In this arrangement the distinguishing feature is the OR gate inputs and AND gate output.

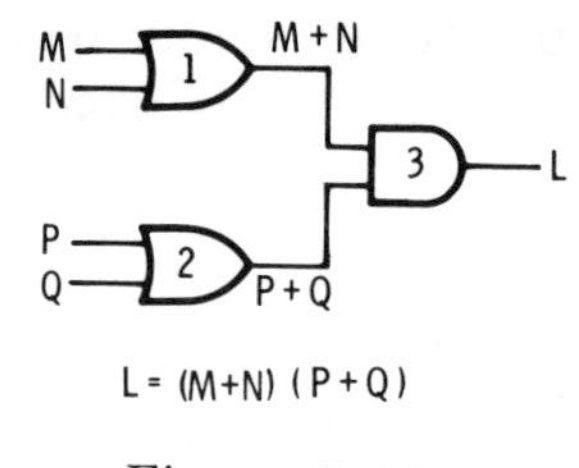

Figure 5-12

Relating Circuits and Equations

You should be able to write the Boolean expression from any logic circuit and draw the logic circuit corresponding to a given Boolean equation. To write the equation of a given logic circuit, you start at the inputs and write the output expression for each gate in the circuit from left to right until the output equation is developed. The unique gate symbols of course will tell you the logic function being performed. The example in Figure 5-13 illustrates this procedure.

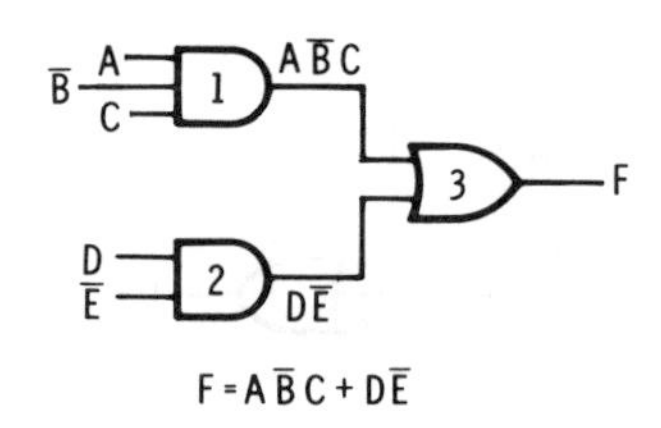

Figure 5-13

You first write the output expressions for the two AND gates. These expressions become the inputs to the OR gate whose output equation is then written. The result is the Boolean expression for the circuit.

$$F = A\overline{B}C + D\overline{E}$$

Now look at the circuit in figure 5-14. Its output equation is $F = B6 \bullet JQ + M8 \bullet X + T \bullet \overline{V} + \overline{Y}$. You simply write the output for each of the AND gates and use these as the inputs to the OR gate. Working this way from left to right quickly produces the complete output expression.

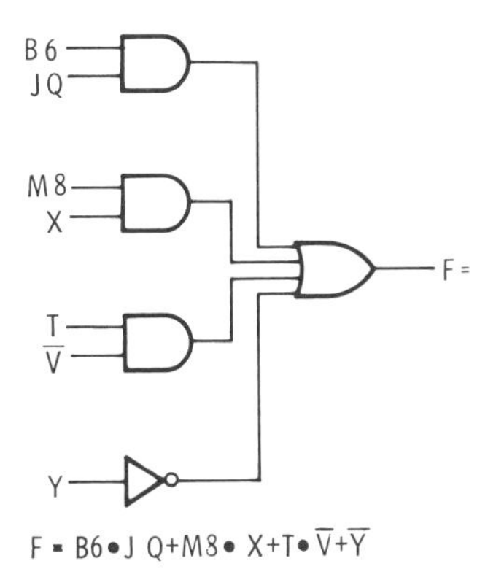

Figure 5-14

This procedure of writing the equation for a given circuit also works on a product-of-sums circuit like the one in Figure 5-15. The output expression of this circuit is $Z = (T + U) \bullet (V + \overline{W}) \bullet X$. The logic sums are formed by gates 1 and 2 and their outputs are combined to form the logic product in the output AND gate 3. Let's take one more example. The output of the circuit in Figure 5-16 is OPR = (A3 + B4) (JMP + T0 + CLK).

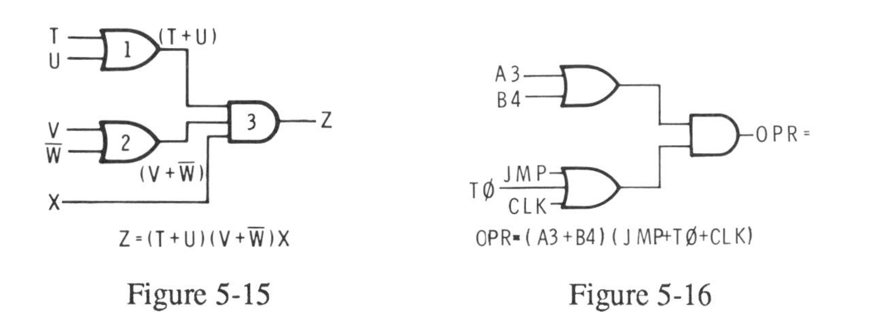

Figure 5-15

Figure 5-16

To draw the diagram corresponding to a given expression you first study the equation to determine whether it is a sum-of-products or product-of sums. This will give you the type of output gate. Then you work backward from the output developing the inputs and outputs from right to left.

For example, consider the expression $K = LM + \overline{C}E$. This is in sum-of-products form so the output gate is an OR. The inputs to this OR gate are LM and $\overline{C}E$. Each of these is a product that is developed by an AND gate with the appropriate inputs. See Figure 5-17.

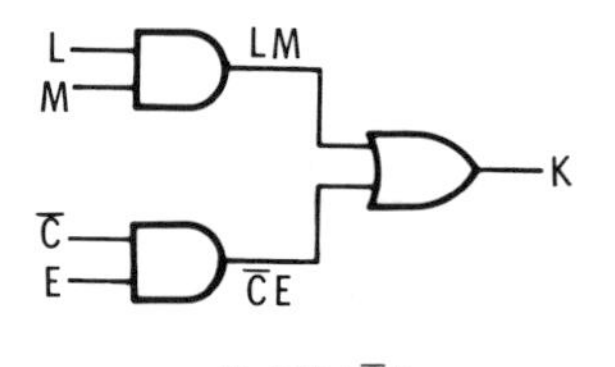

Figure 5-17

Consider the circuit for the expression SH = (CLK + T5) ENB in Figure 5-18. This expression is in product-of-sums form but here there is only one logic sum (CLK + T5). The output is a product, however, and is produced by an AND gate.

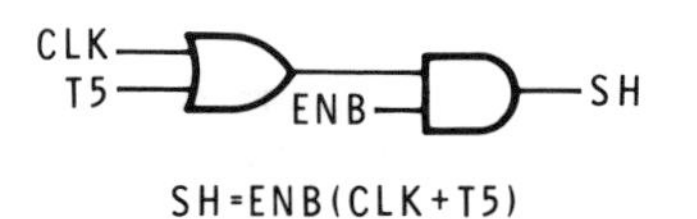

Figure 5-18

One more example is given in Figure 5-19. This is the circuit for the expression $Y = ADD \cdot CY + SUB \cdot \overline{INV} + MPY \cdot ADD \cdot SUB$. This is sum-of-products form. Note that some of the input signals (ADD, SUB) are applied to more than just one of the input gates.

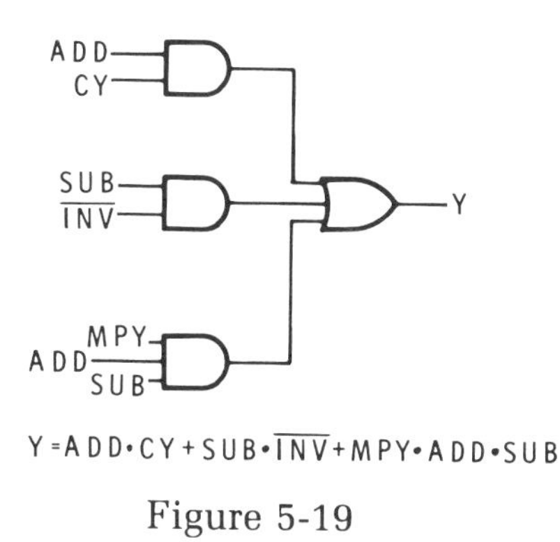

Figure 5-19

So far we have only worked with two levels of logic, that is the inputs are conditioned by two sets or levels of logic gates in cascade: ANDs into OR or ORs into AND. Other more complex logic networks use three, four or even more levels of logic. The expression and circuit in Figure 5-20 is one example. Here both the sum-of-products and product-of-sums formats are combined. There are three levels of logic in this circuit. The input signals must propagate through a series of three gates before a level change occurs at the outputs. Input C on gate 5 only propagates through two levels.

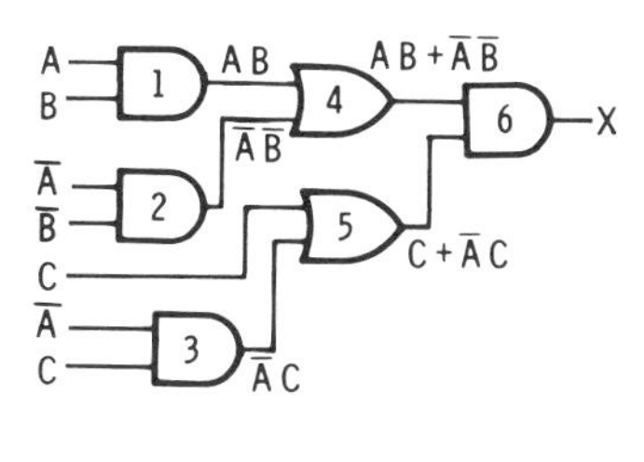

Figure 5-20

Another 3-level logic circuit is given in Figure 5-21. The output expression is $F = (A + \overline{B})(\overline{A} + B) + (B + \overline{C})\overline{A}$. Again you can see that the sum-of-products and product-of-sums are combined to form a three level logic circuit.

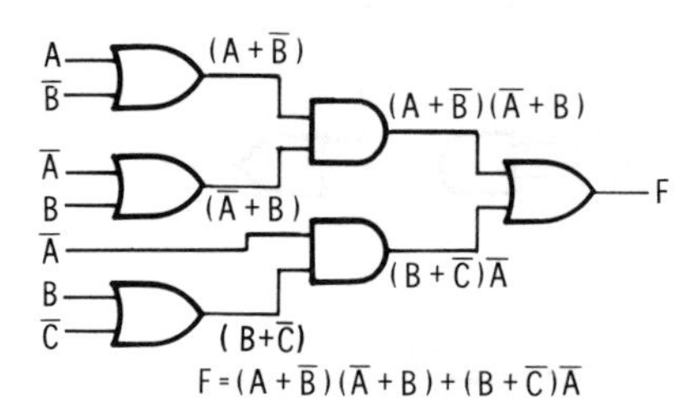

Figure 5-21

Self-Test Review

1. The most commonly used logic format is:

   A. Sum-of-products.
   B. Product-of-sums.
   C. Combination of A. and B.
   D. Neither A. or B.

2. Draw the circuit for the expression $M = \overline{V}W + XY + \overline{W}\overline{X}Y$.

3. Draw the circuit for the expression $F = T(U + \overline{V})(\overline{T} + W)$.

4. Write the Boolean expression for the circuit in Figure 5-22.

5. Write the Boolean equation for the circuit in Figure 5-23.

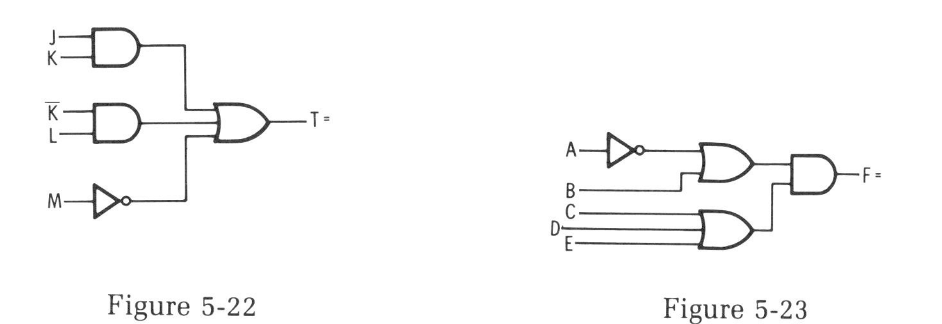

Figure 5-22

Figure 5-23

Truth Tables

One of the most useful tools for analyzing, designing or otherwise working with digital circuits is the truth table. A truth table is a chart that lists all possible input and output signal combinations for a given logic circuit. The truth table is a tabular listing of all input and output states in binary 0 and 1 form. The truth table completely defines the operation of the circuit. You can look at a truth table and quickly identify which specific combination of input states will produce a binary 1 (or binary 0) output.

Truth tables are used in defining the operation of simple logic circuits like inverters and gates as well as more complex combinational logic circuits. You have already seen how truth tables are used in defining the basic logic operations such as AND, OR, and NOT.

INPUT	OUTPUT
A	$\overline{A}$
0	1
1	0

Figure 5-24A

Figure 5-24 shows the truth tables for the three basic logic functions: invert, AND and OR.

In Figure 5-24A, the truth table for an inverter shows both the inputs and corresponding outputs. The output $\overline{A}$ is always the opposite or complement of the input A.

The truth table for a two input AND gate is illustrated in Figure 5-24B. The inputs A and B define all possible input combinations.

INPUTS		OUTPUT
A	B	C
0	0	0
0	1	0
1	0	0
1	1	1

Figure 5-24B

Column C shows the output state corresponding to each input combination. The output is binary 1 only when all inputs are binary 1. This is true of any AND gate.

The truth table defining the operation of an OR gate is given in Figure 5-24C. The output is a binary 1 if any or all inputs are binary 1.

INPUTS		OUTPUT
D	E	F
0	0	0
0	1	1
1	0	1
1	1	1

Figure 5-24C

The total number of possible input conditions in a logic circuit is 2^n where n is the number of inputs. With two inputs there are $2^2 = 4$ possible input conditions. If we treat the inputs as bits in a multibit binary word, we can quickly define and record all input states by using the binary number equivalents. For example, with four possible input states we use the four numbers 0 through 3 or 00, 01, 10, and 11 in binary. These are all possible combinations for a two-bit word.

A logic circuit with three inputs has $2^3 = 8$ different input conditions. We represent the eight possible input conditions with the binary equivalent of the numbers 0 through 7. If the inputs are designated X, Y, and Z, the input states are as shown below.

INPUTS			OUTPUT
X	Y	Z	W
0	0	0	0
0	0	1	1
0	1	0	1
0	1	1	1
1	0	0	1
1	0	1	1
1	1	0	1
1	1	1	1

This particular method of listing all possible input combinations by counting from zero through the upper limit, is orderly and convenient.

There are two basic ways of using truth tables in logic work. First we can develop a truth table from a given logic circuit, and second we can develop an equation or logic circuit from a given truth table. The circuit-to-table method is useful in circuit analysis. The table-to-equation or circuit is useful in circuit design.

Developing the truth table for a given circuit starts with defining all of the inputs. Then the output for each gate in the circuit is developed until the final output is obtained. Consider the circuit shown in Figure 5-25. The Boolean output expression for this circuit is $D = AB + \overline{C}$. The output of gate 1 is AB and the output of inverter 3 is $\overline{C}$. These signals are ORed in gate 2 to produce $D = AB + \overline{C}$.

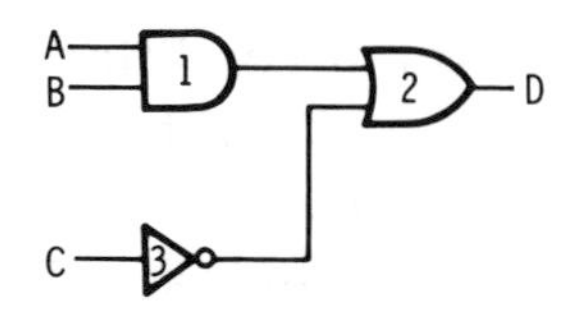

Figure 5-25

To develop the truth table for this circuit, we start with the inputs. Since there are three inputs there are $2^3 = 8$ possible input conditions that we define with the three bit numbers 000 through 111 as indicated in the table below. In the table we also create a column for the output of each gate or element in the circuit.

INPUTS			OUTPUTS		
A	B	C	Gate 1 AB	Inverter 3 $\overline{C}$	Gate 2 D
0	0	0	0	1	1
0	0	1	0	0	0
0	1	0	0	1	1
0	1	1	0	0	0
1	0	0	0	1	1
1	0	1	0	0	0
1	1	0	1	1	1
1	1	1	1	0	1

Observing the inputs, we can fill in the AB and $\overline{C}$ columns. The $\overline{C}$ is simply the complement of the C input column. To complete the AB column, you consider the A and B inputs and their effect on the AND gate output. Next, to find the D output, you note that the AB and $\overline{C}$ outputs are ORed in gate 2. You complete the D column by recording a binary 1 each time either one or both of the AB or $\overline{C}$ columns are binary 1. Check this in the table above.

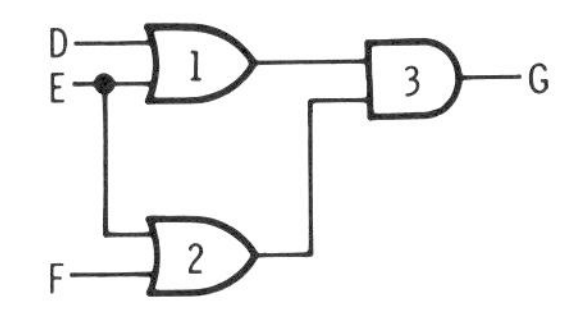

Figure 5-26

Now, consider another example. Let's create a complete truth table for the circuit in Figure 5-26. The results are shown below.

INPUTS			OUTPUTS		
D	E	F	(D + E)	(E + F)	G
0	0	0	0	0	0
0	0	1	0	1	0
0	1	0	1	1	1
0	1	1	1	1	1
1	0	0	1	0	0
1	0	1	1	1	1
1	1	0	1	1	1
1	1	1	1	1	1

To produce this table you first note the number of inputs. There are three different variables D, E, and F so there are $2^3 = 8$ possible input combinations.

Next you create a column for each gate output. In this case, gate 1 output is (D + E), gate 2 output is (E + F), and the final output at gate 3 is G = (D + E) (E + F).

To fill in the (D + E) column you OR together the D and E input columns. You record a binary 1 when either one or both column D or E are binary 1. You complete the (E + F) column in a similar manner considering all eight E and F input combinations.

Finally, you AND together the (D + E) and (E + F) columns, recording a binary 1 in the G column only when both (D + E) AND (E + F) columns are binary 1.

The truth table like the one you developed above completely defines the circuit operation for all possible conditions. And your analysis is thorough because to obtain the final output you had to derive the outputs of all other gates in the circuit.

In designing digital circuits we use the opposite approach. We develop a truth table as the result of our design. In designing a logic circuit we designate the number of inputs and what the output state should be for each set of input conditions. Then we write the Boolean equation from the truth table. From there the equation is readily translated into a logic diagram.

Assume that the circuit we want to design has two inputs A and B. We want a binary 1 output C to occur when A is 0, and B is 1 or when A is 1 and B is 0. Otherwise the output is binary 0.

The truth table outlining these conditions is shown below.

INPUTS		OUTPUT
A	B	C
0	0	0
0	1	1
1	0	1
1	1	0

To write the Boolean equation from this table we observe column C, noting those input states where binary 1s occur in the output. Then we write a sum-of-product Boolean expression based on these inputs. For each binary 1 state in the output we write one product term for the equation then we logically sum (OR) these terms.

The product terms are written from the input states. If the input is binary 1 we write the input letter. If the input is binary 0 we write the complement of the input letter. For example, when A is 0 and B is 1, the product term is $\overline{A}B$. Where A is 1 and B is 0, the product term is $A\overline{B}$. The input conditions for each binary 1 output state are now defined. The product terms are then ORed. The result is $C = \overline{A}B + A\overline{B}$.

Take another example. Write the output equation from the truth table below.

INPUTS		OUTPUT
J	K	L
0	0	1
0	1	0
1	0	0
1	1	1

The correct equation is $L = \overline{J}\,\overline{K} + JK$. A binary 1 output occurs for two of the four possible input combinations. Therefore you know that the sum-of-product output equation will include two product terms. The inputs are ANDed to form these products. The first output occurs when $J = 0$ and $K = 0$. Therefore the corresponding product is $\overline{J}\,\overline{K}$. The second output is binary 1 when $J = 1$ and $K = 1$. The product defining this condition is JK. To obtain the complete output expression we logically sum (OR) these products. $L = \overline{J}\,\overline{K} + JK$.

From here the logic diagram can be drawn. See Figure 5-27.

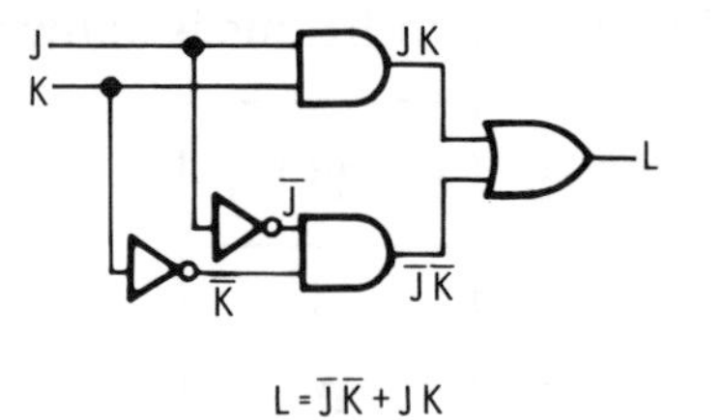

$L = \overline{J}\,\overline{K} + JK$

Figure 5-27

Now let's try a more complex problem. Write the equation and draw the circuit corresponding to the truth table below.

INPUTS			OUTPUT
A	B	C	D
0	0	0	0
0	0	1	1
0	1	0	0
0	1	1	0
1	0	0	1
1	0	1	0
1	1	0	0
1	1	1	1

In this problem there are three inputs, so each product term will have three factors and the number of product terms is set by the number of times a binary 1 output appears in the D output column. You develop each product by looking at the input states and writing the variable when a binary 1 input occurs and the complemented variable when a binary 0 input occurs. The product term when A = 0, B = 0, and C = 1 is $\overline{A}\,\overline{B}C$. Once all the product terms are developed they are ORed together to obtain the output. The final equation is $D = \overline{A}\,\overline{B}C + A\overline{B}\,\overline{C} + ABC$.

The logic diagram is then drawn from the equation. See Figure 5-28. Note in the logic diagram that inputs A, B, and C are considered to be available and signals $\overline{A}$, $\overline{B}$, and $\overline{C}$ are generated with inverters. In some circuits the complement signals may already be available from other sources in which case the inverters can be omitted.

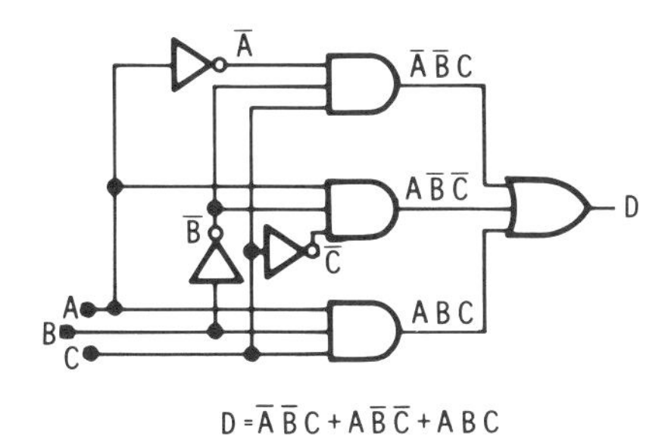

Figure 5-28

6. Develop a truth table for the circuit shown in Figure 5-29.

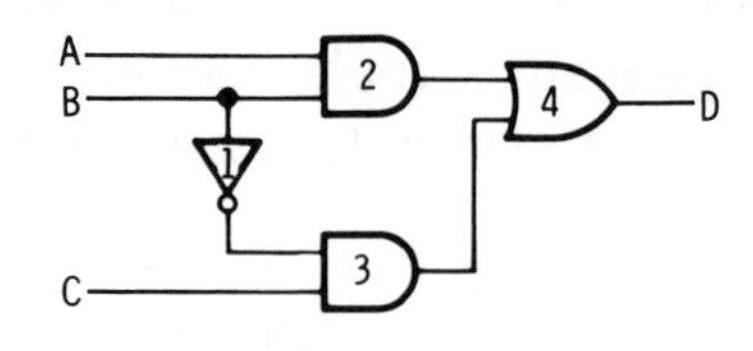

Figure 5-29

7. What is the Boolean equation corresponding to the 1 outputs in the truth table below?

INPUTS			OUTPUT
R	S	T	V
0	0	0	1
0	0	1	0
0	1	0	0
0	1	1	1
1	0	0	1
1	0	1	0
1	1	0	1
1	1	1	0

Boolean Rules

As we mentioned earlier, the primary benefit of Boolean algebra to a technician or engineer today is in analyzing, understanding, and concisely expressing digital logic functions. The availability of a wide variety of integrated circuits has greatly minimized the use of Boolean algebra as a design tool. However, even with modern ICs, the designer can often benefit from the use of Boolean algebra in minimizing or implementing a function.

Boolean algebra is the algebra of two-valued functions. Many of the ordinary rules of algebra such as factoring or expanding a function, apply to Boolean expressions. However, the binary nature of the functions greatly simplifies most of the operations. There are also numerous special rules that apply to handling binary logic functions. We will explain these rules in this section and show how they are used.

The Laws of Intersection, for example, apply to AND gates. The two forms of this law are stated below.

$$A \bullet (1) = A$$
$$A \bullet (0) = 0$$

Remembering that A is a binary signal that can be either binary 0 or binary 1, we can prove the validity of these expressions if we remember how an AND gate works. The first expression simply says that if we apply a binary 1 to one input of an AND gate and the signal A to the other input, the output will be A. The binary 1 input simply enables the gate so that the A input state controls the output. If A = 1, the output will be 1. If A = 0, the output will be 0.

The circuit in Figure 5-30 expresses this relationship.

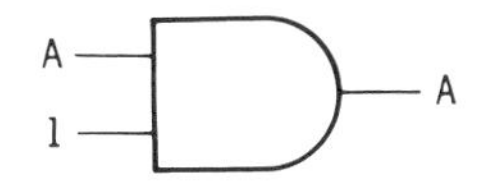

Figure 5-30

The other form of the Laws of Intersection is just as easy to understand.

$$A\ (0) = 0$$

It says that if one input to an AND gate is 0 and the other is A, the output will always be 0. Remember that the only time the output of an AND gate can be 1 is when all inputs are binary 1. If one input is fixed at 0, the output will always be 0. The circuit in Figure 5-31 expresses this. The Law of Intersection works for AND gates with more than two inputs. For example, $D \bullet E \bullet (1) = D \bullet E$ and $D \bullet E \bullet (0) = 0$.

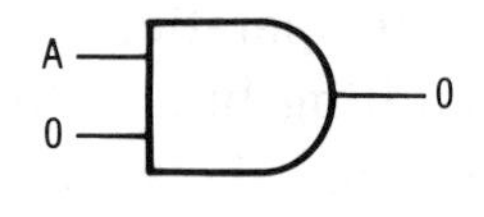

Figure 5-31

Another similar set of rules exist for OR gates. These are called the Laws of Union. Expressed algebraically they are:

$$B + 1 = 1$$
$$B + 0 = B$$

These rules are illustrated in Figure 5-32. These expressions, like those for the AND gate, almost perfectly define the operation of an OR gate. In the first version, if we apply a binary 1 to one input of an OR gate and a signal B to the other, the output will always be binary 1 by definition of an OR gate. If one input to an OR gate is binary 0, the other input B will control the output.

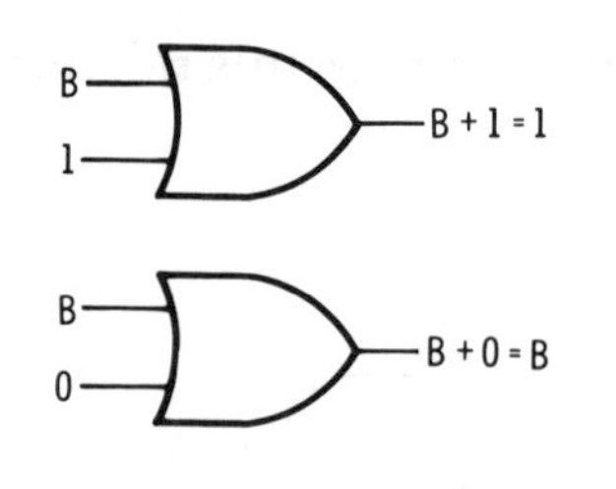

Figure 5-32

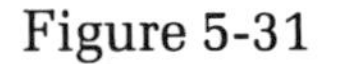

The Laws of Tautology apply to both AND gates and OR gates. The basic rules are given below.

$$A \cdot A = A$$
$$B + B = B$$

The logic symbols illustrate these rules are shown in Figure 5-33.

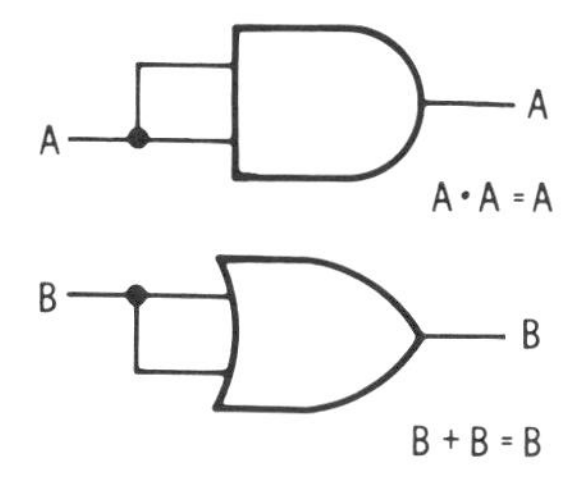

Figure 5-33

What these expressions say is that if you apply the same signal to all inputs of a logic gate, the output will be the same as the input. You can prove this to yourself by looking at the truth tables for AND and OR gates.

We can use the Laws of Tautology to simplify the expression QT = JMX + JMX + F9. Since JMX + JMX = JMX, QT = JMX + F9. The JMX term is redundant. In terms of circuitry you can see the simplification. The circuit in Figure 5-34A implements the original expression. Figure 5-34B shows the simplified but fully equivalent circuit.

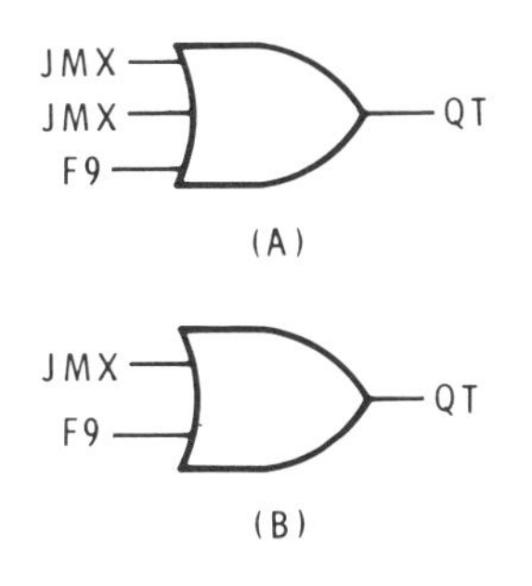

Figure 5-34

This same simplification procedure applies to AND gates.

Consider the expression $X = Q \cdot Q \cdot J$. The original and simplified logic diagrams implementing this equation are shown in Figure 5-35. The original circuit can be implemented as shown in Figure 5-35A. The simplified but equivalent circuit is shown in Figure 5-35B. The logic function is identical. Now you are beginning to see that the value of Boolean algebra is simplifying the design of a circuit.

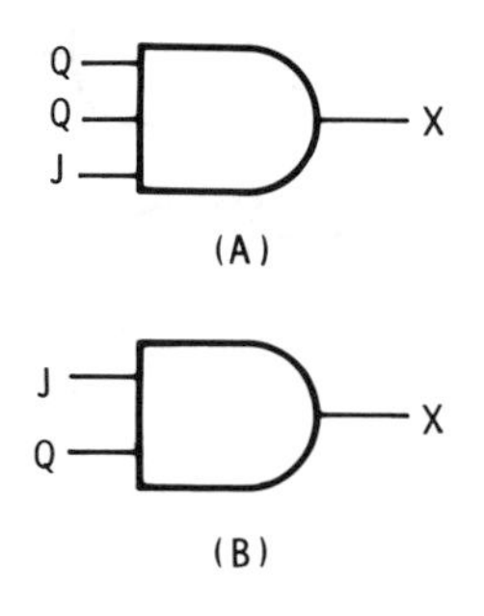

Figure 5-35

Another Boolean law is the Law of Complements. The two versions are:

$$A \cdot \overline{A} = 0$$
$$B + \overline{B} = 1$$

If we apply a logic signal and its complement to a logic gate, the output becomes either a binary 0 or a binary 1 depending on type of logic gate. This is illustrated in Figure 5-36.

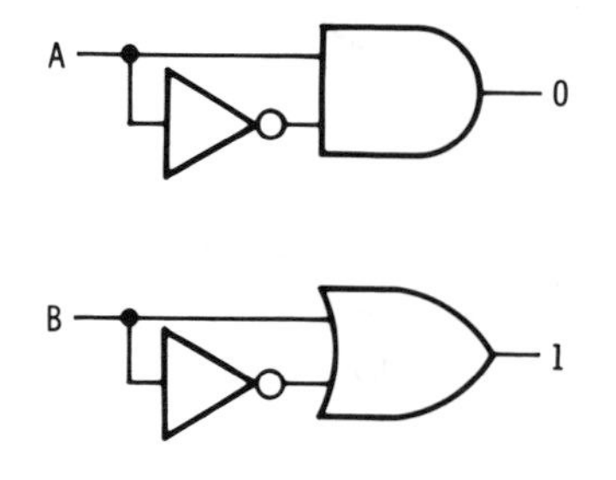

Figure 5-36

If you look closely at these circuits and analyze what happens, you will see that in either case the output is not affected by the state of the input. It can be either a 1 or a 0 and the output will be binary 0 for the AND gate and binary 1 for the OR gate. You can further verify these laws by referring to the AND and OR truth tables. A binary 0 on either input of an AND gate will always produce a binary 0 output. A binary 1 on either input of an OR gate will always produce a binary 1 output.

Now consider the Law of the Double Negative.

$$\overline{\overline{A}} = A$$

It says that the complement of the complement of A is equal to A. Or a signal that is complemented twice is the same as the original signal. You can see this from the circuit in Figure 5-37. If input A is 1, the output of inverter 1 is 0 and the output of inverter 2 is 1. Complementing a signal twice, or any even number of times, gives us the original signal.

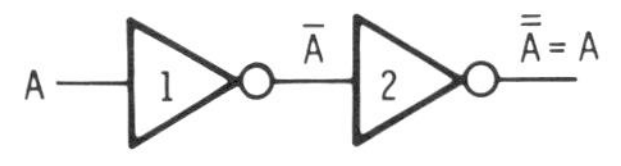

Figure 5-37

For simplicity, if you encounter two inverters in cascade, you can simply remove them and substitute a piece of wire since the effect is the same. Three cascade inverters or any odd number produces the same effect as a single inverter.

Another Boolean rule is the Law of Commutation. This is the same rule from basic algebra. The two forms of it are:

$$A \cdot B = B \cdot A$$
$$A + B = B + A$$

All it really says is that you can arrange the inputs to AND or OR gates in any order and the effect is the same. You can write the input variables in any order and they will mean the same thing.

$$W + X + Y = X + W + Y = Y + W + X$$

Also JML = LJM = MLJ = JLM = LMJ = MJL. The order of the inputs are different, but the logic result is the same.

Now let's give you some practice in using these rules. What are the simplifications of the expressions below?

a. $A + \overline{B} + A =$ ____________
b. $B\,C\,\overline{B} =$ ____________
c. $C + 1 + \overline{B} =$ ____________
d. $\overline{X} + Y + X =$ ____________

Work these problems using the previously discussed rules. The correct answers are given in Figure 5-38.

a. $A + \overline{B}$
b. 0
c. 1
d. 1

In problem (a) you first rearranged it by using the Law of Commutation $A + \overline{B} + A = A + A + \overline{B}$. By the Law of Tautology, you know that $A + A = A$, so the resulting simplified equation is $A + \overline{B}$.

In problem (b) you again rearrange the term using the Law of Commutation. $BC\overline{B} = B\overline{B}C$. From the Law of Complements you know that $B\,\overline{B} = 0$. Substituting this in the expression gives $0 \cdot C$. You know from the Law of Intersection that $0 \cdot C$ or $C \cdot 0 = 0$.

In problem (c) you should recognize the Laws of Union. $C + 1 + \overline{B} = 1$.

In problem (d), you first rearrange the equation by way of the Law of Commutation to $\overline{X} + Y + X = X + \overline{X} + Y$. The Law of Complements says that $X + \overline{X} = 1$. Therefore, the equation becomes $1 + Y$. Of course this reduces to 1 by way of the Law of Union.

Figure 5-38

Now try a few more examples using the previous solutions as a guide. But this time draw the logic diagram of the original expression as well as the simplified version to get a feel for the result of Boolean simplification in terms of circuitry.

a. $L + M + \overline{M}$
b. $JK\overline{K}L$
c. $F + T + F$
d. $\overline{B} + AC\overline{A} + D$

The answers are given in Figure 5-39.

a. $L + M + \overline{M} = L + 1 = 1$

The three input OR and inverter called for by the original expression reduces to a single wire with a binary 1 on it.

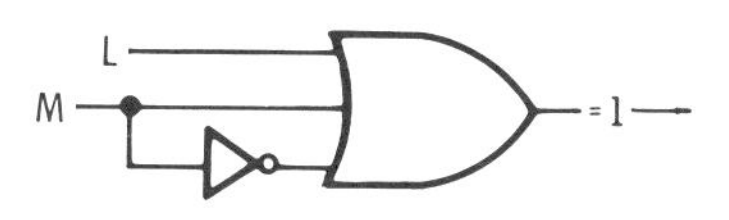

b. $JK\overline{K}L = J \cdot 0 \cdot L = 0$

The reduced expression is simply a binary 0 level.

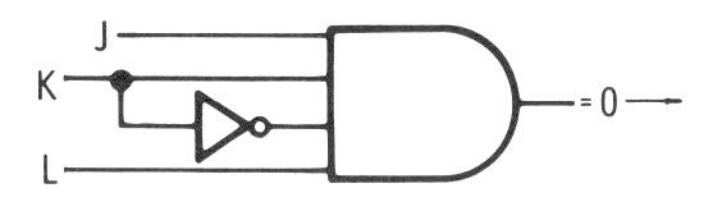

c. $F + T + F = F + F + T = F + T$

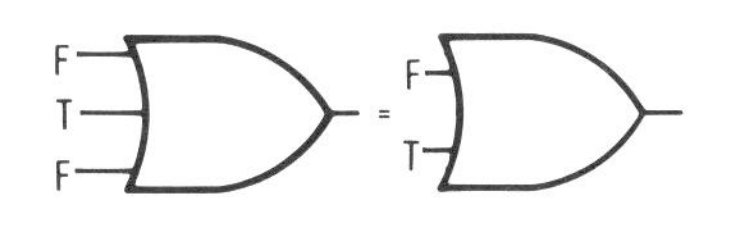

d. $\overline{B} + AC\overline{A} + D = \overline{B} + A\overline{A}C + D = \overline{B} + 0 \cdot C + D =$
$\overline{B} + 0 + D = \overline{B} + D$

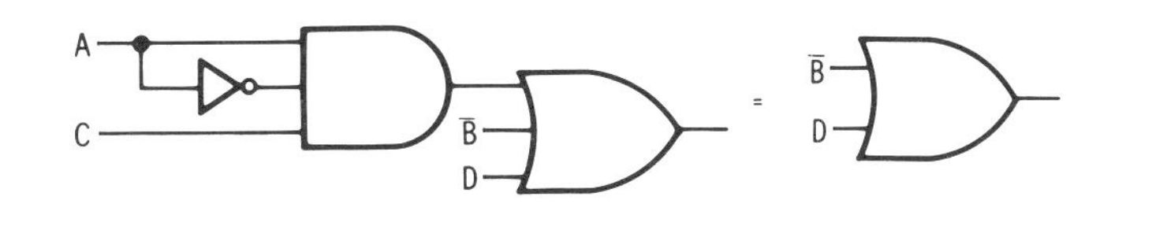

Figure 5-39

By now you should be able to see the value of Boolean algebra in simplifying a logic expression and minimizing the amount of circuitry required to implement it. Fewer parts means lower cost, smaller size and less power consumption.

Another Boolean law identical to the basic algebra rule is the Law of Association. These are:

$$(A \bullet B)\,C = A\,(B \bullet C) = A \bullet B \bullet C$$
$$A + (B + C) = (A + B) + C = A + B + C$$

You can see the circuitry simplification that results by applying these rules. See Figure 5-40. Note that we trade two 2-input AND gates for a single 3-input gate. The OR gate circuit equivalents for the Law of Association are given in Figure 5-41.

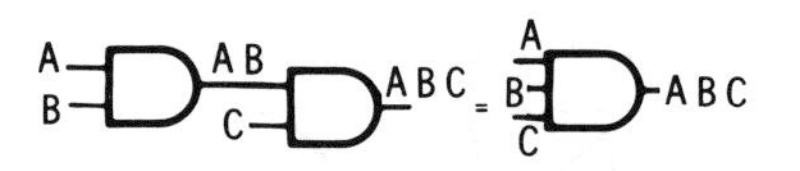

Figure 5-40

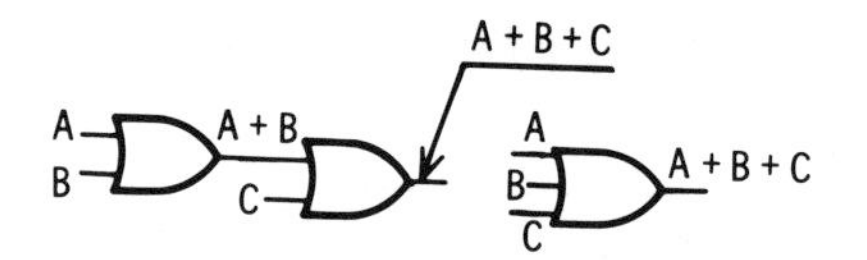

Figure 5-41

Note that the logical effect is the same for either version of the circuit. The three input gate is usually more economical than two 2 input gates.

Now let's consider the Laws of Distribution. We will use some of the rules described earlier to prove this law. The Laws of Distribution are:

$$A\,B + A\,C = A\,(B + C)$$

You should be able to infer this because all you are doing is factoring out one term (A) as you would in basic algebra.

The logic diagrams for each side of the equation on the previous page is shown in Figure 5-42.

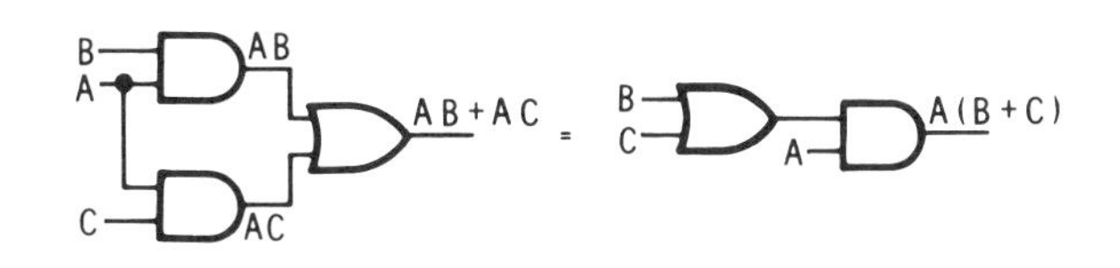

Figure 5-42

Not only is there a reduction in the number of circuits used, but also note that the expression changes from a sum-of-products to a product-of-sums form.

You can also use a truth table to show that the logic effect of both circuits is identical.

The table appears as shown below.

INPUTS			GATE OUTPUTS					
A	B	C	AB	AC	AB + AC	A	B + C	A (B + C)
0	0	0	0	0	0	0	0	0
0	0	1	0	0	0	0	1	0
0	1	0	0	0	0	0	1	0
0	1	1	0	0	0	0	1	0
1	0	0	0	0	0	1	0	0
1	0	1	0	1	1	1	1	1
1	1	0	1	0	1	1	1	1
1	1	1	1	1	1	1	1	1

(AB + AC and A (B + C): equal)

The table shows the eight possible input combinations of the three variables. It also shows the outputs of the intermediate and output gates for both the sum-of-products and product-of-sums forms. And they are equal. This shows you another use of truth tables in analyzing and understanding logic circuits.

Another version of the Laws of Distribution is

$$(A + B)(A + C) = A + BC$$

Note the format of the original and simplified versions.

The original expression is in the product-of-sums form but is changed to the sum-of-products form when is is simplified. The logic diagrams of the two versions illustrated in Figure 5-43 show this difference.

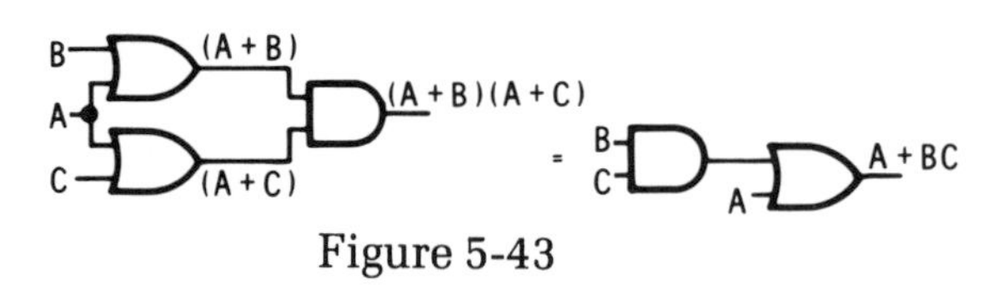

Figure 5-43

You can use truth tables to prove the equality of the two expressions or circuits.

See the table below.

INPUTS			GATE OUTPUTS					
A	B	C	(A+B)	(A+C)	(A+B) (A+C)	A	BC	A+BC
0	0	0	0	0	0	0	0	0
0	0	1	0	1	0	0	0	0
0	1	0	1	0	0	0	0	0
0	1	1	1	1	1	0	1	1
1	0	0	1	1	1	1	0	1
1	0	1	1	1	1	1	0	1
1	1	0	1	1	1	1	0	1
1	1	1	1	1	1	1	1	1

equal

Another way to prove the equality of these expressions is to use some of the Boolean rules learned earlier.

$$(A + B)(A + C) = A + BC$$

First expand the expression on the left side of the equation as you would any algebraic expression. Multiply each term by the others and sum the products as shown.

$$(A + B)(A + C) = AA + AC + AB + BC$$

Next, this can be reduced by substituting A for AA and factoring an A out of the first three terms.

$$A + AC + AB + BC = A(1 + C + B) + BC$$

Then, the Laws of Union will reduce (1 + C + B) to 1 and the expression becomes:

$$A(1) + BC$$

Finally, the Laws of Intersection makes this:

$$A + BC$$

Next there are the Laws of Absorption. There are four versions.

$$A(A + B) = A$$
$$A(\overline{A} + B) = AB$$
$$AB + B = B$$
$$A\overline{B} + B = A + B$$

Now let's use the previously explained Boolean rules to prove the first expression.

$$A(A + B) = A$$

$A(A + B)$
Expand by multiplying (Distribution)

$AA + AB$
Replace AA by A (Tautology)

$A + AB$
Factor out A

$A(1 + B)$
Replace $(1 + B)$ by 1 (Union)

$A(1)$
Replace $A(1)$ by A (Intersection)
$A = A(A + B)$

Next let's prove $A(\overline{A} + B) = AB$

$A(\overline{A} + B)$
Expand by multiplying (Distribution)

$A\overline{A} + AB$
Replace $A\overline{A}$ by 0 (Complements)

$0 + AB$
Replace $AB + 0$ with AB (Union)

$AB = A(\overline{A} + B)$

The other Laws of Absorption are more difficult to prove. You can use truth tables as we did before. But it can be done with Boolean Algebra by using a trick. Let's prove that:

$$AB + \overline{B} = A + \overline{B}$$

There isn't anything we can do with the expression on the right side of the equation. So let's multiply the $\overline{B}$ term by (A + 1). Since A + 1 = 1 and $\overline{B}$ (1) = $\overline{B}$ we will not change the original meaning of the expression. It is equivalent to multiplying a term by 1. Therefore:

$$AB + \overline{B} = AB + \overline{B}(A + 1)$$

Now we will use Boolean rules to further reduce this expression.

$AB + \overline{B}(A + 1)$
Expand by multiplying (Distribution)

$AB + A\overline{B} + \overline{B}$
Factor A out of first two terms (Distribution)

$A(B + \overline{B}) + \overline{B}$
Replace $(B + \overline{B})$ with 1 (Complements)

$A(1) + \overline{B}$
Replace A (1) by A (Intersection)
$A + \overline{B}$

You can use the same trick to prove the expression.

$$A\overline{B} + B = A + B$$

$A\overline{B} + B$
Multiply B by (A + 1) (Distribution)
$A\overline{B} + B(A + 1)$
Expand by multiplying (Distribution)

$A\overline{B} + AB + B$
Factor A out of first two terms (Distribution)
$A(\overline{B} + B) + B$
Replace $(\overline{B} + B)$ by 1 (Complements)

$A(1) + B$
Replace A (1) by A (Intersection)

$A + B = A\overline{B} + B$

DeMorgan's Theorem

Another important Boolean rule is DeMorgan's theorem. There are two basic forms of it as indicated below.

$$\overline{AB} = \overline{A}+\overline{B}$$
$$\overline{A+B} = \overline{A}\,\overline{B}$$

One way to prove the equality of these expressions is by a truth table. The first expression above is proven this way as indicated below.

INPUTS		OUTPUTS				
A	B	$\overline{A}$	$\overline{B}$	AB	$\overline{AB}$	$\overline{A}+\overline{B}$
0	0	1	1	0	1	1
0	1	1	0	0	1	1
1	0	0	1	0	1	1
1	1	0	0	1	0	0

equal

There are two variables A and B so there are four possible input combinations. These are indicated in columns A and B. Columns are also provided for the other terms called for by the expressions:

$$\overline{A}, \overline{B}, \overline{AB} \text{ and } (\overline{A}+\overline{B})$$

Using the inputs as a guide these other columns are completed. Go through each column yourself to be sure you understand how each state is obtained. Note the equality of the $\overline{AB}$ and $\overline{A}+\overline{B}$ columns.

Now let's prove the expression $\overline{A+B} = \overline{A}\,\overline{B}$.

INPUTS		OUTPUTS				
A	B	$\overline{A}$	$\overline{B}$	A + B	$\overline{A+B}$	$\overline{A}\overline{B}$
0	0	1	1	0	1	1
0	1	1	0	1	0	0
1	0	0	1	1	0	0
1	1	0	0	1	0	0

equal

Remember if A = 0, $\overline{A}$ = 1.

The correct logic table of the expression $\overline{A+B} = \overline{A}\overline{B}$ is shown above.

Like other Boolean rules, DeMorgan's theorem is useful in minimizing logic equations. For example, the expression:

$$X = \overline{A\overline{B}C} + \overline{A+\overline{C}}$$

cannot be simplified by first using the previously given Boolean rules. It can only be reduced by using DeMorgan's theorem first, then the previously given Boolean rules.

DeMorgan's theorem is used to split or join vincula (complement bar). When a vinculum is split, every sign over which the splitting takes place changes from OR to AND or AND to OR and the bars are distributed over the individual terms. Let's consider an example where factors are ORed.

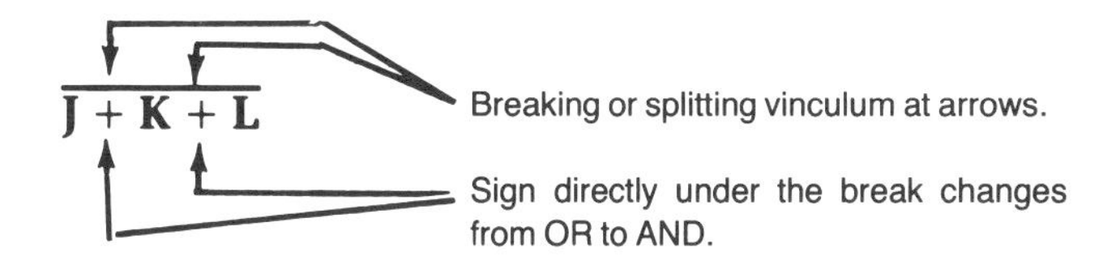

The result is, $\overline{\mathbf{J}}\,\overline{\mathbf{K}}\,\overline{\mathbf{L}}$.

Let's consider an example where the factors in an expression under the vinculum are ANDed such as $\overline{\mathbf{EHDL}}$.

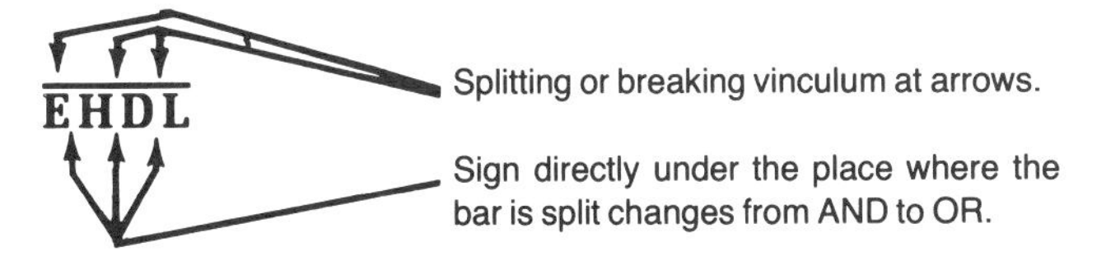

The result is, $\overline{\mathbf{E}} + \overline{\mathbf{H}} + \overline{\mathbf{D}} + \overline{\mathbf{L}}$

When vincula over individual factors or groups of factors are joined, the signs change from AND to OR or OR to AND. Consider an example where the factors are ANDed.

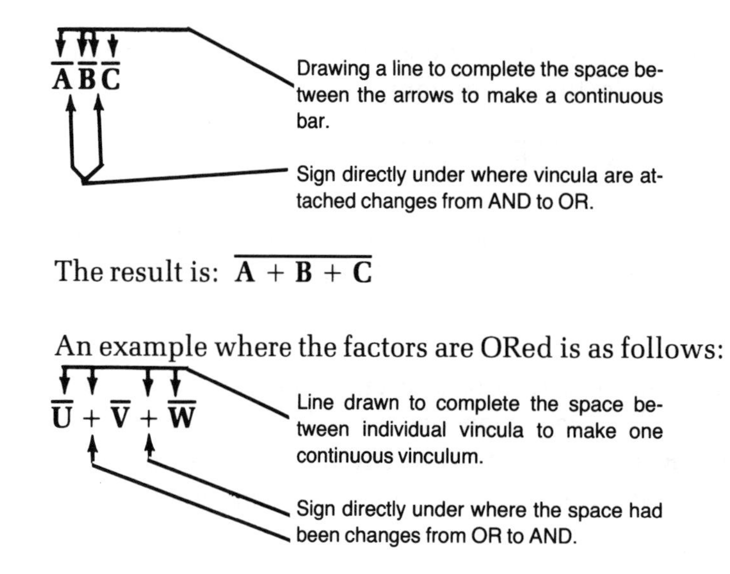

The result is: $\overline{\mathbf{A} + \mathbf{B} + \mathbf{C}}$

An example where the factors are ORed is as follows:

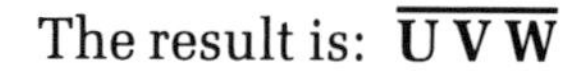

The result is: $\overline{\mathbf{U\,V\,W}}$

Another rule to remember when using DeMorgan's theorem is; when you change signs in an expression, group the same letters that were grouped originally. For example, $\overline{A\,B + C}$ becomes $(\overline{AB})\overline{C} = (\overline{A} + \overline{B})\overline{C} = \overline{A}\overline{C} + \overline{B}\overline{C}$

Notice in the above example that the AND sign between factor A and factor B is a sign of grouping. Breaking the vinculum results in a sign change from AND to OR. Since the resulting OR sign is not a sign of grouping, parenthesis or brackets are used to indicate that the factors A and B were previously grouped.

Make sure you always follow the "signs of grouping" rules; otherwise, you will have errors. If we take the same example $\overline{A\,B + C}$ and do not apply the rule (do not place brackets or parenthesis around AB before breaking the vinculum), we would get the following:

Break Vinculum	$\overline{A\!\!/\,B\!\!/ + C}$	
Becomes	$\overline{A} + \overline{B}\,\overline{C}$	This result indicates that B is grouped with C instead of A.

When the rule is properly applied, we have:

$$\overline{A\,B + C}$$

Insert grouping $\overline{(AB) + C}$

Break Vinculum $\overline{(A{/}B){/} + C}$

becomes $(\overline{A} + \overline{B})\,\overline{C}$ A and B are still grouped as before

Multiplying $\overline{A}\,\overline{C} + \overline{B}\,\overline{C}$

Another type of expression dealing with signs of grouping is, $\overline{(Y + Z)\,X + W}$. In this example, X is grouped with the entire expression Y + Z within the parenthesis. In many cases such as this, you could use any of the previously presented Boolean rules to simplify the expression before splitting the vinculum. Your procedure should be as follows:

- Temporarily ignore vinculum $\overline{(Y + Z)\,X + W}$
- In this case, apply the law of distribution to clear parenthesis. $\overline{XY + XZ + W}$
- Split vinculum at OR signs and change sign of operation. $\overline{XY}\;\overline{XZ}\;\overline{W}$

Note: There are two signs of grouping in the expression up to this point. The vinculum over XY and XZ as well as the AND signs between X and Y and X and Z.

Insert appropriate grouping signs. $[\overline{XY}]\,[\overline{XZ}]\,\overline{W}$

- Split vinculum $[\overline{X} + \overline{Y}]\,[\overline{X} + \overline{Z}]\,\overline{W}$
- Law of Distribution $[\overline{X}\,\overline{X} + \overline{X}\,\overline{Z} + \overline{X}\,\overline{Y} + \overline{Y}\,\overline{Z})\,\overline{W}$
- Law of Tautology $[\overline{X} + \overline{X}\,\overline{Z} + \overline{X}\,\overline{Y} + \overline{Y}\,\overline{Z}]\,\overline{W}$
- Factor out $\overline{X}$ $[\overline{X}\,(1 + \overline{Z} + \overline{Y}) + \overline{Y}\,\overline{Z}]\,\overline{W}$
- Law of Union $[\overline{X}(1) + \overline{Y}\,\overline{Z}]\,\overline{W}$
- Law of Absorption $[\overline{X} + \overline{Y}\,\overline{Z}]\,\overline{W}$
- Law of Distribution $\overline{W}\,\overline{X} + \overline{W}\,\overline{Y}\,\overline{Z}$

The two major facts to remember about the previous procedure is:

1. Watch your signs of grouping.

2. Simplify expression under vinculum as much as possible before splitting vinculum.

There is an alternate method which often can result in fewer steps. Let's use the same example $\overline{(Y + Z)\,X + W}$. However, instead of applying the law of distribution to remove the parenthesis as we did previously, we will add a sign of grouping.

add brackets: $\overline{[(Y + Z)\,X] + W}$

Split vinculum, but be careful to retain signs of grouping.

$$[(\overline{Y}\,\overline{Z}) + \overline{X}]\,\overline{W}$$

Law of Distribution: $\overline{W}\,\overline{Y}\,\overline{Z} + \overline{W}\,\overline{X}$

This second example gives the same result in fewer steps. However, given another expression, the first technique may require fewer steps. The main skill to achieve is accuracy. Only with a lot of practice can you hope to acquire the knack of knowing which procedure will give you an accurate result with the least amount of steps.

Let's look at the result when the same expression, $\overline{(Y + Z)\,X + W}$ is simplified by ignoring signs of grouping and splitting vinculum immediately without retaining groupings by adding brackets.

$$\overline{(\mathbf{Y} \overset{\downarrow}{+} \mathbf{Z})\overset{\downarrow}{\,}\mathbf{X} \overset{\downarrow}{+} \mathbf{W}}$$ Split vinculum above OR and AND signs

$$\overline{\mathbf{Y}}\,\overline{\mathbf{Z}} + \overline{\mathbf{X}}\,\overline{\mathbf{W}}$$

Notice that by splitting the vinculum in the initial step, the factors X and W are grouped together as if the original expression was (Y + Z) (X + W). The result, although arrived at in one step, is obviously wrong because $\overline{(Y + Z)\,X + W}$ is **not** equal to $\overline{(Y + Z)\,(X + W)}$.

Before going on to some additional rules for the proper use of DeMorgan's theorem, practice using the first three DeMorgan's rules previously covered.

Self-Test Review

Apply DeMorgan's theorem to the following expressions.

8. $\overline{DEFG} =$ ______________________

9. $\overline{E + F + G} =$ ______________________

10. $\overline{M} + \overline{N} + \overline{P} + \overline{R} =$ ______________________

11. $\overline{H}\,\overline{J}\,\overline{K} =$ ______________________

12. $\overline{D + E F} =$ ______________________

13. $\overline{R} + \overline{S} + \overline{T} + \overline{U} =$ ______________________

14. $(\overline{H} + \overline{K})\,\overline{L} =$ ______________________

15. $\overline{R + LM} =$ ______________________

16. $\overline{A + BCD} =$ ______________________

17. $\overline{W}\,\overline{X}\,(\overline{Y} + \overline{Z}) =$ ______________________

18. $\overline{A + B\,(C + D)} =$ ______________________

19. The signs or methods used to show grouping in Boolean expressions are:

    ____

    ____

    ____

    ____

DeMorgan's Theorem (Continued)

If a vinculum covers part of an expression such as $\overline{B}\overline{(A+CDE)}$ the following simplification rules apply for splitting vinculum:

- Signs outside the vinculum **do not** change.
- Signs under the vinculum **do** change.

Consider the following example: $\overline{B}\overline{(A + C D E)}$

Place signs of grouping, $\overline{B}\overline{[A + (C D E)]}$

Split vinculum where indicated, $\overline{B}\overline{[A + (C D E)]}$

$$\overline{B}[\overline{A}(\overline{C} + \overline{D} + \overline{E})]$$

At this point, you should recall a rule in ordinary algebra that also applies to Boolean algebra. Where there are signs of grouping within signs of grouping, clear the inside grouping first. In this case, apply the law of distribution to clear inner parenthesis,

$$\overline{B}\,[\overline{A}\,\overline{C} + \overline{A}\,\overline{D} + \overline{A}\,\overline{E}]$$

Law of Distribution again, $(\overline{B}\,\overline{A}\,\overline{C} + \overline{B}\,\overline{A}\,\overline{D} + \overline{B}\,\overline{A}\,\overline{E})$

If a vinculum covers part of an expression such as $B + \overline{C\,D}$, the following simplification rules, when **joining** vinculum, apply:

- You can not extend a vinculum over a factor or term that does not have a vincula or vinculum.

For example, in the expression, $E + \overline{F(G + H)}$, you can not extend the vinculum over E directly so that you have $\overline{E + F(G + H)}$.

- You can extend the vinculum, however, after you have applied the law of double negative. $A = \overline{\overline{A}}$

Let's take the same example used above:

$$E + \overline{F(G + H)}$$

First, apply the law of double negative by placing two vincula over the factor E without changing the value of E.

$$\overline{\overline{E}} + \overline{F(G + H)}$$

Now join the **upper** vincula over E to the original vinculum and change the sign of operation.

$$\overline{\overline{E}\,[F\,(G + H)]}$$

Let's consider some other ways DeMorgan's theorem can be used with additional laws to simplify expressions. Always try to manipulate an expression so that one part is the complement of the other. For example,

	$AB + \overline{A} + \overline{B} + CD$
Apply DeMorgan's to $\overline{A} + \overline{B}$	$AB + \overline{AB} + CD$

Now you have AB and its complement $\overline{AB}$ (which is equivalent to $A + \overline{A} = 1$) so the expression can be simplified to $1 + CD$.

Law of Union, $1 + CD = 1$

Suppose the expression was	$A + B + CD + \overline{AB}$
Law of Commutation	$A + B + \overline{AB} + CD$
DeMorgan's	$A + B + \overline{A} + \overline{B} + CD$
Law of Commutation	$A + \overline{A} + B + \overline{B} + CD$
Law of Complements	$1 + 1 + CD$
Law of Union	$1 + 1 + CD = 1$

Consider the following expression where the double negative law can be used to advantage.

	$\overline{(L + K)\,\overline{(J + M)}}$
DeMorgan's	$\overline{L + K} + \overline{\overline{J + M}}$
Double Negative	$\overline{L + K} + J + M$
DeMorgan's	$\overline{L}\,\overline{K} + J + M$

An alternate method in simplifying the same expression, but using the double negative law twice, is as follows:

	$\overline{(L + K)\,\overline{(J + M)}}$
Place double negative over L + K	$\overline{\overline{\overline{(L + K)}}\,\overline{(J + M)}}$
Join upper vinculum over L + K to vinculum over J + M, and change sign of operation	$\overline{\overline{\overline{(L + K)} + (J + M)}}$
Double Negative	$\overline{L + K} + J + M$
DeMorgan's	$\overline{L}\,\overline{K} + J + M$

Remember, unless you can manipulate an expression so that you have a group of letters and its complement (so that both groups taken together equal 0 or 1), the best procedure for simplifying is:

- First, split or join the vincula according to DeMorgan's theorem.
- Group letters as they were originally grouped.
- Apply other laws, in whatever order seems best.

Self-Test Review

Simplify the following expressions.

20. $\overline{A B \overline{C}} + \overline{\overline{A}\,\overline{B}\,C}$
21. $\overline{(A + \overline{B} + \overline{C})}\,\overline{(A + \overline{C})}$
22. $\overline{E E} + C D + \overline{B} + A + E\,\overline{(C D + A)}$
23. $D + [E + \overline{F(G + H)}]\,[\overline{E}\,F\,(G + H)]$
24. $[W + \overline{X}\,Y + \overline{W}\,(X + \overline{Y})]\,Z$
25. $\overline{\overline{(\overline{A B + C})\,(\overline{A} + \overline{B})\,\overline{C}}}$
26. $\overline{\overline{X}\,\overline{Y} + X\,\overline{Z}}$

Minimizing Logic Circuits

You have already seen how the Boolean rules are used to simplify logic expressions and you have had a little practice in minimizing some logic equations yourself. But now we want you to polish your skill with Boolean so that you can minimize any logic circuit that you might encounter. The discussion presented here will give you the necessary practice.

Let's start with the expression $F = (\overline{A} + B)(B + \overline{C})$. The logic diagram for this expression is given in Figure 5-44.

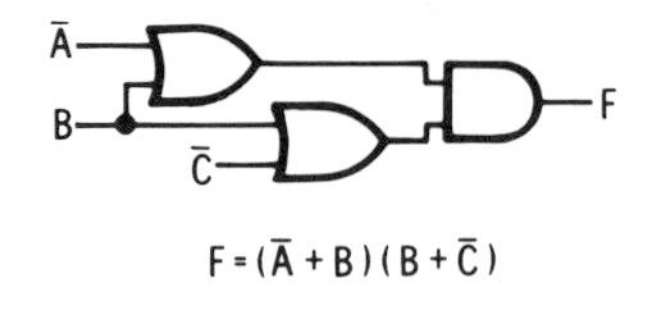

Figure 5-44

Now, using Boolean algebra, let's minimize the equation. The first step is to expand the expression by multiplying as you would in algebra.

$F = (\overline{A} + B)(B + \overline{C}) = \overline{A}B + \overline{A}\overline{C} + BB + B\overline{C}$

Basic Boolean rules can then be used as indicated below to reduce the equation.

$\overline{A}B + \overline{A}\overline{C} + BB + B\overline{C}$
Laws of Tautology (Idempotent) $(B \bullet B) = B$

$\overline{A}B + \overline{A}\overline{C} + B + B\overline{C}$
Laws of Commutation (rearrange equation)

$\overline{A}B + B + B\overline{C} + \overline{A}\overline{C}$

Laws of Absorption	$B(\overline{A} + 1 + \overline{C}) + \overline{A}\overline{C}$
(factor out B)	$B(1) + \overline{A}\overline{C}$

$B + \overline{A}\overline{C}$

The logic diagram of the minimized version of the original expression is shown in Figure 5-45.

Ā
C̄
B
F = B + Ā C̄

Figure 5-45

As you can see, there is a significant simplification in that the minimized circuit uses one less gate.

Just to be sure that the two circuits and expressions do indeed produce the same logical function, we can prove their equality with a truth table. The truth table proves conclusively that:

$$F = (\overline{A} + B)(B + \overline{C}) = B + \overline{A}\,\overline{C}$$

The original and simplified expressions are equivalent.

INPUTS			GATE OUTPUTS						
A	B	C	$\overline{A}$	$\overline{C}$	$(\overline{A}+B)$	$(B+\overline{C})$	$(\overline{A}+B)(B+\overline{C})$	$\overline{A}\,\overline{C}$	$B+\overline{A}\,\overline{C}$
0	0	0	1	1	1	1	1	1	1
0	0	1	1	0	1	0	0	0	0
0	1	0	1	1	1	1	1	1	1
0	1	1	1	0	1	1	1	0	1
1	0	0	0	1	0	1	0	0	0
1	0	1	0	0	0	0	0	0	0
1	1	0	0	1	1	1	1	0	1
1	1	1	0	0	1	1	1	0	1

equal

Next let's try the expression below.

$$X = A\overline{B}\,\overline{C} + AB\overline{C} + A\overline{B}C + \overline{A}B\overline{C}$$

The logic diagram is shown in Figure 5-46.

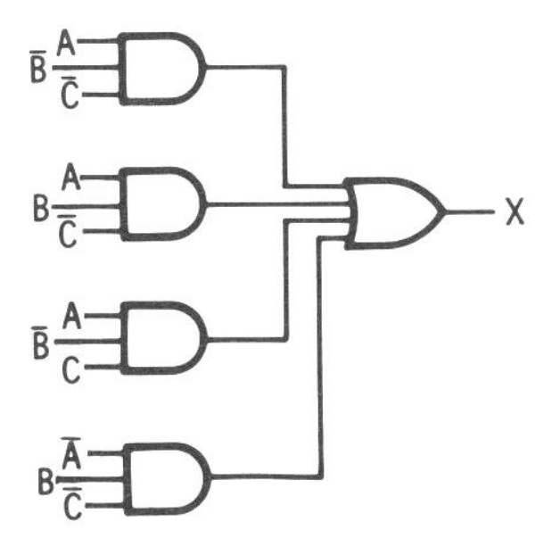

Figure 5-46

Observing the equation, try to spot common factors in each of the terms, then regroup the terms and rearrange the factors using the Laws of Commutation.

$$X = A\overline{B}\overline{C} + AB\overline{C} + A\overline{B}C + \overline{A}B\overline{C}$$
$$X = A\overline{B}\overline{C} + A\overline{B}C + B\overline{C}A + B\overline{C}\overline{A}$$

Next we factor out the common expressions, $A\overline{B}$ in the first two terms and $B\overline{C}$ in the last two terms.

$$X = A\overline{B}(\overline{C} + C) + B\overline{C}(A + \overline{A})$$
$$A\overline{B}(1) + B\overline{C}(1)$$

By the Laws of Complements this becomes:

$$X = A\overline{B} + B\overline{C}$$

The corresponding logic diagram is given in Figure 5-47.

Comparing this circuit with the one in Figure 5-46, you can see the result of minimization. The three gate circuit performs exactly the same logic function as the original five gate circuit at a considerable savings.

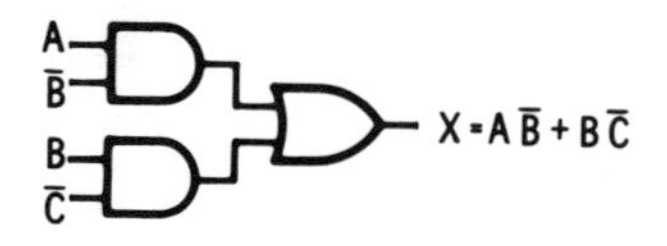

Figure 5-47

Next, let's minimize a logic equation with DeMorgan's theorem.

Reduce the equation

$$G = \overline{\overline{\overline{(A\,\overline{B}\,\overline{C}} + B\,C)}\,(A\,\overline{B})}$$

The correct solution is shown below.

$$G = \overline{\overline{\overline{(A\,\overline{B}\,\overline{C}} + B\,C)}\,(A\,\overline{B})}$$

DeMorgan's

$$G = \overline{(A\,\overline{\overline{B}}\,\overline{\overline{C}}} + BC) + \overline{(A\,\overline{\overline{B}})}$$

DeMorgan's

$$G = \overline{A} + B + C + B\,C + \overline{A} + B$$

Law of Commutation

$$G = \overline{A} + \overline{A} + B + B + C + B\,C$$

Law of Tautology

$$G = \overline{A} + B + C + B\,C$$

Law of Distribution

$$G = \overline{A} + B + C\,(1 + B)$$

Law of Union

$$G = \overline{A} + B + C\,(1)$$

Law of Intersection

$$G = \overline{A} + B + C$$

Self-Test Review

Simplify the following logic equations using Boolean Algebra.

27. $X = AB\overline{C}D + ABC\overline{D} + B\overline{C}D + \overline{A}BC\overline{D}$

28. $F = (A + B + \overline{C})(\overline{A} + B + \overline{C})$

29. $X = \overline{A\overline{B}C} + \overline{A + \overline{C}}$

30. $M = \overline{(A + \overline{B})(\overline{A} + C)(B + C)}$

31. $D = \overline{A}B\overline{C} + \overline{A}BC + AB\overline{C} + ABC$

Using NAND/NOR Gates

Throughout this unit, we have shown logic equations implemented with AND and OR gates. However, most modern digital systems and circuits are made with NAND or NOR gates. As you saw in an earlier unit, any of the three basic logic operations can be realized with either NAND or NOR circuits.

A NAND gate or a NOR gate can be used as an inverter by tying all of the inputs together as shown in Figure 5-48. Both circuits produce an output that is the complement of the input.

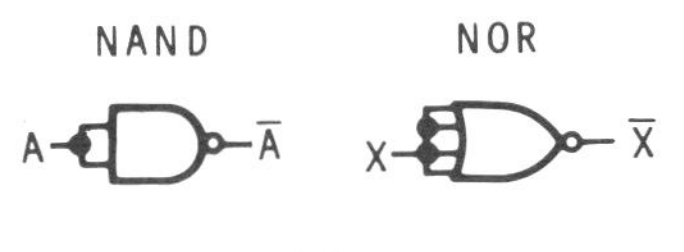

Figure 5-48

When used as inverters NAND and NOR gates can be represented by the inverter symbol. See Figure 5-49.

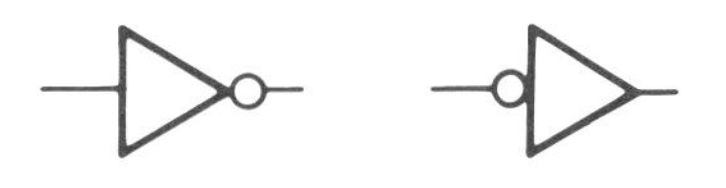

Figure 5-49

A NAND gate can be used for AND operations by inverting its output as shown in Figure 5-50. The inversion of the NAND is cancelled by the added inverter producing the pure AND function.

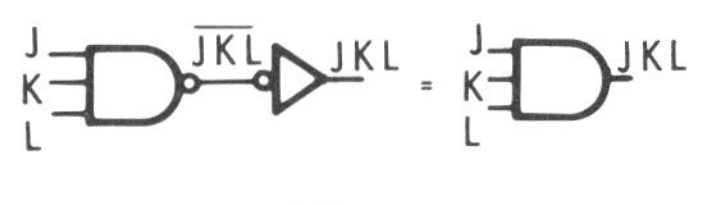

Figure 5-50

When you use inverters to complement the inputs to a NAND, the OR function will be performed. The output equation of this combination circuit, shown in Figure 5-51, is $C = \overline{\overline{A}\,\overline{B}}$. Using DeMorgan's theorem the output expression reduces to $A + B$.

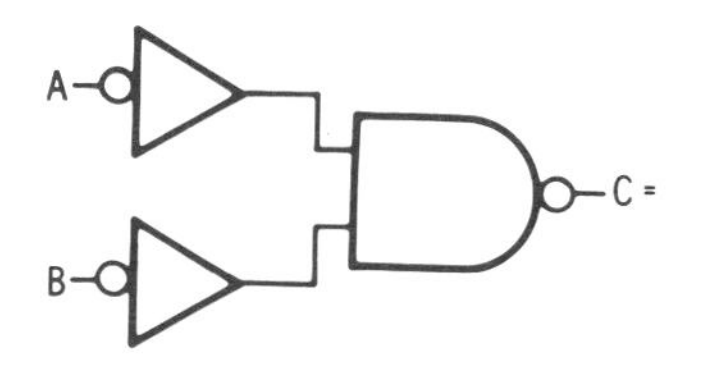

Figure 5-51

DeMorgan's theorem tells that a NAND can also perform the negated OR function.

$$\overline{AB} = \overline{A} + \overline{B}$$

When the NAND is used for the negated OR function the symbol in Figure 5-52 is used. This makes it clear what function is being performed.

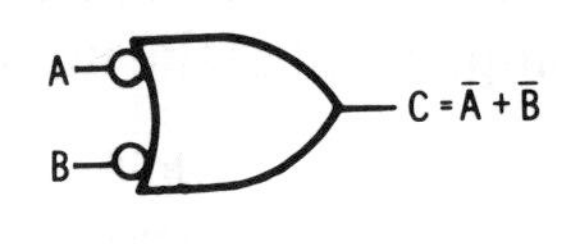

Figure 5-52

Putting inverters ahead of the inputs creates the pure OR function as indicated in Figure 5-53.

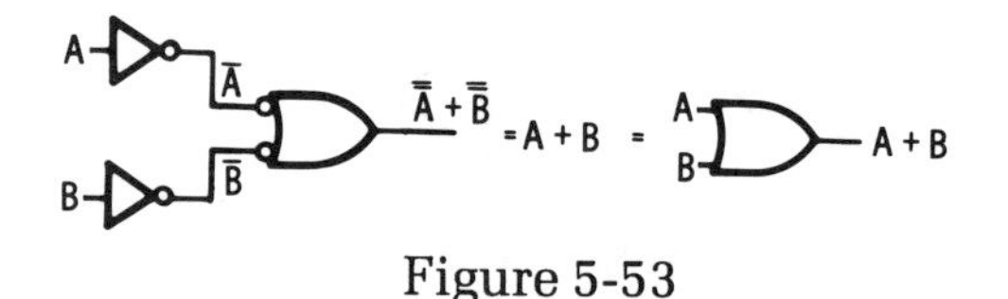

Figure 5-53

You should realize that the symbol used for the negated OR shows circles or inverters at the inputs. In a true physical sense there are no inverters there, but the logic effect produced is as if there were.

In writing the Boolean equation from a logic diagram simply treat the symbol literally and interpret each circle as an inversion and each gate as the designated logic function.

The equation of the circuit in Figure 5-54 is $\overline{E} + H + \overline{F}$. If you had drawn this circuit with the equivalent NAND symbol as indicated in Figure 5-55, you might expect a different logic operation to be performed. The equation for this circuit is $X = \overline{E\overline{H}F}$.

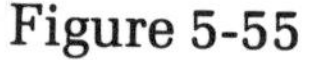

Figure 5-54

Figure 5-55

Using DeMorgan's theorem on this expression it becomes $\overline{E} + H + \overline{F}$.

The NOR gate can also be used to perform any logic function. By inverting its output the OR operation is performed as shown in Figure 5-56.

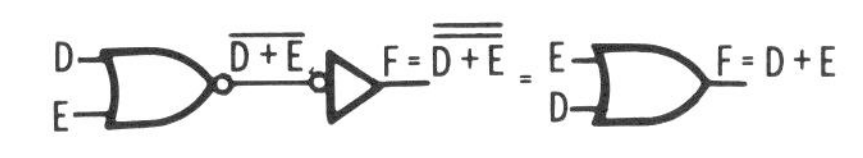

Figure 5-56

In an earlier unit you saw how using inverters at the input of a NOR could also be used to express the AND function. The logic symbols illustrating this are shown in Figure 5-57.

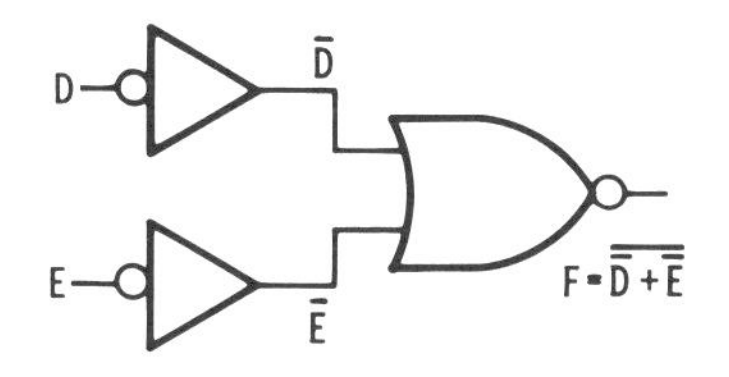

Figure 5-57

The output equation of this circuit is $F = \overline{\overline{D} + \overline{E}}$. Reducing it with DeMorgan's theorem we get $F = \overline{\overline{D} + \overline{E}} = \overline{\overline{D}} \cdot \overline{\overline{E}}$. This is of course the AND function $D \cdot E$.

DeMorgan's theorem tells us that the positive NOR can also perform as a negated AND. The DeMorgan's expression for this relationship is $\overline{D + E} = \overline{D} \cdot \overline{E}$.

When the negated AND function is used, the symbol in Figure 5-58 indicates the function.

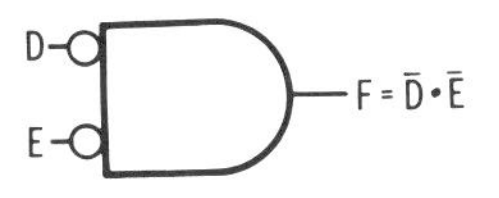

Figure 5-58

The negated AND connected as a standard AND is shown in Figure 5-59.

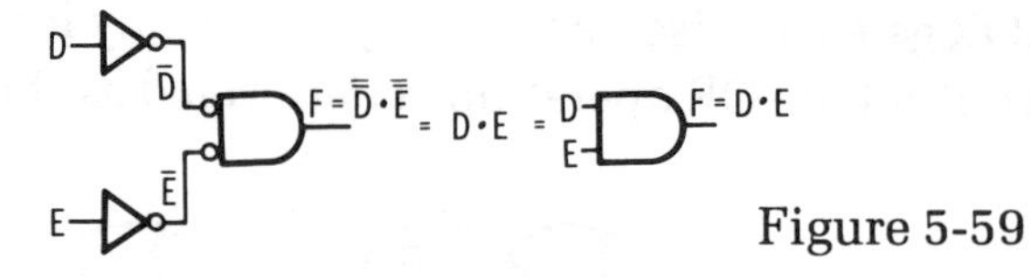

Figure 5-59

Interpret the negated AND logic symbol literally for the purpose of writing equations, even though in reality no inverters are physically present at the inputs where circles are indicated.

Figure 5-60 summarizes the functions and symbols of NAND and NOR gates.

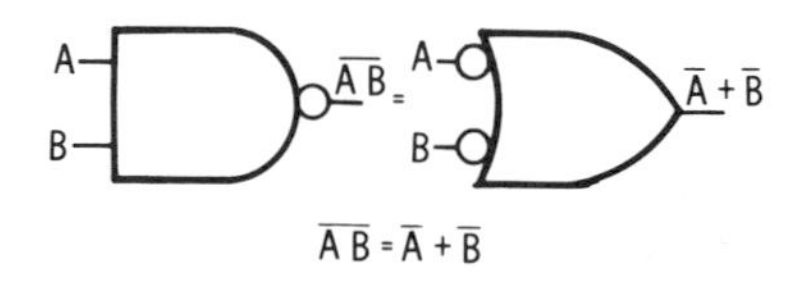

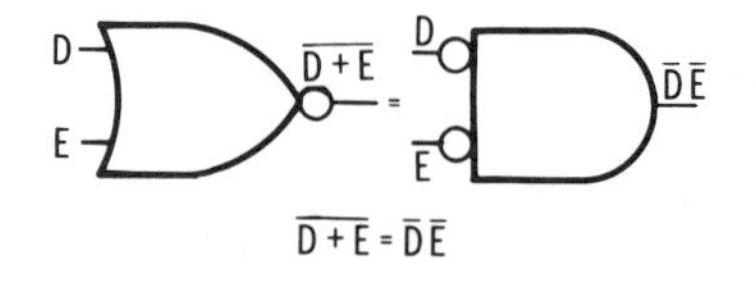

NAND TRUTH TABLE

A	B	OUTPUT
L	L	H
H	L	H
L	H	H
H	H	L

D	E	OUTPUT
L	L	H
H	L	L
L	H	L
H	H	L

NOR TRUTH TABLE

Figure 5-60

The AND and OR equivalent circuits with NANDs and NORs are summarized in Figure 5-61.

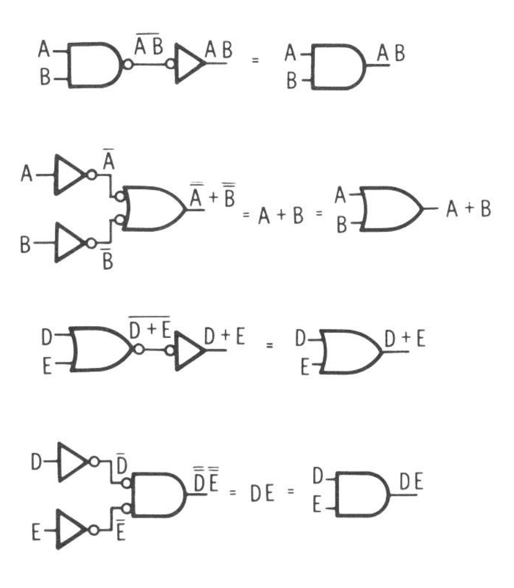

Figure 5-61

We will show how any Boolean equation can be implemented with NAND or NOR gates in the following section.

NOR Logic Equivalent Circuits

The procedure for implementing any Boolean expression with NOR gates is as follows:

Step 1. Minimize the equation using Boolean algebra.

Step 2. Draw the logic circuit of the reduced equation using standard AND and OR symbols.

The first example we will use is, $F = X + \overline{Y}Z$, which is already in its simplest form. The circuit is shown in Figure 5-62.

Step 3. Draw the output NOR gate showing the reduced equation at its output as in Figure 5-63.

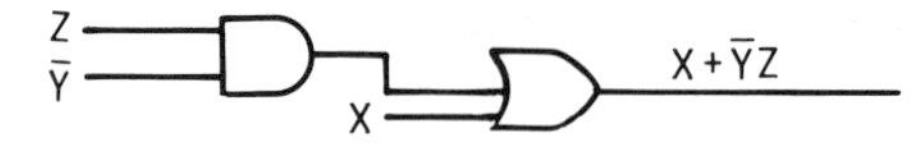

Figure 5-62

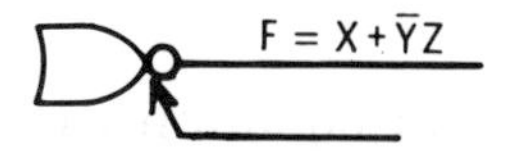

Figure 5-63

Note: With this method, we start at the output gate and the final output expression working from right to left (output to input). Both sections of the NOR gate must be considered but only one section at a time.

Step 4. Complement the output. Working from right to left in Figure 5-63, the inverter is the part of the NOR gate first encountered. Now you know that at the point indicated by the arrow in Figure 5-63, the signal must pass through the inverter to become $F = X + \overline{Y}Z$. Therefore, the expression describing the signal at the arrow is the complement or $\overline{X + \overline{Y}Z}$. Figure 5-64 shows the results of this fourth step in our procedure.

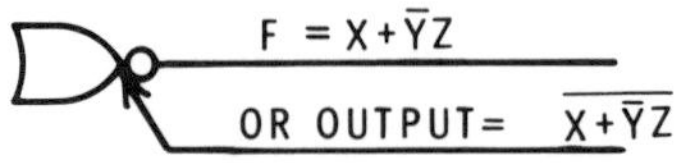

$F = X+\overline{Y}Z$

OR OUTPUT= $\overline{X+\overline{Y}Z}$

Figure 5-64

Step 5. Simplify the output expression of the OR gate. This is the expression shown at the arrow in Figure 5-64.

	$F = \overline{X + \overline{Y}Z}$
DeMorgan's	$(\overline{X})\ (\overline{\overline{Y}Z})$
DeMorgan's	$(\overline{X})\ (Y + \overline{Z})$
Distribution	$\overline{X}\ Y + \overline{X}\ \overline{Z}$

Step 6. The result indicates two terms.
Therefore, the output gate is a 2-input NOR with $\overline{X}Y$ one input and $\overline{X}\,\overline{Z}$ the other input. The result is shown in Figure 5-65.

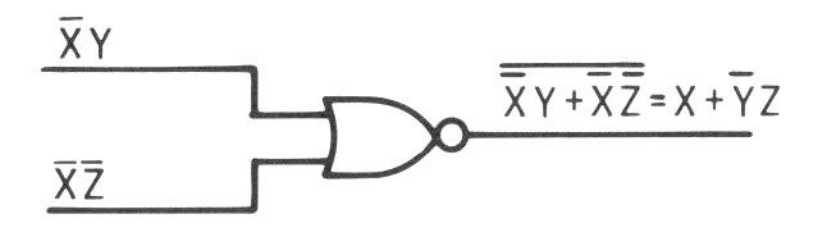

Figure 5-65

Step 7. Draw a NOR gate connected to each input line of the output NOR. This is shown in Figure 5-66.

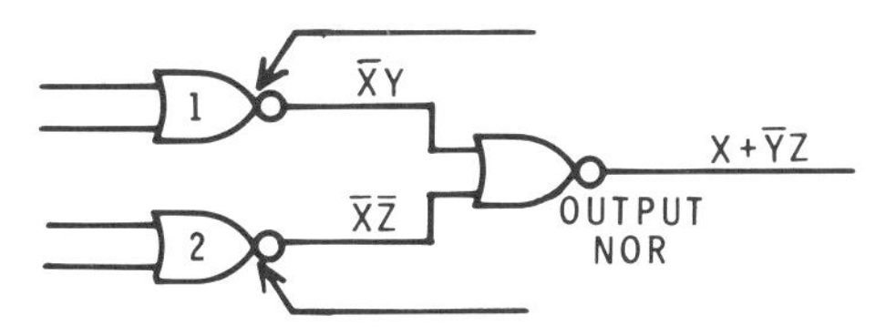

Figure 5-66

In steps 8 and 9 of this procedure, you must consider both sections of these NOR gates. The inverter, then the OR.

Step 8. Complement the output expressions of the NORs at the point indicated by the arrow in Figure 5-66, the signal must pass through the inverter to become $\overline{X}Y$ for gate 1 and $\overline{X}\overline{Z}$ for gate 2. The expression describing the signal at the arrow then is the complement. $\overline{\overline{X}Y}$ for gate 1. $\overline{\overline{X}\overline{Z}}$ for gate 2.

Step 9. Determine the NOR inputs by simplifying the complemented expression. To find the inputs for gate 1, you apply DeMorgan's theorem to $\overline{\overline{X}Y}$. The result is $X + \overline{Y}$. Applying DeMorgan's theorem to $\overline{\overline{X}\,\overline{Z}}$ results in $X + Z$, the inputs to NOR gate 2. The procedure in step 8 and 9 and the results are shown in Figure 5-67.

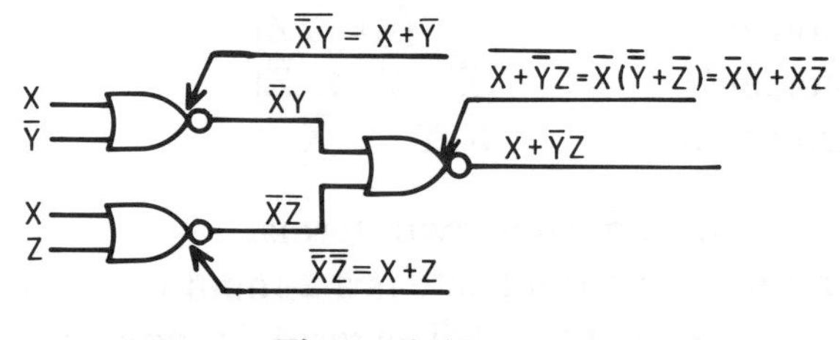

Figure 5-67

Step 10. Remove all but the input signals from your diagram.

Step 11. Using the inputs, determine the outputs of each gate. See Figure 5-68.

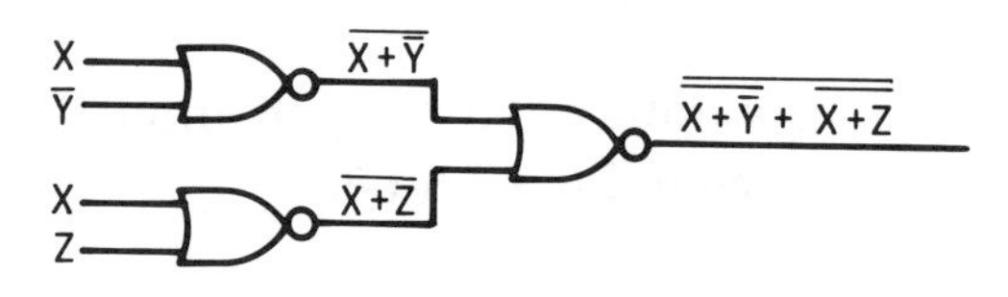

Figure 5-68

Step 12. Simplify the output shown in Figure 5-68 proving that the equivalent circuit is correct if the result is equal to the original equation, $X + \overline{Y}Z$.

Insert signs of grouping	$\overline{\overline{(X+\overline{Y})}+\overline{(X+Z)}}$
DeMorgan's	$\overline{\overline{(X+\overline{Y})(X+Z)}}$
Double Negative	$(X+\overline{Y})(X+Z)$
Distributive	$XX + XZ + X\overline{Y} + \overline{Y}Z$
Tautology	$X + XZ + X\overline{Y} + \overline{Y}Z$
Absorption	$X + \overline{Y}Z$

Let's try the example, shown in Figure 5-69.

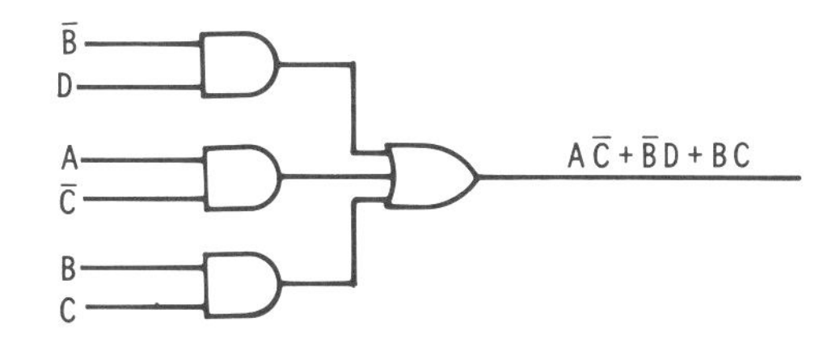

Figure 5-69

Since the circuit and expression are both already in simplified form, steps 1 and 2 of our procedure are complete, so we can begin with step 3, drawing the output NOR gate with its output equation. See Figure 5-70.

Step 3.

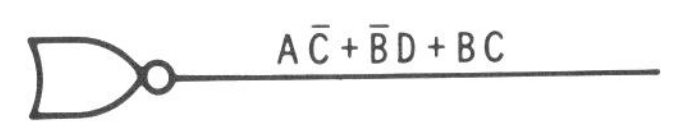

Figure 5-70

Step 4. Working from output to input (right to left), complement the output equation to show the action of the inverter. This is shown in Figure 5-71.

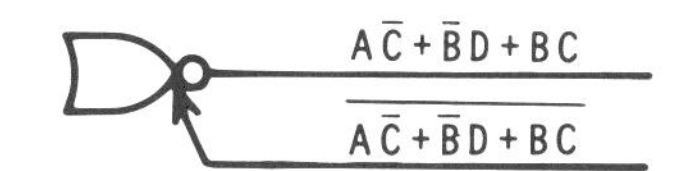

Figure 5-71

Step 5. Find inputs to the OR section by simplifying the complemented expression.

$$\overline{A\bar{C} + \bar{B}D + BC}$$

Place signs of grouping	$\overline{(A\bar{C}) + (\bar{B}D) + (BC)}$
DeMorgan's	$(\bar{A} + C)(B + \bar{D})(\bar{B} + \bar{C})$
Distribution $B\bar{B} = 0$	$(\bar{A} + C)(B\bar{B} + B\bar{C} + \bar{B}\bar{D} + \bar{C}\bar{D})$
Complement	$(\bar{A} + C)(B\bar{C} + \bar{B}\bar{D} + \bar{C}\bar{D})$
Distribution	$\bar{A}B\bar{C} + \bar{A}\bar{B}\bar{D} + \bar{A}\bar{C}\bar{D} + \bar{B}C\bar{D} + \cancel{BC\bar{C}} + \cancel{C\bar{C}\bar{D}}$
Complement and Tautology	$\bar{A}B\bar{C} + \bar{A}\bar{B}\bar{D} + \bar{A}\bar{C}\bar{D}(1) + \bar{B}C\bar{D}$
Intersection	$\bar{A}B\bar{C} + \bar{A}\bar{B}\bar{D} + (\bar{A}\bar{C}\bar{D})(B + \bar{B}) + \bar{B}C\bar{D}$
Complements	$\bar{A}B\bar{C} + \bar{A}\bar{B}\bar{D} + \bar{A}B\bar{C}\bar{D} + \bar{A}\bar{B}\bar{C}\bar{D} + \bar{B}C\bar{D}$
Distribution Factor $\bar{A}B\bar{C}$ and $\bar{A}\bar{B}\bar{D}$	$\bar{A}B\bar{C}(1 + \bar{D}) + \bar{A}\bar{B}\bar{D}(1 = \bar{C}) + \bar{B}C\bar{D}$
Absorption	$\bar{A}B\bar{C} + \bar{A}\bar{B}\bar{D} + \bar{B}C\bar{D}$

Step 6. Determine number of inputs and draw a NOR gate on each input. The result of step 5 above is an expression with three terms. This indicates that the output gate must have three inputs. The three inputs of the output gate each must be driven by a NOR gate. These conclusions are shown in Figure 5-72.

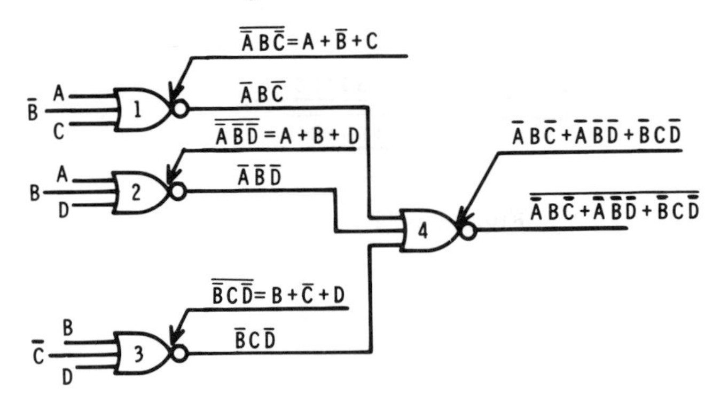

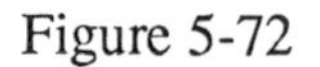
Figure 5-72

Step 7. Now complement each of the NOR gate outputs to account for the inverting part of each NOR. This is shown in Figure 5-72.

Step 8. Using DeMorgan's theorem, simplify each of the complemented outputs as in Figure 5-72.

Step 9. Complete the diagram in Figure 5-72 by showing the inputs to each of the NOR gates. The inputs are the results of step 8 above.

Step 10. Draw the completed diagram showing only the input signals.

Step 11. Now, using these inputs, determine the outputs of each gate to acquire the final output equation. See Figure 5-73.

Step 12. This is a check step. Simplify the output equation. The simplified result should be the original output equation in Figure 5-69. If it is, the equivalent circuit in Figure 5-73 is accurate.

Step 11.

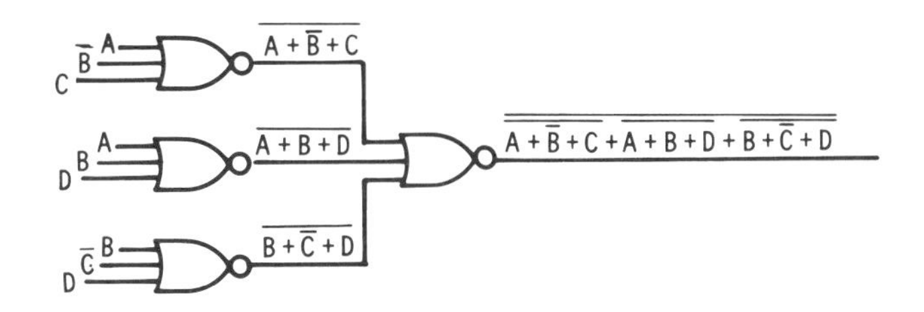

Figure 5-73

Step 12. STEP BY STEP SIMPLIFICATION

FROM FIGURE 5-73 $\overline{\overline{A + \overline{B} + C} + \overline{A + B + D} + \overline{B + \overline{C}D}}$

DeMorgan's and Grouping Terms $\overline{\overline{(A + \overline{B} + C)(A + B + D)(B + \overline{C}D)}}$

Drop Double Negative $(A + \overline{B} + C)(A + B + D)(B + \overline{C} + D)$

Expand Equation $(AA + AB + AD + A\overline{B} + B\overline{B} + \overline{B}D + AC + BC + CD)(B + \overline{C} + D)$

Factor A $[A(1 + B + D + \overline{B} + C) + (B\overline{B} + \overline{B}D + BC + CD)](B + \overline{C} + D)$

Union $(A + B\overline{B} + \overline{B}D + BC + CD)(B + \overline{C} + D)$

Complement $(A + \overline{B}D + BC + CD)(B + \overline{C} + D)$

Expand Equation $AB + A\overline{C} + AD + \overline{B}BD + \overline{B}\overline{C}D + \overline{B}DD + BBC + B\overline{C}C + BCD + BCD + C\overline{C}D + CDD$

Complements $AB + A\overline{C} + AD + \overline{B}\overline{C}D + \overline{B}DD + BBC + BCD + BCD + CDD$

Tautology $AB + A\overline{C} + AD + \overline{B}\overline{C}D + \overline{B}D + BC + BCD + CD$

Factor $\overline{B}D$ and CD $AB + A\overline{C} + AD + \overline{B}D(\overline{C} + 1) + CD(B + 1) + BC$

Union $AB + A\overline{C} + AD + \overline{B}D + CD + BC$

Multiply by 1 $AB + A\overline{C} + AD + \overline{B}D + CD(B + \overline{B}) + BC$

Expand Equation $AB + A\overline{C} + AD + \overline{B}D + BCD + \overline{B}CD + BC$

Factor $\overline{B}D$ and BC $AB + A\overline{C} + AD + \overline{B}D(1 + C) + BC(D + 1)$

Union $AB + A\overline{C} + AD + \overline{B}D + BC$

Multiply by 1 $AB + A\overline{C} + AD(B + \overline{B}) + \overline{B}D + BC$

Expand Equation $AB + A\overline{C} + ABD + A\overline{B}D + \overline{B}D + BC$

Factor AB and $\overline{B}D$ $AB(1 + D) + A\overline{C} + \overline{B}D(A + 1) + BC$

Union $AB + A\overline{C} + \overline{B}D + BC$

Multiply by 1 $AB(C + \overline{C}) + A\overline{C} + \overline{B}D + BC$

Expand Equation $ABC + AB\overline{C} + A\overline{C} + \overline{B}D + BC$

Factor BC and $A\overline{C}$ $BC(A + 1) + A\overline{C}(B + 1) + \overline{B}D$

Union $BC + A\overline{C} + \overline{B}D$ The original equation.

The key to multiplying by 1 is to ensure that each term contains the needed variables.

Single-Letter Term Expression

One type of expression cannot be handled in the same way as those previously discussed. This type has all single-letter terms. For example, the expression, $E + D + H + \overline{F}$ contains all single-letter terms. It is neither a product-of-sums nor a sum-of-products expression. Let's determine the NOR circuit for this single-term expression.

1. Draw the output NOR as in Figure 5-74.

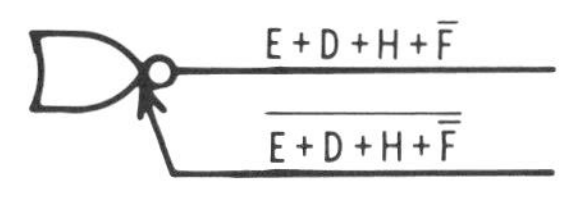

Figure 5-74

2. Complement the output expression.

3. Simplify the complemented expression to determine the NOR gate inputs using DeMorgan's theorem.

$\overline{E + D + H + \overline{F}}$

$\overline{E}\,\overline{D}\,\overline{H}\,F$

As you can see by the result of step 3, there is no way to split $\overline{EDHF}$ into two or more inputs. Therefore the correct way to diagram this type of expression is to perform steps 1 and 2 as usual. Then, instead of simplifying the expression as in step 3, merely make the complemented expression a single input to the output NOR, which in turn, is connected as an inverter. See Figure 5-75.

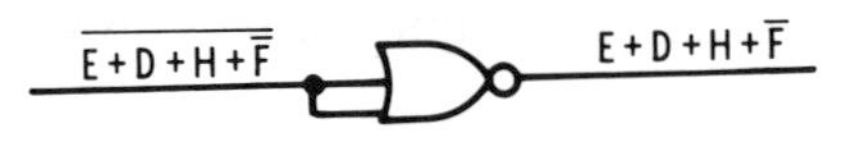

Figure 5-75

Now, instead of using DeMorgan's theorem to simplify the complemented expression, as you previously have done, use the individual terms or factors under the vinculum as the inputs to a NOR. The completed circuit is shown in Figure 5-76.

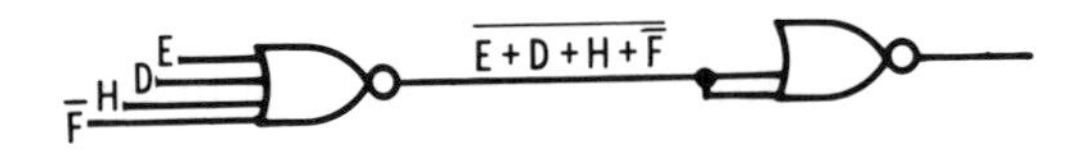

Figure 5-76

32. Write the equation for the circuit below, simplify using Boolean algebra.

    Draw the circuit for the simplified expression using AND and OR gates. Then, draw the NOR equivalent circuit.

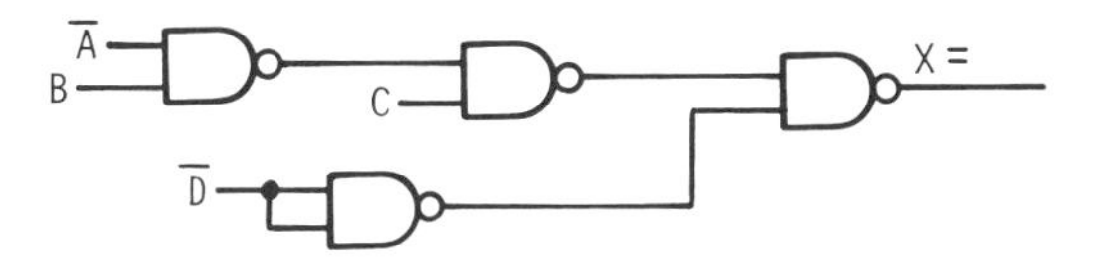

33. Implement the logic expression $F = C(A + \overline{B})$ with conventional AND and OR gates. Then use all NOR gates.

34. Construct a NOR logic circuit for the expression, $\overline{A} + \overline{B} + C + \overline{D} + \overline{E}$.

NAND Logic Equivalent Circuits

The procedure that is used in changing a logic circuit to an equivalent circuit using all NAND gates, will depend on whether the output expression is in a product-of-sums or in a sum-of-products form. However, any one of the two procedures is much simpler than the previously discussed procedure implementing NOR gates. Let's begin with an example previously used when implementing NOR gates. It is the expression $X + \overline{Y}Z$ which is a sum-of-products form.

Sum-Of-Products Equations

The expression $X + \overline{Y}Z$ is already in its simplest form and the circuit using standard AND and OR gates is shown in Figure 5-62. Therefore, the first two steps of the procedure are already accomplished, so we will proceed with the third step.

Step 3. Draw the output NAND gate showing the output expression. See Figure 5-77.

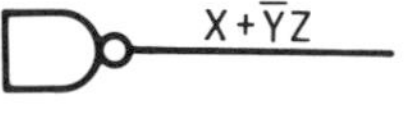

Figure 5-77

Step 4. Working from output to input, place a double vinculum over the output expression as shown in Figure 5-78.

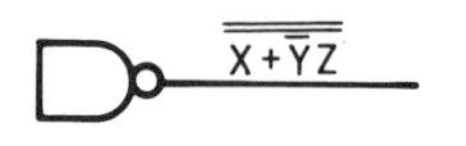

Figure 5-78

Step 5. Passing through the inverter symbol from right to left (from output to input), results in dropping one vinculum. The result is the output of the AND portion of the NAND gate. See Figure 5-79.

Now notice that the uppermost vinculum remains on the right side of the inverter because you are proceeding from right to left through one inverter. The left side of the inverter now has the complement of the original expression.

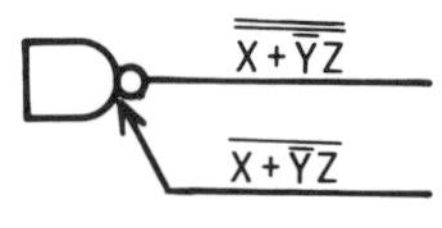

Figure 5-79

Step 6. Working with the expression at the output of the AND, break the vinculum just above the OR sign. Be careful with your signs of grouping. The result is $(\overline{X})\ (\overline{\overline{Y}Z})$. The terms within the signs of grouping are the inputs to the output gate. See Figure 5-80.

There are two terms indicating that the output NAND will have two inputs. One single input another driven by a NAND.

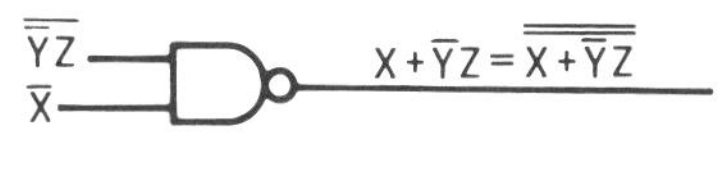

Figure 5-80

Step 7. Draw a NAND gate on the line that has the $\overline{\overline{Y}Z}$ expresssion. See Figure 5-81.

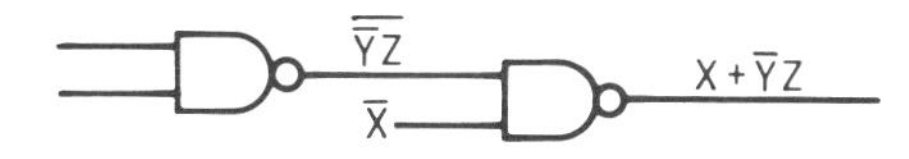

Figure 5-81

Step 8. Proceeding from output to input through the inverter of the NAND results in removing a vinculum. Therefore, the output of the AND portion of the NAND gate is $\overline{Y}Z$. See Figure 5-82. Note $\overline{\overline{\overline{Y}Z}} = \overline{Y}Z$.

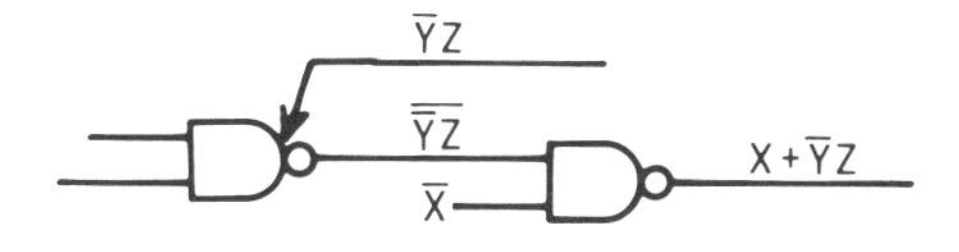

Figure 5-82

Step 9. Determine inputs. To get $\overline{Y}Z$ at the output of the AND portion of the NAND, the inputs must be $\overline{Y}$ and Z.

Step 10. Draw the equivalent NAND circuit showing inputs and all outputs as in Figure 5-83.

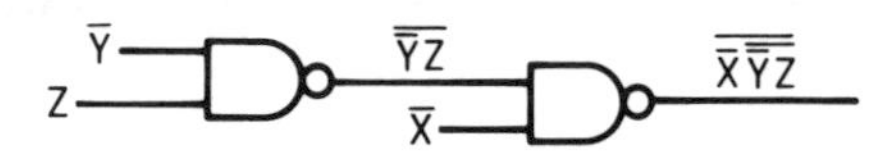

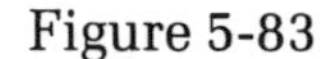
Figure 5-83

Step 11. Check Step. Simplify the output expression of Figure 5-83; the result should be the original expression.

DeMorgan's $\overline{\overline{X}\,\overline{\overline{Y}\,Z}}$

$\overline{\overline{X}} + \overline{\overline{\overline{Y}Z}}$

Double Negative $X + \overline{Y}\,Z$ = Original expression.

Let's try another expression previously used for NOR logic, $A\,\overline{C} + \overline{B}\,D + B\,C$. The circuit using standard AND and OR symbols is shown in Figure 5-69. Since the circuit and output expression are already in simplified form, we can start our conversion to all NAND gates by beginning at step 3.

Step 3. Draw the output NAND gate showing the simplified expression at its output. See Figure 5-84.

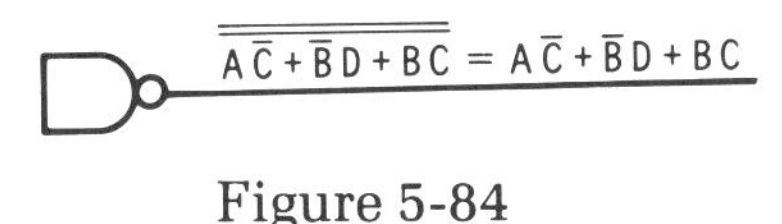

Figure 5-84

Step 4. Place a double vinculum over the output expression as shown in Figure 5-84.

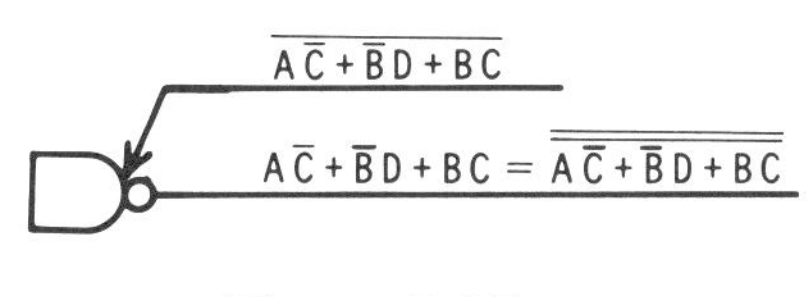

Figure 5-85

Step 5. Show the output of the AND portion of the NAND. Note if the output of the NAND is $\overline{\overline{A\overline{C}+\overline{B}D+BC}}$ then, after going through the inverter portion (proceeding from right to left), the expression must be $\overline{A\overline{C}+\overline{B}D+BC}$ which is the complement of the original expression. See the result in Figure 5-85.

Step 6. Use DeMorgan's theorem on the complemented expression by splitting the vinculum. Split the vinculum only at the OR signs as follows:

$$\overline{A\overline{C}+\overline{B}D+BC}$$

DeMorgan's $\overline{A\overline{C}}\quad \overline{\overline{B}D}\quad \overline{BC}$

Step. 7. Determine the number of inputs to the output NAND gate and draw a NAND for each. The result is three complemented terms. Each is the output of a NAND driving an input of the output NAND gate as shown in Figure 5-86.

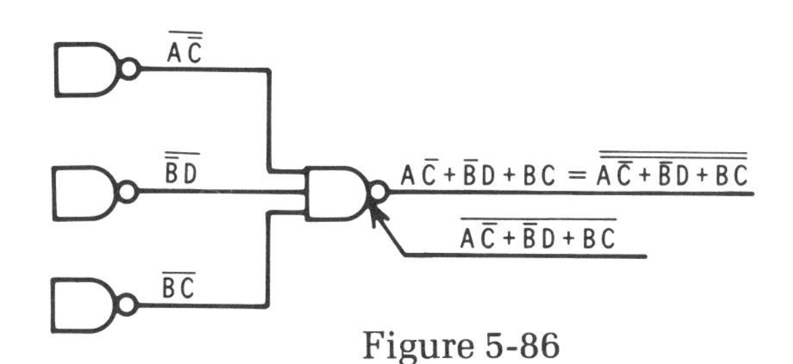

Figure 5-86

Step 8. Determine the output of the AND portion of each NAND gate.

Note: Proceeding from output to input of the inverters results in the complement of the $\overline{A\overline{C}}$, $\overline{\overline{B}D}$, and $\overline{BC}$ terms at their respective AND gate outputs.

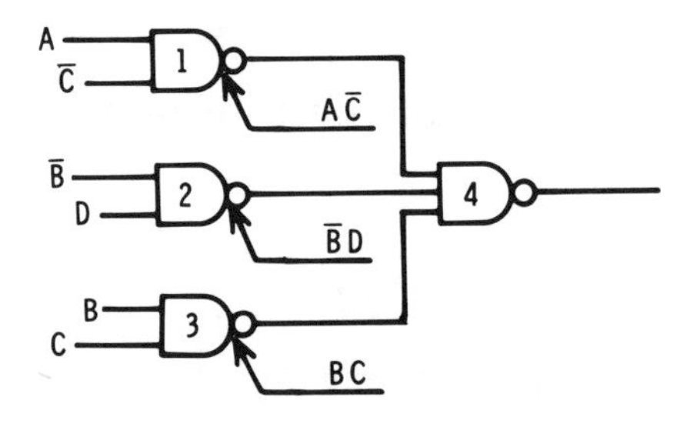

Figure 5-87

Step 9. Determine the inputs to each NAND gate. To get $A\overline{C}$, $\overline{B}D$ and BC at the output of AND gates 1, 2 and 3, the inputs to these gates must be as shown in Figure 5-88.

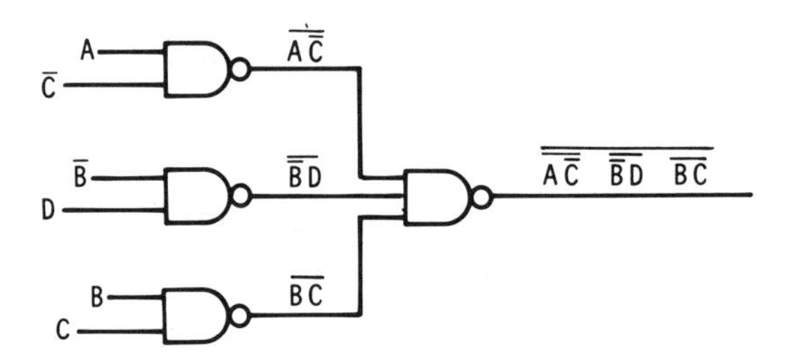

Figure 5-88

Step 10. Now, proceeding from inputs to outputs in the alleged completed diagram, show all input and output signals. When completed, your diagram should appear as in Figure 5-88.

Step 11. Prove that the diagram in Figure 5-88 is equivalent to Figure 5-71. Use DeMorgan's theorem and any other Boolean laws to simplify the output expression shown in Figure 5-88. The result will match the original expression if there were no mistakes in any of the previous operations.

	$\overline{\overline{A\overline{C}}\;\overline{\overline{B}D}\;\overline{BC}}$
DeMorgan's	$\overline{\overline{A\overline{C} + \overline{B}D + BC}}$
Double Negative	$A\overline{C} + \overline{B}D + BC$ = Original expression.

Product-Of-Sums Expressions

The procedure for implementing NAND logic from product-of-sums expressions such as $(A + \overline{B})(C + \overline{D})$ is somewhat different than the procedure for sum-of-products equations. Let's use the expression $(A + \overline{B})(C + \overline{D})$. It is already in its simplest terms; therefore we will begin the procedure at the second step.

Step 2. Draw the circuit using standard AND and OR symbols. See Figure 5-89A.

Step 3. Draw the output NAND gate. See Figure 5-89B.

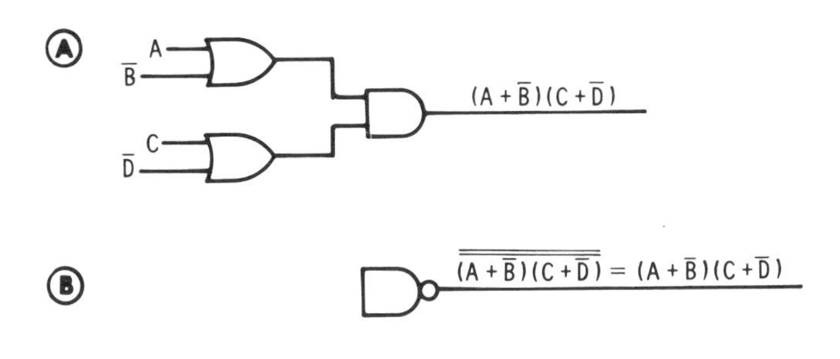

Figure 5-89

Step 4. Place a double vinculum over the output expression.

Step 5. Proceeding from output to input of the inverter show the output of the AND portion of the NAND gate.

Step 6. Using DeMorgan's theorem simplify the expression at the AND gate output of Figure 5-90.

Note: This step is different than Step 6 for the sum-of-products expression. In that procedure the expression is partially simplified. In this case, you simplify completely to acquire the simplest form as follows:

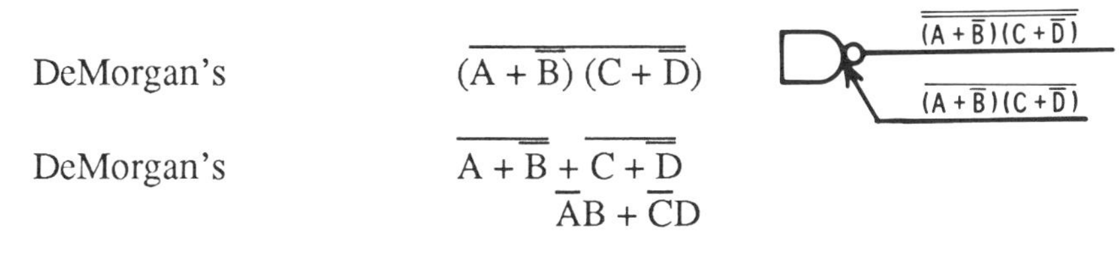

Figure 5-90

Step 7. Determine the inputs to the output NAND gate and draw a NAND gate on each of these inputs. See Figure 5-91.

Step 8. Show each term in the result of step 6 above as the output of the input NAND gates.

Step 9. Determine the inputs to the NAND gates. See Figure 5-91.

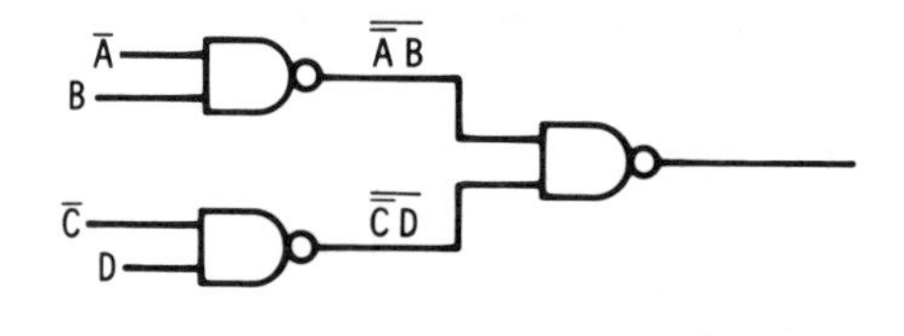

Figure 5-91

Step 10. Show inputs and outputs of all gates. See Figure 5-92.

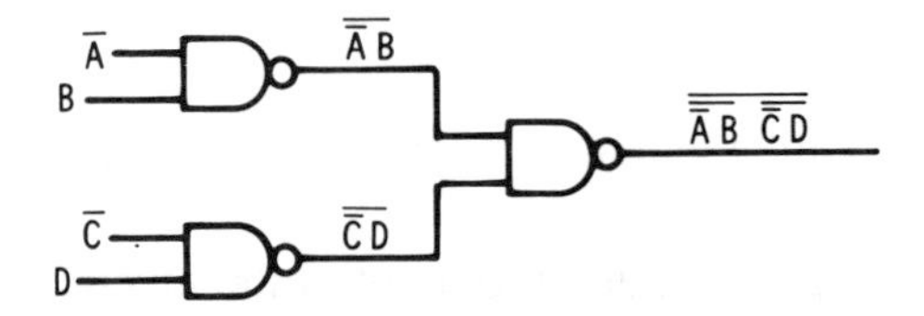

Figure 5-92

Step 11. This is a check step. As in the other procedures, the output expression is now simplified as a check step. If the simplification results in the original expression, the circuit is accurate and complete. So, let's perform the check.

DeMorgan's	$\overline{\overline{\overline{\overline{A}\,B + \overline{C}\,D}}}$
Double Negative	$\overline{A}\,B + \overline{C}\,D$

Notice that the result is not the original expression. So let's try again. However, instead of connecting the two vincula as we did previously, let's split the vincula.

	$\overline{\overline{\overline{A}B}\;\;\overline{\overline{C}D}}$
DeMorgan's	$\overline{(\overline{\overline{\overline{A}}} + \overline{B})\,(\overline{\overline{\overline{C}}} + \overline{D})}$
Signs of Grouping	$\overline{(\overline{\overline{\overline{A}}} + \overline{B})\,(\overline{\overline{\overline{C}}} + \overline{D})}$
Double Negative	$\overline{(A + \overline{B})\,(C + \overline{D})}$

Now notice the expression matches the original except for the vinculum over it. Further simplification, DeMorgan's etc., will not result in the original expression. Try it. So what can be done to the circuit to eliminate the vinculum? Add an inverter as in Figure 5-93. Remember the double negative law says $\overline{\overline{(A + \overline{B})(C + \overline{D})}} = (A + B)(C + \overline{D})$

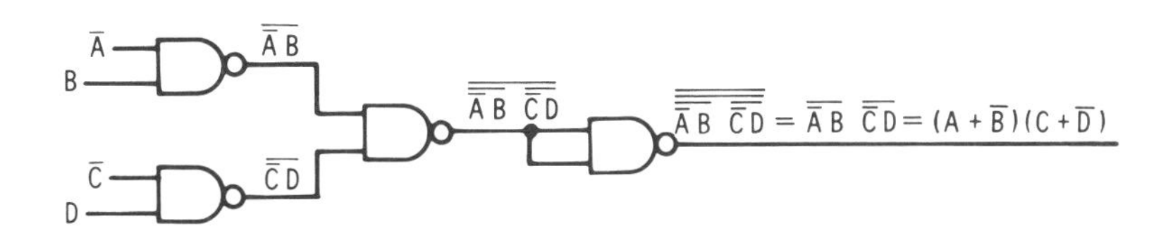

Figure 5-93

Once you become familiar with DeMorgan's theorem and its relationship with NAND and NOR gates, the procedure you have seen here will come naturally to you. A little practice and experience will make you competent in dealing with NAND and NOR integrated circuits to implement logic functions. Keep in mind that your goal is to arrive at the minimum circuit for your application.

Self-Test Review

Given the diagram in Figure 5-94, do the following:

35. Determine the output expression.

36. Simplify the expression.

37. Diagram the simplified expression using standard AND and OR gates.

38. Diagram the simplified expression using all NAND gates.

39. Check your final result.

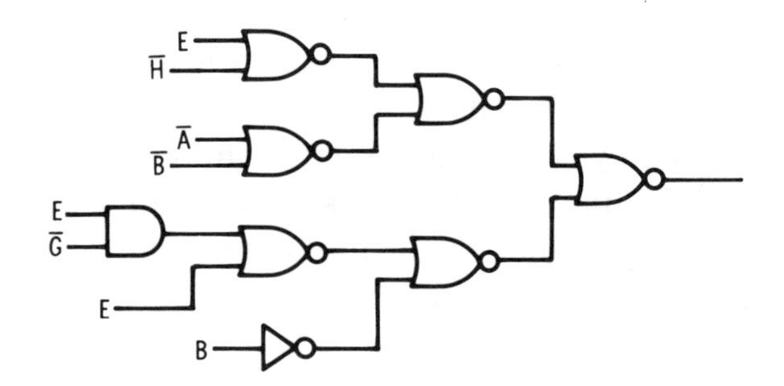

Figure 5-94

Rules of Boolean — Summary

Here is a handy tabulation of all the commonly used Boolean algebra rules.

Laws of Intersection

$$A \cdot (1) = A$$
$$A \cdot (0) = 0$$

Laws of Union

$$B + 1 = 1$$
$$B + 0 = B$$

Laws of Tautology (Idempotent)

$$A \cdot A = A$$
$$B + B = B$$

Laws of Complements

$$A \cdot \overline{A} = 0$$
$$B + \overline{B} = 1$$

Law of the Double Negative

$$\overline{\overline{A}} = A$$

Laws of Commutation

$$A \cdot B = B \cdot A$$
$$A + B = B + A$$

Laws of Association

$$(A \cdot B)C = A(B \cdot C) = A \cdot B \cdot C$$
$$A + (B + C) = (A + B) + C = A + B + C$$

Laws of Distribution

$$AB + AC = A(B + C)$$
$$(A + B)(A + C) = A + BC$$

Laws of Absorption

$$A(A + B) = A$$
$$A + AB = A$$
$$\left[\begin{array}{l} A(\overline{A} + B) = AB \\ A + \overline{A}B = A + B \end{array}\right] \quad \text{Common Identities}$$

DeMorgan's Theorem

$$\overline{AB} = \overline{A} + \overline{B}$$
$$\overline{A + B} = \overline{A}\,\overline{B}$$

Karnaugh Mapping

Karnaugh mapping is preferred over Boolean algebra because it makes the simplification process faster, easier, and more effective. In fact, Karnaugh mapping completely eliminates the need for using Boolean algebra, and it allows you to translate the truth table directly into a simplified equation. In this section, you will learn how to perform Karnaugh mapping for problems with two, three, and four input variables. You will find that this is adequate to solve most application tasks.

Two Input Variables

The first thing you must do when performing a Karnaugh map, or K-map, is to construct the grid that will be used during the mapping process. A two-variable grid is shown in Figure 5-95a. Here, the two input variables are A and B. The possible logic states for A are listed in the left column, while those for B are listed in the top row. The intersection of a row and a column in the grid is called a **cell**. Once the grid is set-up, the process involves three operations: plotting, grouping, and reading. The best way to teach you how to plot, group, and read is to look at some examples.

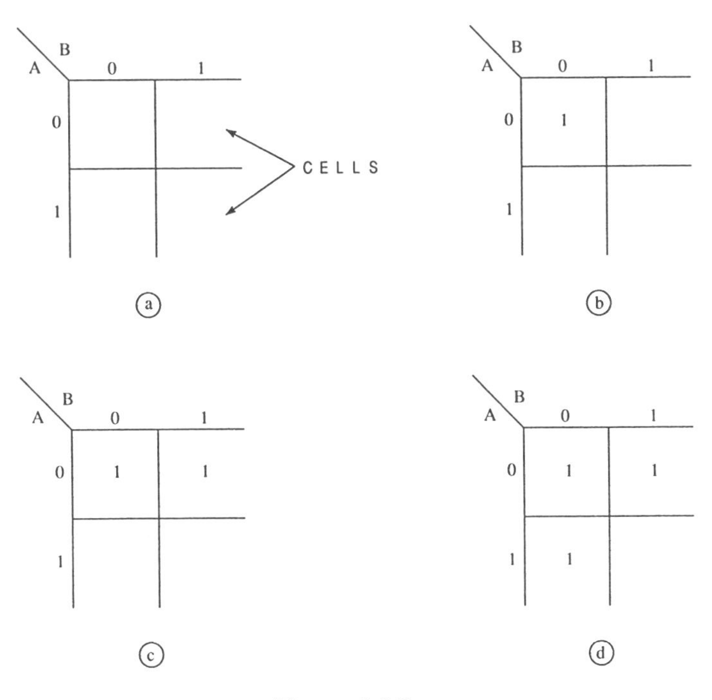

Figure 5-95

The two-variable grid **a** is used to plot the logic 1 outputs of the truth table in **b**,**c**, and **d**.

Plotting

Suppose you have arrived at the following truth table:

INPUTS		OUTPUT
A	B	y
0	0	1
0	1	1
1	0	1
1	1	0

To plot a truth table on a K-map grid, you must transfer the logic 1 outputs of the truth table to the grid cells. The first logic 1 output in the preceding truth table appears for an input of A = 0 and B = 0. To plot this output, place a 1 in the grid cell where the A = 0 column and B = 0 row intersect as shown in Figure 5-95b. Notice that this is the same way that you plot points on an x-y coordinate system in algebra class.

The next logic 1 output in the truth table appears at A = 0 and B = 1. Again, place a 1 in the grid cell where the A = 0 column and B = 1 row intersect, as shown in Figure 5-95c. Finally, the last logic 1 appears at A = 1 and B = 0. This output is shown plotted in Figure 5-95d. The fourth possibility, A = 1 and B = 1, is zero. Because it is zero, it's grid cell location is not plotted.

Grouping

The grouping operation requires that you combine the cell plots that you marked on the K-map grid, if possible. The following rules apply to the grouping process (study them!):

1. Only **adjacent** vertical and horizontal cells can be grouped.

2. Diagonal groups are illegal.

3. Make your groups as large as possible. However, group sizes must be in powers of two, i.e. 2 cells, 4 cells, 8 cells, and so on.

4. All plots must be grouped, if possible, using the above rules.

5. A given plot may be used to form more than one group, thereby creating overlapping groups.

6. If no grouping is possible, the equation is in its simplest form and cannot be reduced further.

Now, apply the above rules to the final plot in Figure 5-95d. How many groups do you see? You were right if you said, "two." First, the two adjacent vertical plots can be grouped as shown in Figure 5-96a. Then, the two adjacent horizontal plots can be grouped as shown in Figure 5-96b. Notice that the two groups overlap (share a plot). As a result, you end up with two groups of two. Let's label the vertical group, group 1, and the horizontal group, group 2, as shown in the figure. The grouping shown in Figure 5-96c will not work, since diagonal cell groups are illegal.

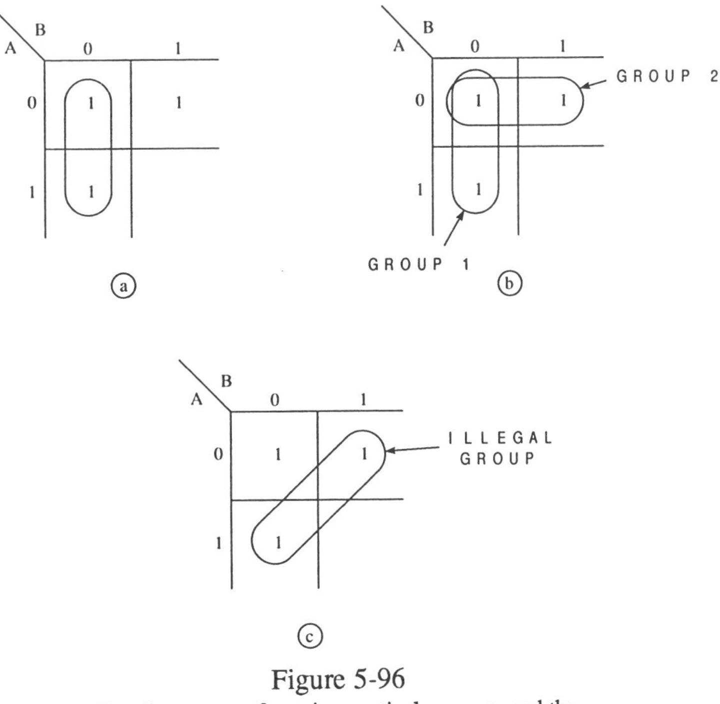

Figure 5-96
The first group of two is a vertical group **a**, and the second group of two is a horizontal group which overlaps the first group **b**. Diagonal groups are illegal **c**.

Reading the Groups

The final step in performing a K-map is to read the groups and generate the simplified equation. You must read **each** group within the K-map and generate a fundamental product term for each group. The fundamental product terms generated by each group are then ORed together to produce the final sum-of-products equation.

To read a group, you must go from one cell within the group to the next, asking yourself: "what doesn't change within the group?" For example, consider group 1 in Figure 5-96b. Notice that the input variable A changes from one cell to the next. The variable A had to be a 0 for the top cell plot and a 1 for the bottom cell plot. Since A has changed within the group, it is ignored. Now look at what the input variable B does within group 1. For the top cell plot, B had to be a 0. Also, B had to be a 0 in the bottom cell plot. Thus, B **doesn't change** and remains a 0 within the group. Since B didn't change, the fundamental product representation for group 1 is $\overline{B}$.

Next, consider group 2 and ask yourself, "what doesn't change within the group?" Notice that A had to be zero in both cell plots. Thus, $\overline{A}$ doesn't change within the group. However, B changes since it was a 0 to get the plot in the left cell and a 1 to get the plot in the right cell. As a result, B is discarded and the fundamental product representation for group 2 is simply $\overline{A}$.

Combining (ORing) the fundamental products for groups 1 and 2, the simplified equation becomes: $y = \overline{B} + \overline{A}$. Is this the simplest equation possible? The associated truth table shown is that of a 2-bit NAND gate whose Boolean expression is: $y = \overline{AB}$. How can this be, since a K-map is supposed to produce the simplest equation? Remember DeMorgan's second theorem? By this theorem, the two expressions are equivalent. Selecting the simplest expression depends on the digital ICs you use to implement the operation. In most cases, the NAND gate requires fewer ICs than the bubbled OR gate. This goes to show you that a K-map might not give you the easiest equation to implement. By applying one of DeMorgan's theorems to the final K-map equation, you might get an equation that requires fewer ICs.

For example, use a K-map to get the simplified equation for the following truth table:

INPUTS		OUTPUT
J	K	L
0	0	1
0	1	0
1	0	0
1	1	1

The resulting K-map plot is shown in Figure 5-97. No groups are possible, since diagonal groups are illegal. You could say the the K-map reduces to two groups of one cell each. This means that the equation cannot be simplified using a K-map.

Reading the two groups of one, the fundamental product that produced the plot in the upper left cell is $\overline{J}\overline{K}$. The fundamental product that produced the plot in the lower right cell is JK. The equation then becomes $\overline{J}\overline{K}$ + JK.

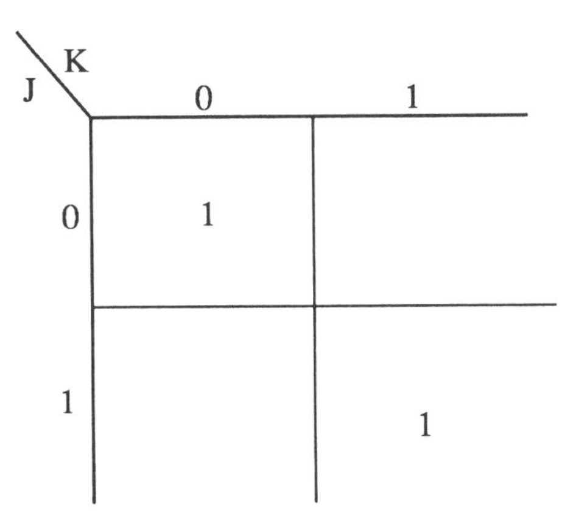

Figure 5-97
If a K-map plot cannot be grouped, the Boolean expression is in its simplest form.

This same equation was obtained earlier in this unit directly from the truth table.

Three Input Variables

Two variable maps are rather trivial, since you can usually apply a little common sense to the truth table and come up with the simplest possible equation. On the other hand, three and four variable maps are more challenging.

To demonstrate a three-variable map, we will use the following truth table:

INPUTS			OUTPUT
A	B	C	y
0	0	0	0
0	0	1	0
0	1	0	0
0	1	1	1
1	0	0	0
1	0	1	1
1	1	0	1
1	1	1	1

The structure for a three variable grid is shown in Figure 5-98a. Notice that all possible combinations of A and B inputs are listed in the left column. However, notice the order of the listing. This is not how you might ordinarily list the four logic combinations of two inputs; however, it is very important that this order be maintained. If not, the K-map will not work. Finally, the two logic possibilities for the third variable, C, are listed in the top row.

Figure 5-98b shows the cell plots generated by the logic 1 outputs in the truth table. Figure 5-98c shows how the plots should be grouped. Observe that the four plots form three overlapping groups of two.

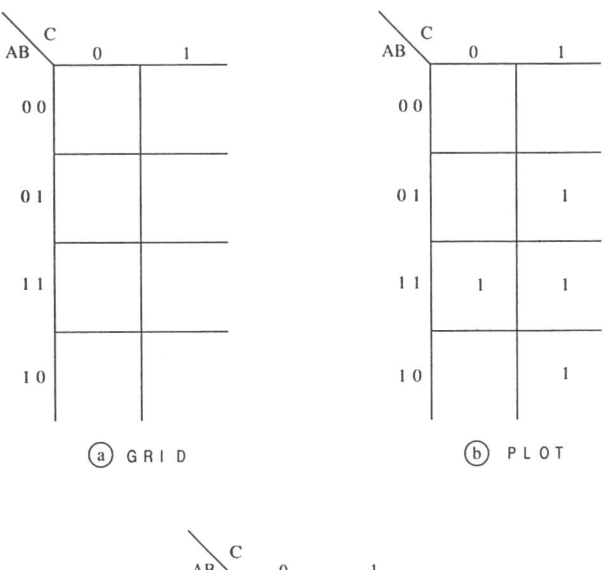

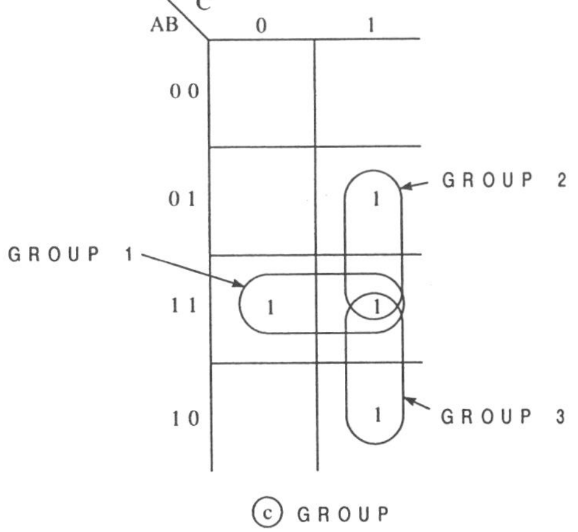

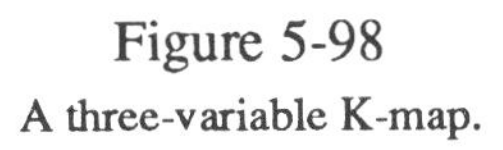

Figure 5-98
A three-variable K-map.

Reading the groups (asking yourself: "what doesn't change?"), the respective fundamental product terms are:

Group 1: AB

Group 2: BC

Group 3: AC

The resulting simplified equation is therefore:

$$y = AB + BC + AC$$

Since you don't observe a possible application of DeMorgan's theorems, the above equation will most likely produce the simplest circuit.

Four Input Variables

You can really appreciate the power of K-mapping when you perform a four variable map. To demonstrate such a map, let's use a K-map to reduce the following truth table.

INPUTS				OUTPUT
A	B	C	D	e
0	0	0	0	0
0	0	0	1	1
0	0	1	0	0
0	0	1	1	1
0	1	0	0	1
0	1	0	1	1
0	1	1	0	0
0	1	1	1	1
1	0	0	0	0
1	0	0	1	1

The grid for a four variable map is shown in Figure 5-99a. The A and B input combinations are listed in the left column and the C and D input combinations are listed in the top row. Again, notice the order of the input listings. This order must be followed or the K-map will not work. Figure 5-99b shows the result when each of the logic 1 outputs from the truth table are plotted.

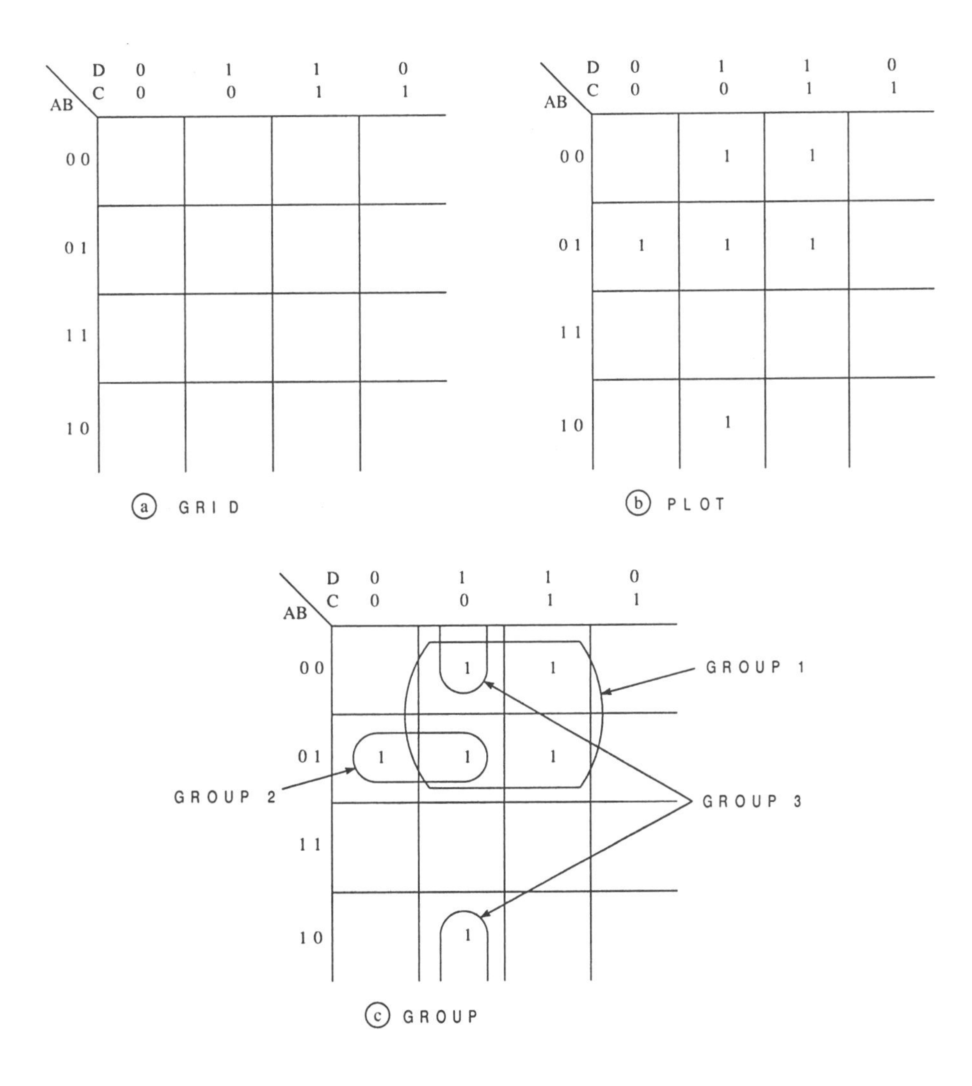

Figure 5-99
A four variable grid **a**, plot **b**, and grouping **c**.

Now, with three and four variable maps, the grouping can get a little tricky because there are several unique possibilities. Remember that you must form the largest groups possible and the size of each group must be some power of 2. Figure 5-100 illustrates several possible ways that groups can be formed. The groups of four and eight cells that are completely circled in Figure 5-100 should be self-explanatory. Each group consists of four or eight adjacent plots. However, notice the plots that are only half-circled. These can also be used to form groups by thinking of the K-map grid as a sphere. In other words, you can mentally roll the grid so that the top touches the bottom and the left side touches the right side. Then, the two-dimensional grid becomes a sphere with the top cells adjacent to the bottom cells and the left cells adjacent to the right cells. This allows you to form bigger groups using the plots on the edges of the grid as shown in the figure. In fact, as you can see, the four corners can even be used to form a group of four plots. With this in mind, Figure 5-99c shows the proper grouping for the four variable map in our example.

The next step is to read the groups in Figure 5-99c. In the large group of four, group 1, $\overline{A}$ and D remain constant within the group. Notice that A had to be a logic 0 to get each plot in the group, while D had to be a logic 1. However, B changes from row-to-row and C changes from column-to-column and are, therefore, discarded. Thus, the resulting fundamental product is $\overline{A}D$.

The horizontal group of two, group 2, produces a fundamental product of $\overline{A}B\overline{C}$. Here, A and C are 0 and B is a 1 to get both plots. The variable D changes from column-to-column and is discarded.

Finally, the half-circled plots in the top and bottom row form a group, group 3, of two that produces a fundamental product of $\overline{B}\overline{C}D$. Notice that B and C are 0 for both plots, while D is a 1 for both plots. Because A alternates, it is discarded.

The three fundamental products combine as follows to give you the simplified equation:

$$e = \overline{A}D + \overline{A}B\overline{C} + \overline{B}\overline{C}D$$

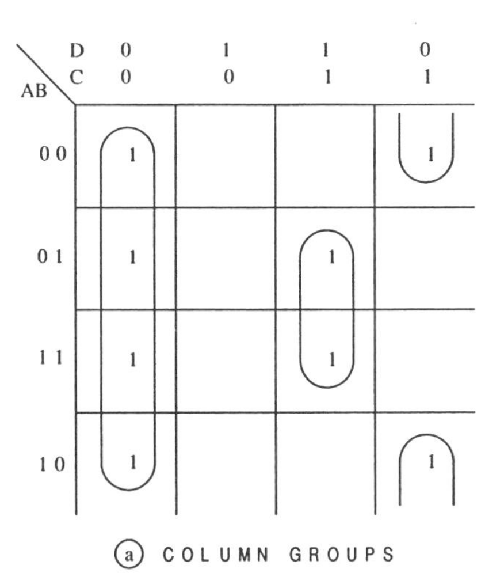

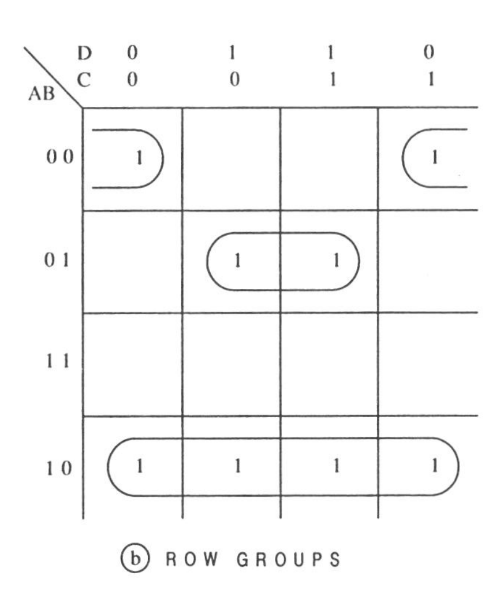

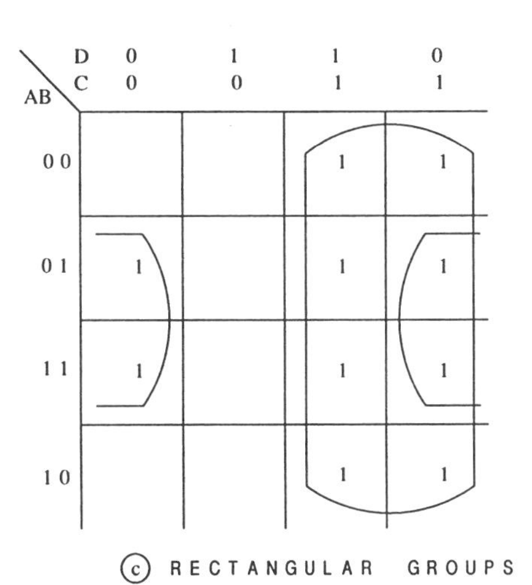

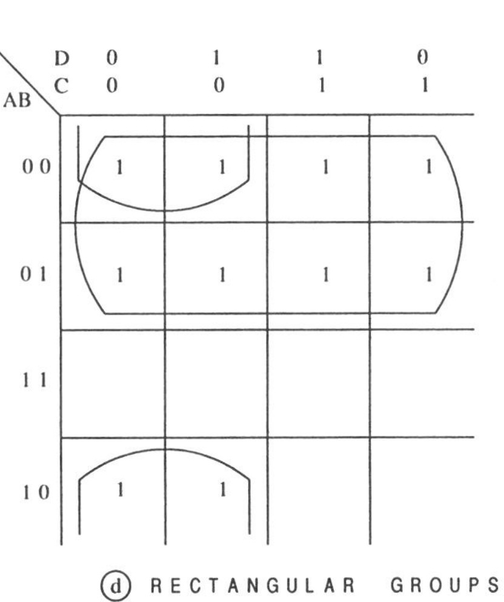

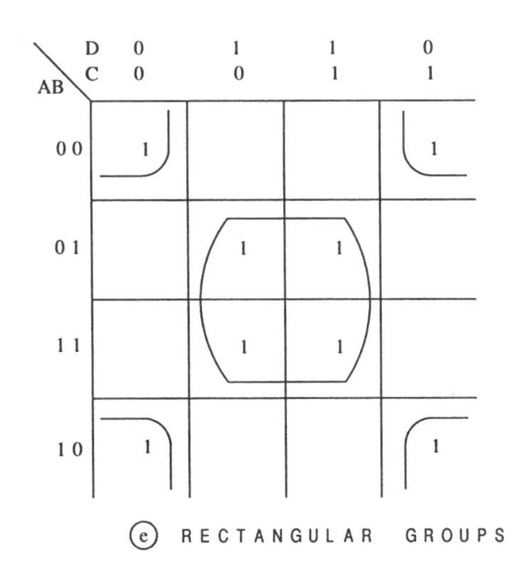

Figure 5-100
There are several possible ways to form groups in three- or four-variable K-maps.

Let's try some examples using equations instead of truth tables to map from.

1. $y = \overline{A}\,\overline{B}\,\overline{C}\,\overline{D} + \overline{A}B\overline{C}\,\overline{D} + AB\overline{C}\,\overline{D} + \overline{A}\,\overline{B}\,\overline{C}D + \overline{A}\,\overline{B}C\overline{D} + A\overline{B}C\overline{D}$

2. $y = \overline{A}B\overline{C} + \overline{A}BCD + \overline{A}BC\overline{D} + AB\overline{C}\,\overline{D} + AB\overline{C}D + ABCD + ABC\overline{D}$

The first equation requires the four variable grid shown in Figure 5-101a. To plot a Boolean equation, rather than a truth table, you simply interpret the fundamental products as logic 1's and 0's. As a result, $\overline{A}\,\overline{B}\,\overline{C}\,\overline{D}$ = 0000, $\overline{A}B\overline{C}\,\overline{D}$ = 0100, $AB\overline{C}\,\overline{D}$ = 1100, and so forth. You then plot each fundamental product in the equation. The resulting plot is shown in Figure 5-101b.

Figure 5-101c shows the most efficient grouping of the plots. There is a vertical group of four plots and a four-corner group of plots. Reading the vertical group produces a fundamental product of $\overline{C}\,\overline{D}$, while the four-corner group produces $\overline{B}\,\overline{D}$. The simplified equation then becomes:

$$y = \overline{C}\,\overline{D} + \overline{B}\,\overline{D}$$

The second equation also requires a four variable map. However, notice that the first term ($\overline{A}B\overline{C}$) in the equation only contains three variables. To perform a K-map, **all** of the terms must contain **all** of the input variables. If a given term does not, you must multiply (AND) that term with the missing variable and its complement.

The first term in this equation is missing the D variable. Thus, you must multiply (AND) this term by the quantity (D + $\overline{D}$). This does not change the logic meaning of the equation since by the Law of Complements, (D + $\overline{D}$) = 1. The resulting equation is:

$$y = \overline{A}B\overline{C}(D + \overline{D}) + \overline{A}BCD + \overline{A}BC\overline{D} + AB\overline{C}\,\overline{D} + AB\overline{C}D + ABCD + ABC\overline{D}$$

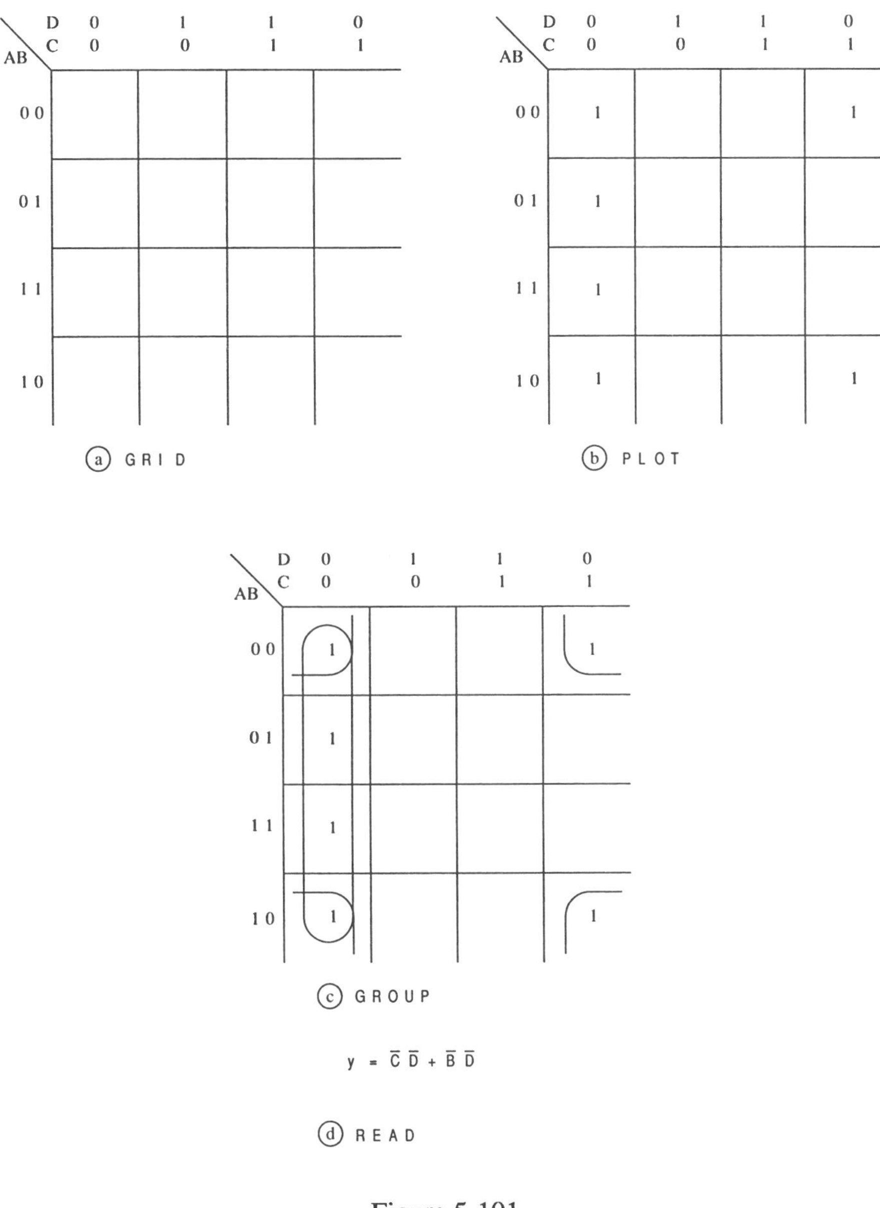

Figure 5-101
The K-map for the first equation.

Multiplying (actually ANDing) through by the $(D + \overline{D})$ quantity you get:

$$y = \overline{A}B\overline{C}D + \overline{A}B\overline{C}\,\overline{D} + \overline{A}BCD + \overline{A}BC\overline{D} + AB\overline{C}\,\overline{D} + AB\overline{C}D + ABCD + ABC\overline{D}$$

Now the equation can be plotted and grouped as shown in Figure 5-102. As you can see, the K-map contains one big group of eight cells. Reading the group, you find only one variable, B, that "doesn't change within the group." Consequently, the equation reduces to simply:

$$y = B$$

Try doing that as easily with Boolean algebra!

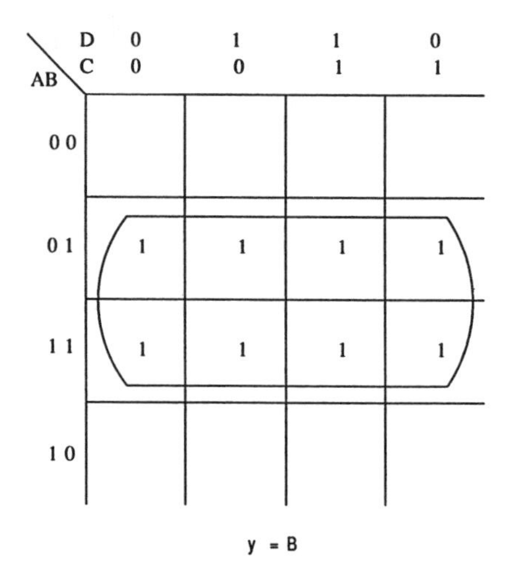

Figure 5-102
The K-map for the second equation.

"Don't Care" States

The last thing you need to know about K-mapping is how to use "don't cares." There are some design situations where all combinations of the input variables will not occur. For example, you may have identified the need for four input variables and your design calls for the use of only ten of the sixteen possible input states. You can usually determine by the application which input combinations can never occur. In other situations, there are various combinations of input states which will not affect the operation of the circuit; and therefore, you do not care whether they occur, or not. It is useful to identify these "don't care" states for use in Karnaugh mapping. The "don't care" states are plotted on the Karnaugh map along with the logic 1 outputs. In most cases, they will aid in the reduction of the circuitry required to implement the desired function.

The previous example is illustrated in the following truth table:

INPUTS				OUTPUT	
A	B	C	D	e	
0	0	0	0	0	
0	0	0	1	1	
0	0	1	0	0	
0	0	1	1	1	
0	1	0	0	1	
0	1	0	1	1	
0	1	1	0	0	
0	1	1	1	1	
1	0	0	0	0	
1	0	0	1	1	
1	0	1	0	X	Don't Care Conditions
1	0	1	1	X	
1	1	0	0	X	
1	1	0	1	X	
1	1	1	0	X	
1	1	1	1	X	

Since our example application only uses the 4-bit binary values 0000 thru 1001, the remaining six 4-bit values are "don't cares." An **X** is placed in the output column to indicate the don't care condition. The **X** indicates that the output for these conditions can be treated as either a 1 or a 0, we simply "don't care," since the conditions should never occur in the circuit anyway. However, if you treat the don't care conditions as producing logic 1 outputs, you can plot them in the K-map and use them to form larger groups. Larger groups result in simpler equations.

Figure 5-103a shows the logic 1 outputs of the truth table plotted as 1's. In addition, the don't care conditions of the truth table are plotted using X's. In Figure 5-103b, you see that larger groups can be formed by using the don't cares. The equation now reduces to simply

$$e = B\overline{C} + D$$

from our earlier

$$e = \overline{A}D + \overline{A}B\overline{C} + \overline{B}\overline{C}D$$

The idea is to plot the don't care conditions and use them, if you can, to make larger groups. **Do not** use them if they are not needed. In other words, don't try to group all the X's! They are only used in conjunction with the real "1's" to generate larger groups. A group of all X's will produce an unneeded term in the final equation.

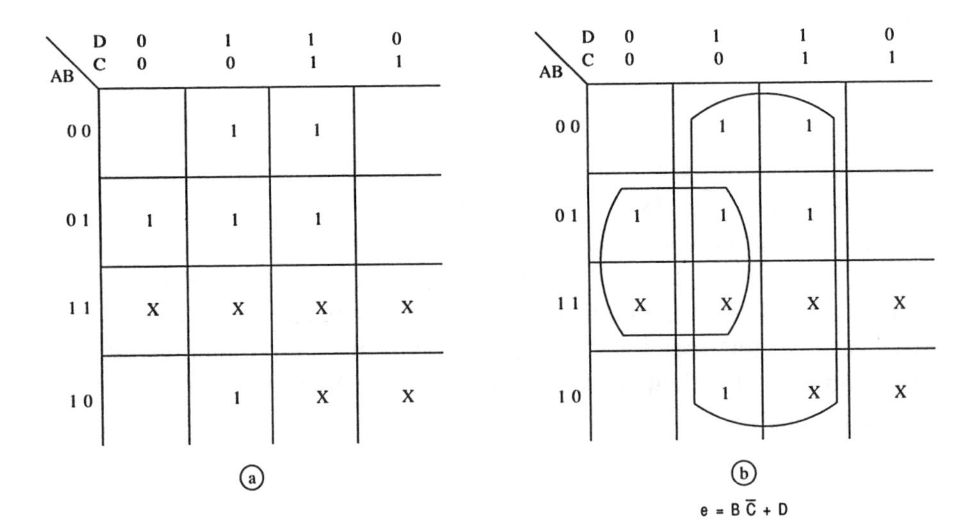

Figure 5-103
Don't cares are plotted **a** and used
as needed to form larger groups **b**.

The power of the Karnaugh map is evident from these examples. With a little practice in plotting, grouping, and reading K-maps, you can quickly reduce logic expressions to their minimum form.

40. What are the three operations used in Karnaugh mapping?

41. Given the following truth table, perform a K-map to find the simplified Boolean expression:

INPUTS				OUTPUT
A	B	C	D	f
0	0	0	0	X
0	0	0	1	0
0	0	1	0	0
0	0	1	1	0
0	1	0	0	1
0	1	0	1	0
0	1	1	0	1
0	1	1	1	1
1	0	0	0	1
1	0	0	1	1
1	0	1	0	X
1	0	1	1	X
1	1	0	0	X
1	1	0	1	X
1	1	1	0	X
1	1	1	1	X

42. Simplify the following equation:

$$z = ABCD + AB\overline{C}D + ABC\overline{D} + A\overline{B}\,\overline{C}D + AB\overline{C}\,\overline{D} + A\overline{B}\,\overline{C}\,\overline{D} + A\overline{B}C$$

Summary

Boolean Algebra is the mathematical system with a set of rules for analyzing logic circuits and reducing logic expressions. If necessary, review the Rules of Boolean.

Each Boolean variable can have only two values — zero or one. The variables (A, B, C, etc) can be arranged in sum-of-products (AB + BC + ABC) or product-of-sums (A + B) (A + C) format. In both cases, it is a method of combining OR and AND logic functions.

The Boolean equation identifies each term that will provide an output of 1. The terms are then ORed or ANDed together, to provide all of the logic terms that provide a 1 in the output. The resulting equation is a Boolean expression (equation) that completely describes the logic circuit. The Boolean equation that completely describes a logic circuit can be written directly from the logic circuit's truth table.

From the Boolean equation you can determine the number of AND and OR gates, how many inputs each gate contains, and how many inverters are required. Using the Rules of Boolean or Boolean Algebra, the equation can be reduced to the minimum number of components to accomplish the same functions. By using Boolean Algebra, you can save money and time in designing discrete logic circuits.

Using the traditional approach to designing, you will first build the circuit, and once it is operating properly, you will see which functions could be combined by experimentation. Sometimes referred to as the trial-and-error method or cut-and-paste method.

When you use Boolean Algebra to reduce the equation, you already know the minimum number of components required and their circuit arrangement.

DeMorgan's theorems are used to distribute the NOTs over the individual variables or terms. This allows you to separate the ones which appear in the output column, of a circuit's truth table. DeMorgan's theorems are extremely important in designing discrete digital circuits using Karnaugh Maps. Unless the NOTs are distributed a Boolean equation can not be plotted in a Karnaugh Map.

A Karnaugh Map provides a method of plotting the logic circuit's outputs. It also provides a convenient format for combining like terms and equivalent terms. The Karnaugh Map requires a square for each term that represents a possibility of 1. Thus, if the equation has 4 variables ($2^4 = 16$), the truth table will require 16 steps, and the Karnaugh Map will require 16 squares to plot all of the output possibilities.

Karnaugh mapping is an alternative to using Boolean Algebra. With a little practice, K-mapping can be used to quickly reduce logic equations to their minimum form.

Unit 6
Flip-Flops And Registers

Contents

Introduction 6-3

Unit Objectives 6-5

RS Flip-Flops 6-6

D Flip-Flops 6-20

JK Flip-Flops 6-29

Summary 6-39

Introduction

In this unit you are going to learn about flip-flops. A flip-flop is a digital logic element used for storing one bit of binary data. It has two stable states, one representing a binary 1 and the other a binary 0.

The flip-flop is the basic logic element used in sequential logic circuits. The primary characteristics of a sequential circuit is memory. Such circuits are used for a variety of storage, counting, sequencing and timing operations.

A major use of the flip-flop is in storage registers where a multibit binary word is stored. A register is made up of a number of flip-flops, each storing one bit of the number.

Look closely at the Unit Objectives that follow, to determine the specific knowledge and skills that you will have when you complete this Unit.

Unit Objectives

When you complete this unit you will have the following skills, knowledge and capabilities:

1. You will be able to write a definition for a flip-flop.

2. You will be able to name the three basic types of flip-flops.

3. Given a logic diagram, you will be able to identify each of the three types of flip-flops from their symbols or logic gate connections.

4. You will be able to explain the operation of RS, D, and JK flip-flops, showing the output states for all possible input states.

5. Given a set of input waveforms for the RS, D or JK flip-flop, you will be able to recognize the corresponding output waveforms.

6. You will be able to give a practical application for each of the three types of flip-flops.

7. You will be able to write a definition for a register.

8. Given a register made with any type of flip-flop, you will be able to measure the output states and determine the binary number stored there.

RS Flip-Flops

A flip-flop is a digital logic circuit, whose basic function is memory, that is capable of storing a single bit of binary data. It can assume either of two stable states, one representing a binary 1 and the other a binary 0. If the flip-flop is put into one of its two stable states, it will remain there as long as power is applied or until it is changed.

A flip-flop remembers to which state it was set. It effectively memorizes the data it is given. You give it this data by applying appropriate logic inputs to it. To determine the value of the bit stored in the flip-flop, you look at its outputs.

There are three basic types of flip-flops; the latch or RS, the D and the JK. Let's start with the simplest, the latch, also called a set-reset or RS flip-flop. This is the simplest form of binary storage element. The symbol shown in Figure 6-1 is used to represent this type of flip-flop.

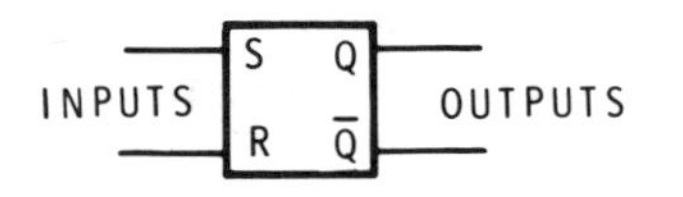

Figure 6-1
RS flip-flop symbol.

The flip-flop has two inputs, S and R, and two outputs Q and $\overline{Q}$. Applying the appropriate logic signal to either the S or R input will put the latch into one state or the other. The S input is used to set the flip-flop. When a flip-flop is set, it is said to be storing a binary 1. The R input is used to reset the flip-flop. A flip-flop that is reset is said to be storing a binary 0.

To determine which state the flip-flop is in, you look at the outputs. The latch has two outputs labeled Q and $\overline{Q}$. These are called the *normal* and *complement* outputs respectively. As in other logic circuits, any letter or alphanumeric mnemonic can be used to designate logic signals. See Figure 6-2. For example, the designation FF2 (meaning flip-flop number 2) could be used.

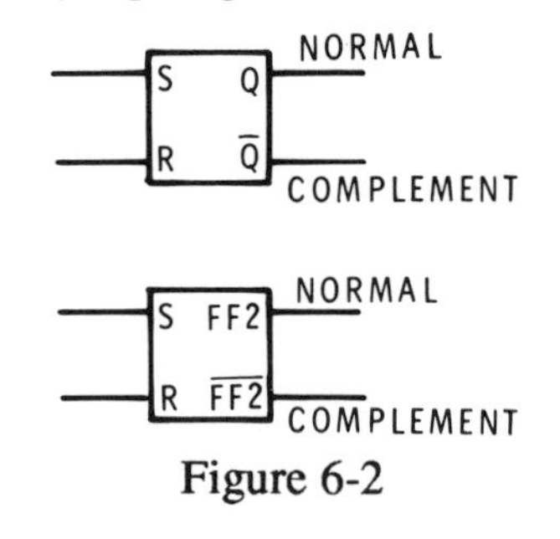

Figure 6-2

To tell what state the flip-flop is in, you look at the *normal* output. The logic level present there tells you which bit, 0 or 1, is being stored. If the normal output is a binary 0 level then the flip-flop is reset or storing a binary 0. If the normal output is the binary 1 level, the flip-flop is set and is storing a binary 1. The normal output always tells the state of the flip-flop. At the same time, the complement output has the state opposite that of the normal output. The complement output is just as useful in determining the output state of the flip-flop as long as you remember the above relationship. The simple table below sums up the states of an RS flip-flop.

FLIP-FLOP STATE	OUTPUTS Q	$\overline{Q}$
SET	1	0
RESET	0	1

This relationship is true for the latch and all other types of flip-flops.

A latch is readily constructed with logic gates as shown in Figure 6-3. Here two NAND gates are wired back-to-back so that the output of one feeds the input to the other.

Three methods of drawing the latch are illustrated in Figure 6-3. They are all electrically the same, but the version in Figure 6-3A is the most widely used. The other versions are used occasionally so it is a good idea to be familiar with the various configurations so that you will recognize them on a logic diagram when you see them.

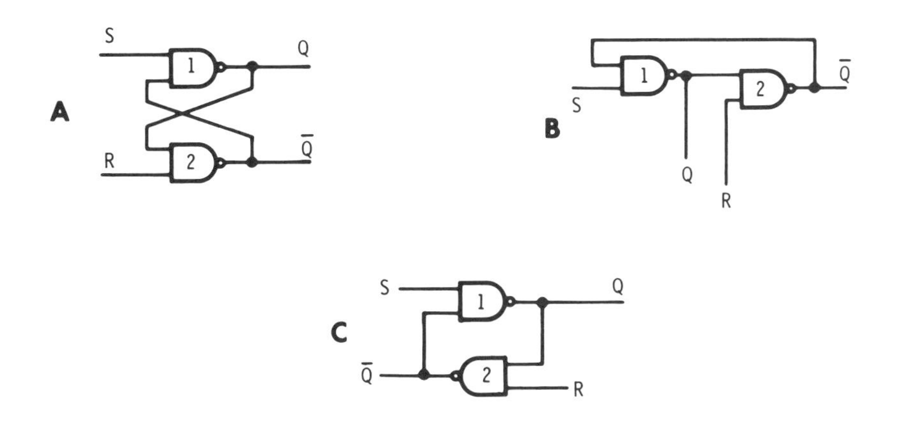

Figure 6-3

The latch is also sometimes drawn using the negative logic NOR symbols. See Figure 6-4. Either NAND or NOR logic symbols can be used to illustrate a latch. Let's consider a latch using NAND gates.

Recall that if both inputs to a 2 input TTL NAND gate are binary 1, the output will be binary 0. In order for the output to go low, both (all) inputs must be binary 1 or high. Any other combination of inputs will produce a binary 1 (high) output. If both inputs are open, the output will also go low. For that reason, an open input has the same effect on the gate as a binary 1 input. The operation of the NAND gate is summarized by the truth table below.

INPUTS		OUTPUT
A	B	C
low	low	high
low	high	high
high	low	high
high	high	low

High usually refers to the most positive logic voltage level while low refers to the least positive level.

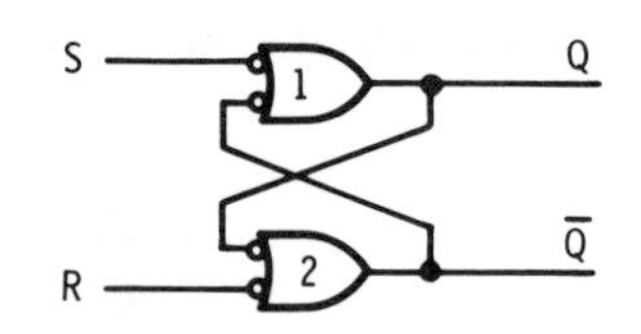

Figure 6-4

A look at the NAND gate truth table shows that of the four output states, three of them are high. The high output state is created by one or more low inputs. For that reason, we say that the predominant input state is a low or binary 0 for this type of gate. Now, let's consider the operation of the latch. Refer to Figure 6-5.

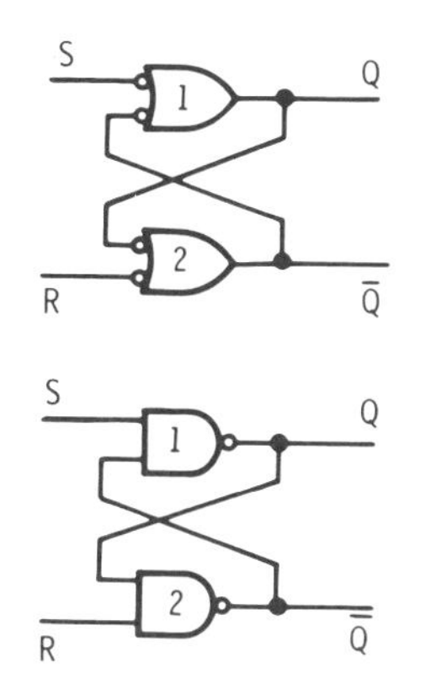

Figure 6-5

If the S and R inputs are both binary 1 (or open), which is the normal condition for this type of latch, the circuit is simply storing a bit put there by an earlier manipulation of the inputs. For example, if the flip-flop is set, the normal (Q) output from gate 1 (the set gate) will be high (binary 1). This output is fed back around to the upper input on gate 2 (the reset gate). The lower input to gate 2 is a binary 1 (or open) so its output $\overline{Q}$ is low. The output from gate 2 is fed to the lower input of gate 1. This input holds the Q output high. You can see now why they call this circuit a latch. Because of this feedback arrangement, the flip-flop is latched into this state. It will stay this way until you change it. And the way you change it is by applying a low level to either the set or reset inputs.

If you apply a low to the R input of the latch, it will reset. The low level on the R input will force the output of gate 2 high. This will cause both inputs to gate 1 to be high so its output will go low, thereby indicating the reset state.

If the flip-flop is set, applying a low to the S input will not do anything. The low level from the $\overline{Q}$ output fed back to the set gate keeps the Q output high. In the same way, applying a low level to the R input while the latch is reset will not produce a state change.

So, summing it all up we can say that to set the latch you must apply a binary 0 to the S input. To reset it you must apply a binary 0 to the R input. The waveform timing diagrams in Figure 6-6 shows the effect of various inputs on the outputs.

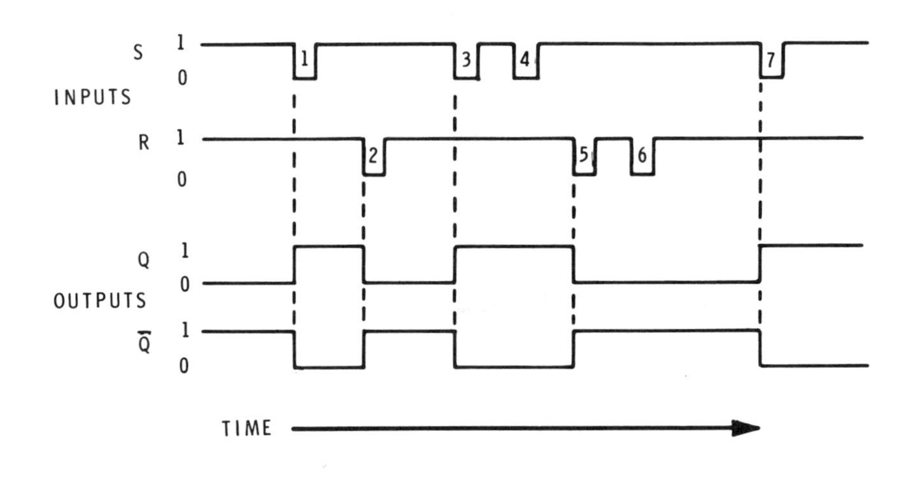

Figure 6-6

Go through these waveforms from left to right observing the effect of each input pulse on the outputs.

Looking at the waveforms above, you can determine what state the flip-flop is in prior to the application of pulse 1. Since the Q output is low and the $\overline{Q}$ output is high, before the occurrence of (to the left of) pulse 1, the latch is in the reset state storing a binary 0. Now look at these waveforms again.

When pulse 1 occurs on the S input, the latch sets with the outputs going to their proper levels. Pulse 2 comes along next on the R input so the latch resets. Pulse 3 again sets the flip-flop. Note that pulse 4 also occurs on the S input. Since the flip-flop is already set naturally nothing will happen. Pulse 5 then resets the latch. Pulse 6, also occuring on the R input, has no effect on the state of the latch. Finally, pulse 7 again sets the latch.

Both inputs should normally be high on a NAND gate latch unless you are changing its state. The high inputs do not disturb the state of the latch, so either a binary 1 or binary 0 may be stored there. Short duration input pulses that switch from high to low should be used when the latch is to be set or reset.

Now look at the latch circuit in Figure 6-7. Let's see what happens if both inputs go low at the same time.

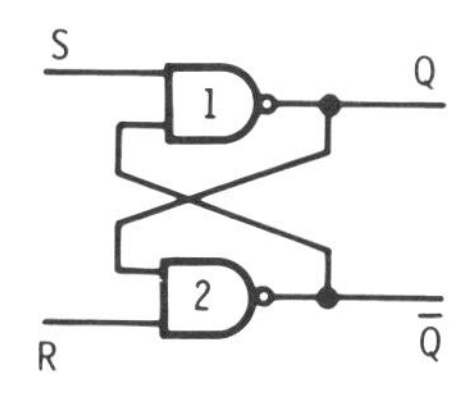

Figure 6-7

With both S and R inputs low, the Q and $\overline{Q}$ outputs will *both* be high. No longer are the outputs complementary, therefore, we really don't know what state the flip-flop is in. It is in some ambiguous state and is neither set or reset. This condition is one of the peculiarities of a latch. When you are using it you have to be careful to avoid simultaneous low inputs on the S and R terminals. This ambiguous state is generally undesirable, because it can produce undesirable operation of a logic circuit if it is not avoided or accounted for. The ambiguous condition actually represents a third state in which the latch can exist. This state is sometimes referred to as the "limbo" state.

One way to avoid this condition is to modify the latch as shown in Figure 6-8. The normal and complement outputs are both derived from gate 2. The inverter ensures that the outputs are always complementary even if both inputs do go low simultaneously.

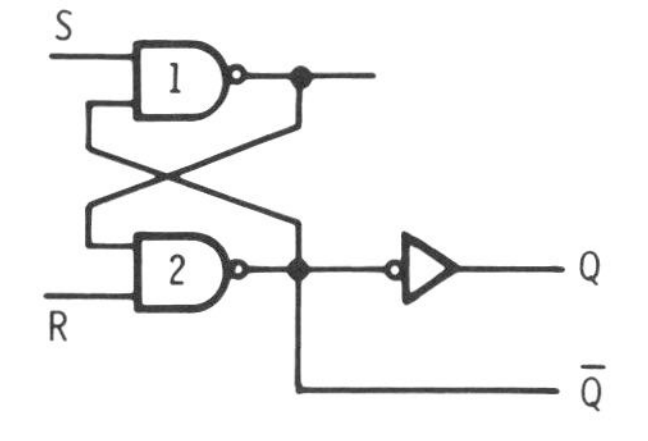

Figure 6-8

The complete operation of a NAND gate latch is summarized by the truth table below.

INPUTS		OUTPUTS		STATE
S	R	Q	$\overline{Q}$	
0	0	1	1	Limbo
0	1	1	0	Set
1	0	0	1	Reset
1	1	X	$\overline{X}$	Either set or reset

The truth table accounts for all possible input and output states. Note that when both S and R inputs are binary 1, the output state of the flip-flop is designated X, where X can be either a 0 or a 1 as determined by previous input conditions.

The latches we've discussed so far use positive logic NAND gates. We can also make latches out of positive logic NOR gates. Such a latch is shown in Figure 6-9.

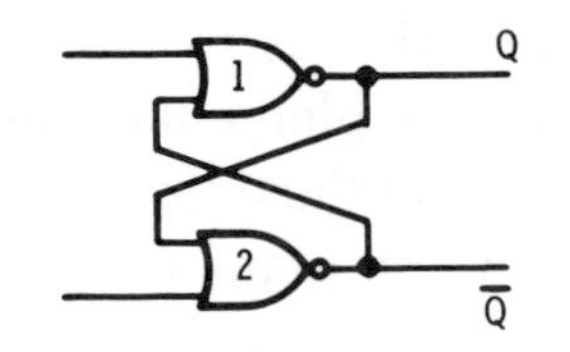

Figure 6-9

It is identical to the other latches just discussed in that the two gates are wired back-to-back. Even the logic symbol is the same. But first, refresh your memory on positive NOR gate operation by referring to the truth table below.

INPUTS		OUTPUTS
A	B	C
low	low	high
low	high	low
high	low	low
high	high	low

A high or binary 1 on either or both inputs produces a low or binary 0 output.

While NOR and NAND latches have exactly the same function, they achieve it in a slightly different way. To set the NOR latch you apply a binary 1 to the S input. To reset it you apply a binary 1 to the R input. And, if both inputs are made binary 1 simultaneously, the "limbo" or ambiguous state occurs. This is the exact opposite set of input conditions that exist in the NAND latch. Take a look at the circuits in Figure 6-10.

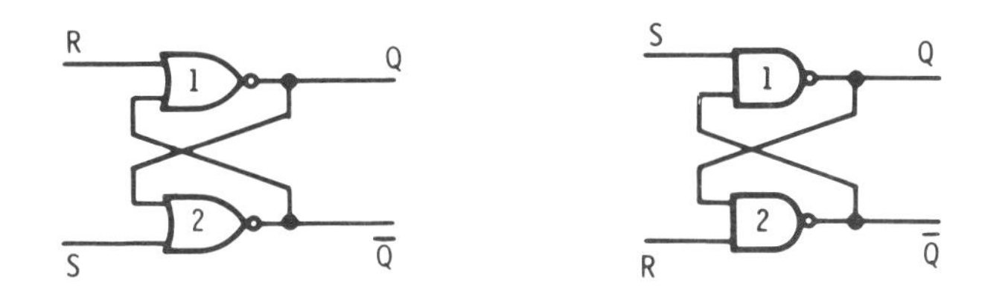

Figure 6-10

Note a subtle difference. The R and S inputs are reversed from those on the NAND latch. The reason for this has to do with the characteristics of the NOR gate. Applying a binary 1 to the R input forces the output of gate 1 low. This makes the upper and lower inputs to gate 2 low or binary 0 so its output is a binary 1. With this arrangement ($Q = 0$, $\overline{Q} = 1$) the flip-flop is clearly reset. As you can see, the interpretation of the outputs is the same. In fact, it is the same for *any* flip-flop.

Both outputs will go to the binary 0 state if a binary 1 level is applied to the R and S inputs simultaneously. This is exactly the opposite of what happens in the NAND latch. Nevertheless, this ambiguous condition is generally avoided unless there is some specific application for it.

The operation of a NOR latch is summarized in the truth table below.

INPUTS		OUTPUTS		
S	R	Q	$\overline{Q}$	STATE
0	0	X	$\overline{X}$	Either set or reset
0	1	0	1	Reset
1	0	1	0	Set
1	1	0	0	Ambiguous

As in the NAND latch, the X output indicates either set or reset.

One of the most common and useful applications for a latch flip-flop is in switch buffering. Pushbutton switches are used in digital equipment to control various aspects of its operation. However, most pushbutton switches produce contact bounce. This means that when the button is depressed or released, the switch contacts do not make an immediate solid electrical or mechanical connection. The contacts "bounce" open and closed for a brief period of time.

The waveform in Figure 6-11 indicates this effect.

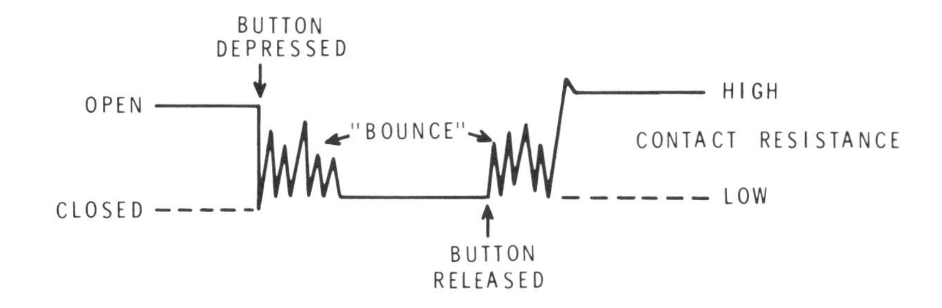

Figure 6-11

Naturally, if current is being switched, this waveform would represent the voltage across the switch. Instead of getting solid off-on switching, you get pulses. Such pulses can repeatedly trigger digital circuits. In pressing the button once, you would expect to get a single pulse or level change. Instead, the contact bounce gives you several. This effect is usually detrimental to the performance of digital circuits.

The circuits in Figure 6-12 show two ways of using a pushbutton switch to supply a logic pulse or level change. Such circuits usually produce a considerable amount of contact bounce.

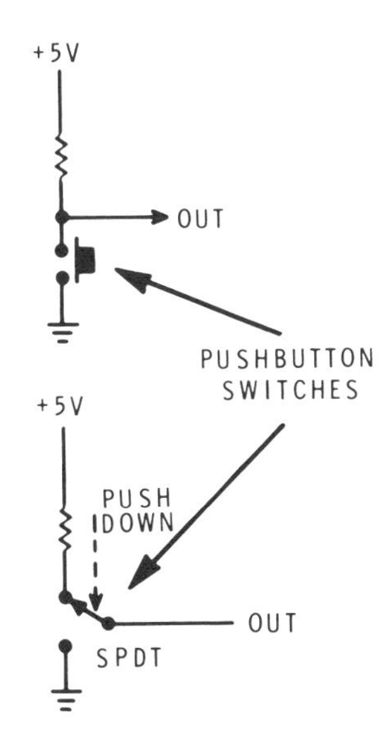

Figure 6-12

To overcome this problem, the switch can be combined with a latch as shown in Figure 6-13. An SPDT break-before-make (non-shorting) momentary contact pushbutton switch is normally used. With the switch in position A (not depressed or normally closed, N.C.), the output of gate 1 is held high. Depressing the switch, so that the grounded arm contacts position B, forces the output of gate 2 high and the output of gate 1 low. So how is the "bounce" removed? Well, as the button is depressed the arm of the switch breaks contact with point A. Even though it may bounce several times between open and ground, it has no effect on the state of the latch. The effect is the same as trying to repeatedly set a latch that is already set. Nothing happens. As the contact arm is in transit between points A and B, both inputs to the latch are open so the latch simply remains set. As point B is contacted, the latch resets. The slightest disturbance will trigger the state change through quickly. Even if switch bounce occurs, the latch is insensitive to it. The result is a single clean logic level change at the output. Releasing the pushbutton causes the latch to change back to its original state.

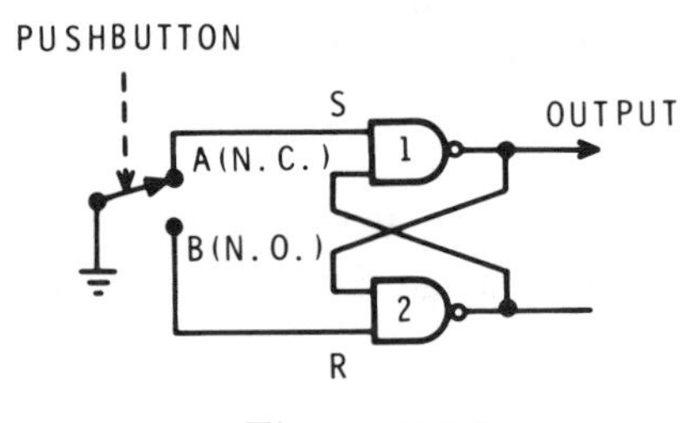

Figure 6-13

A NOR latch can also be used to buffer contact bounce. This is illustrated in Figure 6-14. The NOR latch removes contact bounce just as well as the NAND latch, only the reference R and S need be reversed on the NOR latch.

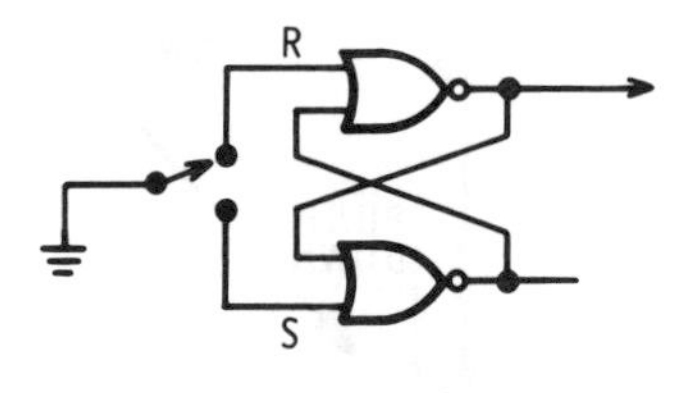

Figure 6-14

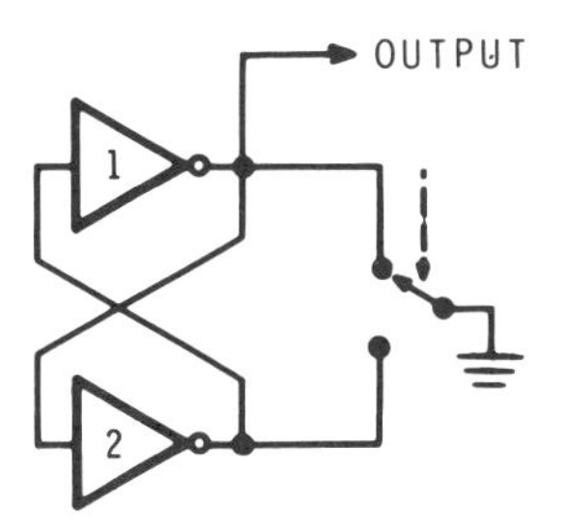

Figure 6-15

Another switch buffer latch circuit is shown in Figure 6-15. The latch is made of inverters so the outputs and inputs are common. The switch normally holds the output of inverter 1 low so that inverter 2 output is high. Pressing the switch reverses this state. The output is a "bounce-less" level change.

The most important requirement for a switch used with a latch buffer is that it must have two terminals, so an SPDT unit is required. And it is important that it be a break-before-make type so that the A and B contact points are not shorted momentarily in switching from one position to the other. This would put the latch into its "limbo" state briefly and false triggering will occur.

Another point is that the switch doesn't necessarily have to be a momentary contact type pushbutton. Any SPDT switch, slide or toggle, can be used. But remember, if it supplies logic level changes to a digital circuit, it will probably need buffering.

Self-Test Review

1. What will the normal output level of a latch be if it is set?

    a. high.
    b. low.

2. The complement output of a latch is low. What is the bit value stored?

    a. binary 0.
    b. binary 1.

3. Normally the duration of the pulses applied to the set or reset inputs should only be long enough to put the latch in the proper state.

    a. True.
    b. False.

4. Which of the following is *not* a typical name for the circuit discussed in this section?

    a. latch.
    b. RS flip-flop.
    c. set-reset flip-flop.
    d. multivibrator.

5. The ambiguous state in a latch is indicated by which of the following conditions?

    a. both outputs low.
    b. both outputs high.
    c. either a or b.
    d. one output low, the other high.

6. Unless the state of a NAND gate latch is being changed its inputs should both be:

    a. high.
    b. low.
    c. open.

7. Both inputs of a NAND latch are low. The state of the latch is:

   a. set.
   b. reset.
   c. ambiguous.

8. Both inputs to a NAND latch are low. The S input goes high. Shortly thereafter, the R input goes high. The state of the latch is:

   a. set.
   b. reset.
   c. ambiguous.

9. Both inputs to a NOR latch are high. The R input goes low, then the S input goes low. What is the value of the bit stored in the latch?

   a. binary 0.
   b. binary 1.

10. Besides the storage of binary data, latches are also commonly used for ____________________ ____________________.

11. The most important requirement for a switch being used with a latch buffer is to have __________________ __________________.

D Flip-Flops

Now let's consider the D flip-flop. Its symbol is shown in Figure 6-16.

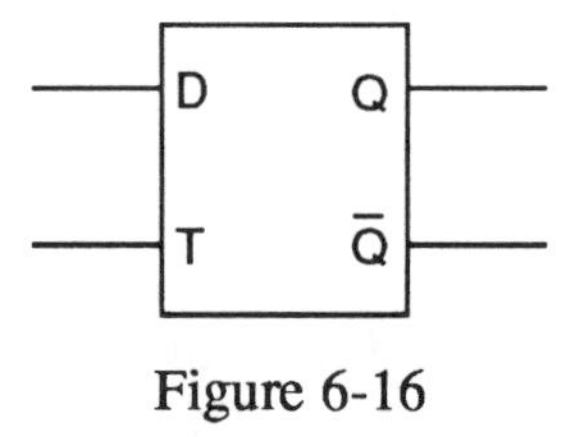

Figure 6-16

Like any other flip-flop the D flip-flop has two outputs that are used to determine its contents. That is, the outputs indicate what bit is stored there. The Q output tells you the state of the flip-flop directly. If it is a binary 0, the flip-flop is reset. If it is a binary 1, the flip-flop is set.

Now look at the inputs. Like on the latch there are two. But they work differently. The D input is where you apply the data or bit to be stored. Of course, it can be either a binary 1 or a binary 0. The T input line controls the flip-flop. It is used to determine whether the input data is recognized or ignored. If the T input line is high or binary 1, the data on the D line is stored in the flip-flop. As long as the T line is high, the normal output will simply follow or track the D input. If the T line is low or binary 0, the D input line is not recognized. The bit stored in the flip-flop previously is retained. The D line can essentially do anything and it will just be ignored if T is low.

You can get a better idea about how the D flip-flop works by taking a look at its insides. The logic diagram of one type of D flip-flop is shown in Figure 6-17.

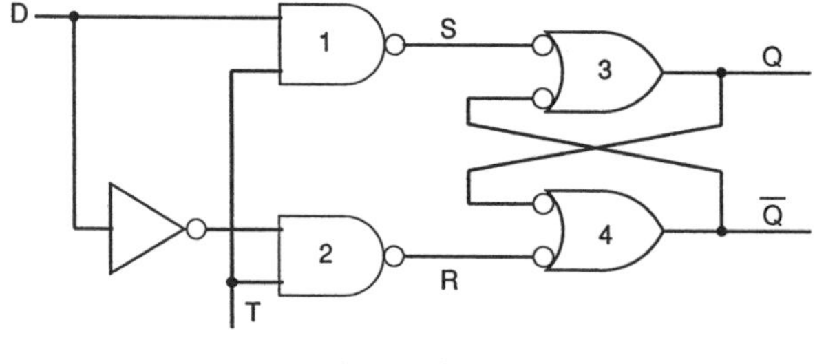

Figure 6-17

Gates 3 and 4 form a latch where the bit is stored. Gates 1 and 2 are enabling gates that pass or inhibit the input. The inverter makes sure that the S and R inputs to the latch are always complementary to avoid any possibility of the ambiguous state occurring.

With a low input on the T line, the outputs of gates 1 and 2 are high. This is the normal state for the inputs of a NAND latch to assume. In this state the latch is undisturbed.

Suppose a binary 1 is applied to the D input. Of course, nothing happens if the T input is still low. Now, make the T input go high. This enables both gates 1 and 2. The binary 1 on the D input makes gate 1 output go low. The inverter puts a low on the input to gate 2 so its output stays high. The low output of gate 1 sets the latch causing it to store the binary 1. Returning the T input low disables the input, but the binary 1 is retained.

Now look at the waveforms in Figure 6-18. These represent the D and T inputs and the Q output of a D flip-flop. The output is identical to the D input as long as the T input is high. When the T line goes low, the flip-flop stores the *last* state it sees on the D input.

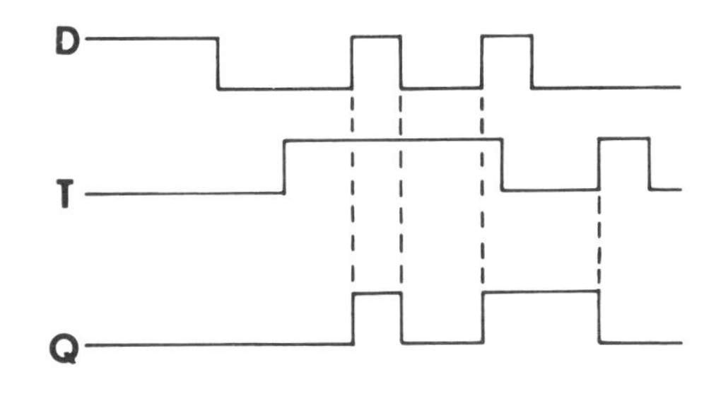

Figure 6-18

The circuit in Figure 6-19 shows another method of implementing the D flip-flop. As in the other circuit, gates 3 and 4 form the storage latch while gates 1 and 2 handle the input control.

Note that no separate inverter is needed. This arrangement functions exactly like the other circuit but is more economical of logic circuits. This circuit is quickly and easily made from a common quad 2 input NAND IC.

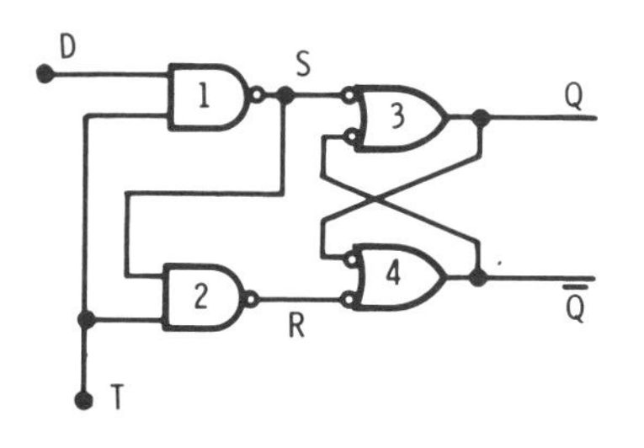

Figure 6-19

The operation of a D flip-flop is completely described by the truth table below.

INPUTS		OUTPUTS	
D	T	Q	$\overline{Q}$
0	0	X	$\overline{X}$
0	1	0	1
1	0	X	$\overline{X}$
1	1	1	0

Note that when T is binary 1, the Q output is the same as the D input. When T is binary 0, the Q output can be either binary 0 or 1 depending upon a previous input. This is indicated by the X state in the table. Note that a D flip-flop does not have an ambiguous state.

A D flip-flop can also be constructed with positive NOR gates as indicated in Figure 6-20.

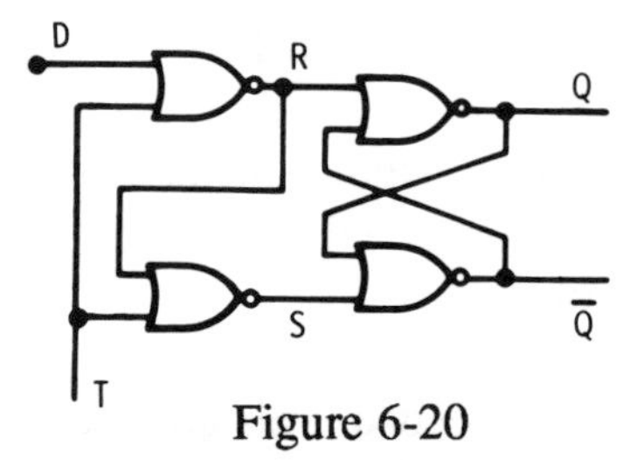

Figure 6-20

To explain the NOR latch better, however, it is desirable to redraw it so that the gates are shown as they are used. See Figure 6-21.

Gates 3 and 4 make up the latch that can be set or reset by the inputs from gates 1 and 2. Gates 1 and 2 control the input in that they determine whether the D input will be transferred to the latch. Functionally they perform the *AND* operation.

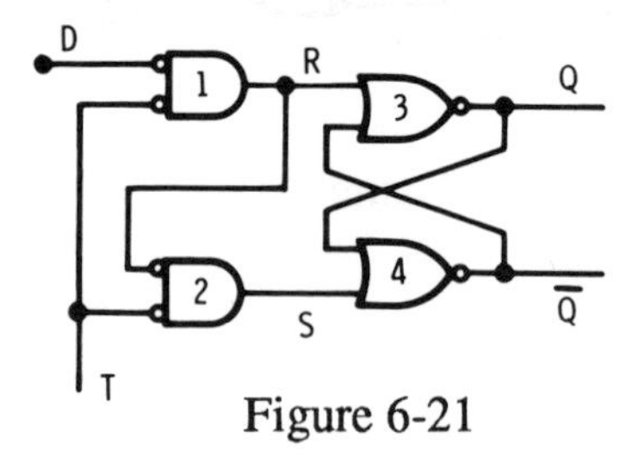

Figure 6-21

The NOR flip-flop does not perform exactly like the NAND flip-flop, but it is similar. Both circuits store one bit of information. The recognition of the D input is determined by the state of the T input. And, here lies the difference. In the NAND flip-flop, the T line has to be high in order for the flip-flop to store the D input state. In the NOR flip-flop, the T line must go *low* in order to recognize the D input. Bringing the T line high disables the D input. The last D input state prior to the T input going high is stored.

Storage Registers

The most common application of the D flip-flop is as an element in a storage register. A register is a group of flip-flops used to store a binary word. Each flip-flop stores one-bit of the data word. For example, a single BCD digit consists of four-bits. To store this word, we need one D flip-flop for each bit. The result is a 4-bit storage register.

Figure 6-22 below illustrates a 4-bit register.

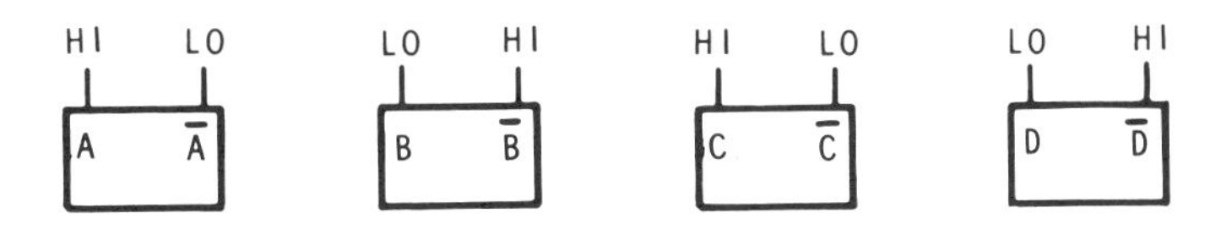

Figure 6-22

Each flip-flop is labeled with its own designation, A through D, so that it can be identified. Also shown here are the states of the flip-flop.

With the information given in Figure 6-22, you really can't tell what number is stored. True, you can look at normal outputs of the flip-flop and write down the corresponding bit values. This will give you two possible bit patterns depending upon whether you read from right to left or left to right. These bit patterns are 1010 (left to right) and 0101 (right to left).

There is one missing ingredient. Which bit is the most significant (MSB)? The answer is, it could be A or it could be D. Usually the LSB is designated as the earliest letter of the alphabet, or the lowest number if the number designations are used. If A is the LSB, then the number stored there is 0101 or a decimal 5. If D is the LSB the number is 1010 or decimal 10. It's always necessary to identify the LSB and/or MSB positions on a register in a logic diagram.

To be sure you understand this, let's take another example. A five-bit register with flip-flops A, B, C, D and E is storing a number. The flip-flop states are: A-reset, B-set, C-set, D-reset and E-set. If the A flip-flop is the LSB, the binary number is $E\overline{D}CB\overline{A}$ or 10110. This converts to a decimal 22.

Another type of register you should be familiar with is the switch register. This is exactly what its name implies, a register made of switches. The group of switches form a register for storing a single word or bit pattern using one switch per bit. The position of the switch (up/down, on/off, open/close, etc.) determines the bit value.

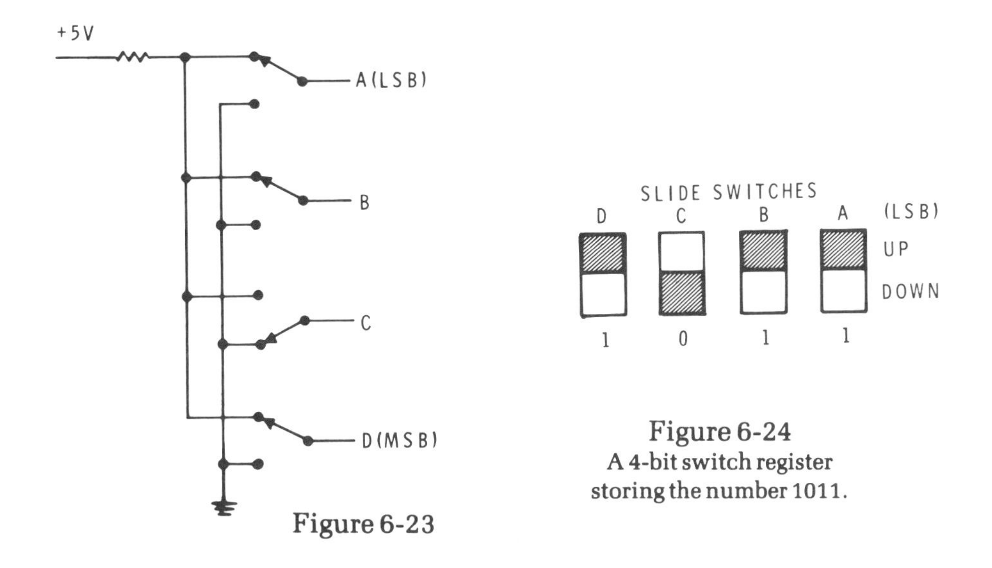

Figure 6-23

Figure 6-24
A 4-bit switch register storing the number 1011.

A 4-bit switch register is shown in Figure 6-23. Four single pole double throw (SPDT) switches store the bit value as a physical position. The A, B, C, and D outputs are ground (0) or +5 (1) depending upon their position. The binary number stored in the switch register is 1011 or decimal 11. You can determine the switch register contents by monitoring its electrical outputs. Or in most switch registers, the switches are mounted adjacent to one another horizontally with the LSB on the right and their position (usually up or down) is readily observable. Up usually means 1, down means 0. Therefore, a visual identification of the switch register contents is possible. See Figure 6-24.

A frequent operation in digital equipment is the transfer of data from one register to another. Figure 6-25 illustrates how the data in a switch register can be transferred to a register made of D flip-flops. The switch outputs are fed to the D inputs. The control of the transfer is by the common T line on the flip-flops.

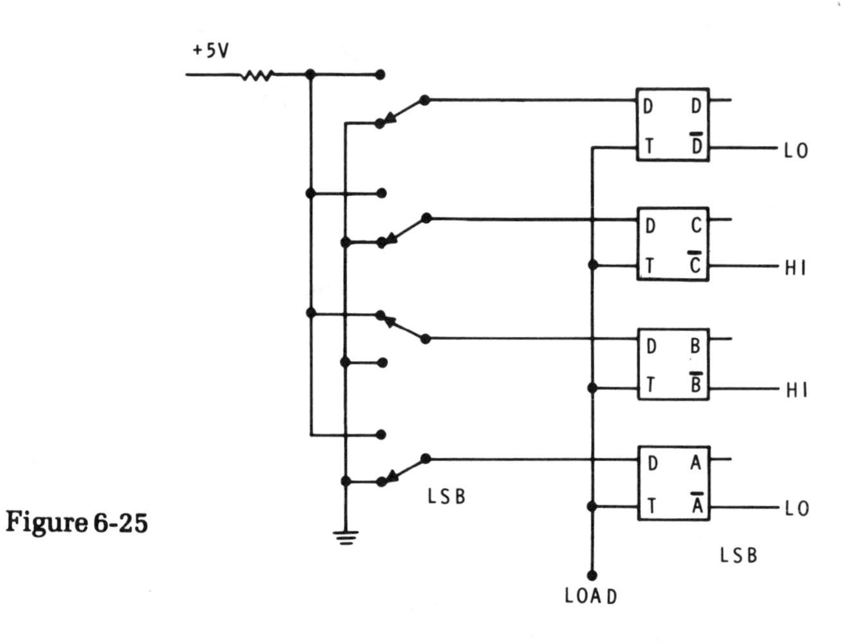

Figure 6-25

The content of the flip-flop register in Figure 6-25 is 1001. The data given in the figures is the complement output states. From this, you can determine the normal outputs and hence the contents of the register. You can also determine the output of the switch register, 0010, by inspection. With the T inputs to the flip-flop at binary 0, the data input from the switch register is not recognized by the flip-flops. But if the LOAD control line goes high momentarily, the flip-flop register contents will become the same as the switch register, 0010.

There are two important points to note here. First, the LOAD input controls the transfer of the data from the switch register to the flip-flop register. This LOAD input is the parallel or simultaneous control of all the flip-flop T inputs. This line is also sometimes called the STROBE input since it is usually only enabled or "strobed" momentarily with a binary 1 pulse to transfer the data.

Second, the data transfer is a parallel one. That is all bits from the switch register are loaded into the flip-flop register simultaneously.

Instead of drawing the individual flip-flops, most registers are shown as only a single box with the inputs and outputs identified as shown in Figure 6-26.

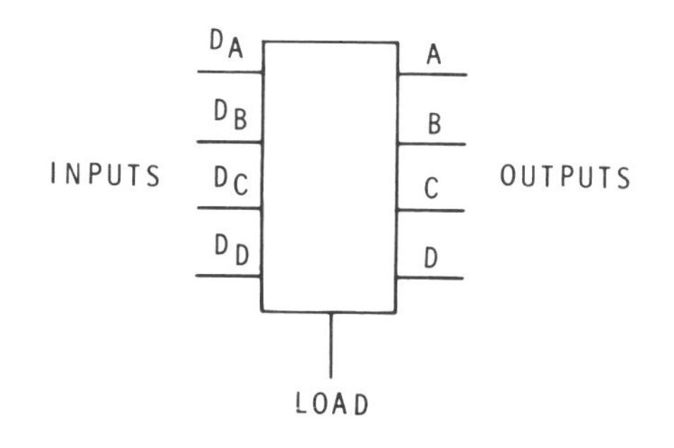

Figure 6-26

This is particularly true of MSI integrated circuit registers. Many IC registers also do not have the complement outputs available.

Self-Test Review

12. The T input of a D flip-flop determines its state.

    a. True.
    b. False.

13. D flip-flops are widely used to form ______________________________
    ______________________________.

14. Complete the truth table of a NOR gate D flip-flop.

INPUTS		OUTPUTS	
D	T	Q	$\overline{Q}$
0	0		
0	1		
1	0		
1	1		

15. What is the decimal equivalent output of the register shown in Figure 6-27? Assume positive logic. ______________

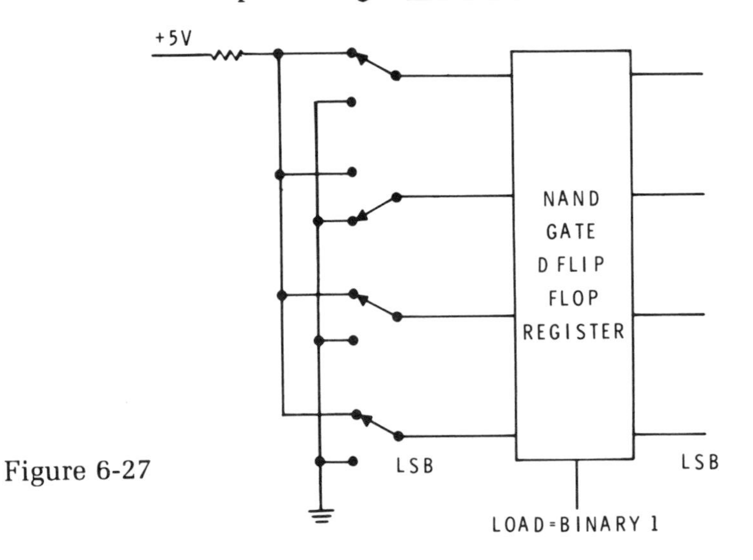

Figure 6-27

16. Given the input waveforms shown in Figure 6-28, sketch the normal output waveform of a NAND gate D flip-flop.

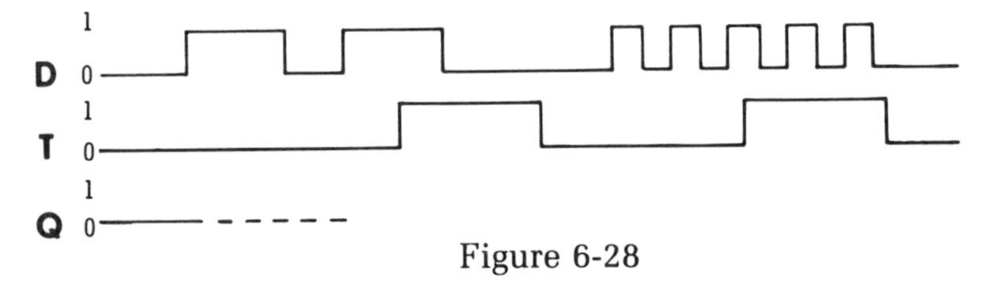

Figure 6-28

JK Flip-Flops

The JK flip-flop is the most versatile type of binary storage element in common use. It can perform all of the functions of the RS and D type flip-flops described earlier plus it can do several other things that these simple flip-flops cannot. Naturally, it is more complex and expensive than the other types so for that reason it isn't always used where simpler and less expensive circuits will do.

An integrated circuit JK flip-flop is really two flip-flops in one. It usually consists of two latches, one feeding the other, with appropriate input gating on each. See Figure 6-29.

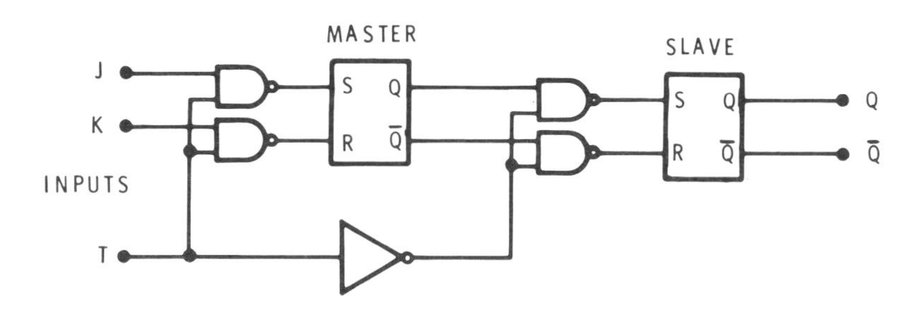

Figure 6-29

The arrangement is called a master-slave JK flip-flop. The master flip-flop is the input circuit. Logic signals applied to the JK flip-flop set or reset this master latch. The slave flip-flop is the latch from which the outputs are taken. The slave latch gets its input from the master latch. Both latches are controlled by a clock pulse. Since there are *two places* to store bits in a JK flip-flop, there are times when both master and slave latches are identical or times they are complementary. But only one of these latches is responsible for indicating the state of the JK flip-flop. The slave latch designates the state being stored. If it is set, the JK flip-flop is storing a binary 1.

Refer to Figure 6-30. The logic gates are the positive NAND type. Gates 3 and 4 make up the master latch while its input is controlled by gates 1 and 2. The slave latch is made up of gates 7 and 8. Gates 5 and 6 control the transfer of the master latch state to the slave latch. Note that clock signal T controls the input gating circuits. The inverter keeps the clock to the master and slave input gates complementary. The clock pulse controls the JK flip-flop while the J and K inputs determine exactly how it will be controlled. (Note: You will also see the T input referred to as C or CLK designating clock pulse or clock.)

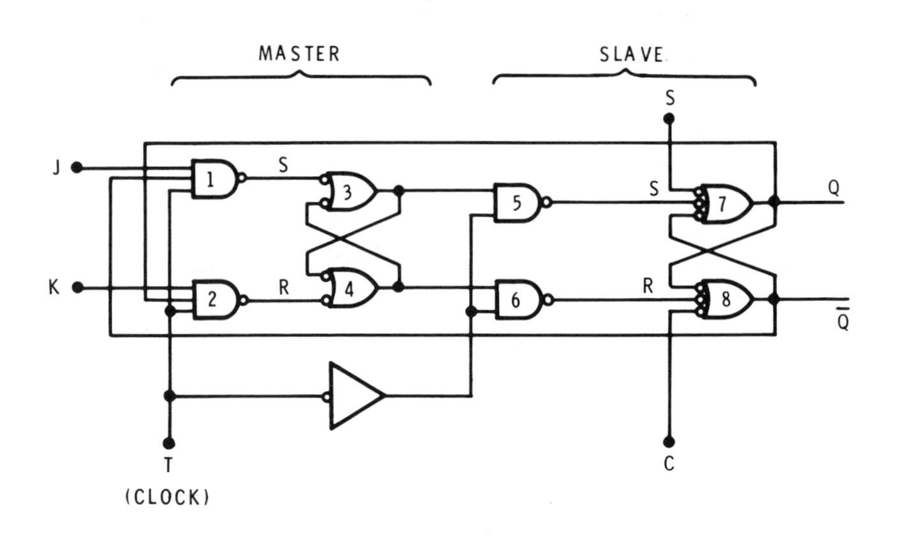

Figure 6-30.

The set (S) and clear (C) inputs also control the JK flip-flop. These are inputs to the slave latch that can be used to set or reset (clear) the flip-flop. These inputs override all other circuitry in the JK flip-flop. These inputs are used to preset the state of the flip-flop prior to any other operation involving the JK inputs and the clock. They work just like the inputs on any latch.

To set the slave latch *and* the JK flip-flop, the S input should be low, the C input high. This forces the normal Q output high indicating that a binary 1 is being stored. To reset the JK flip-flop, the C input is made low while S is high. Normally, the S and C inputs will be high when they are not being used to preset the flip-flop. This arrangement is identical to that for the NAND latch.

Now let's consider how the J K and T (clock) inputs affect the flip-flop. Refer to Figure 6-30. Consider the time when the clock input is low. Gates 1 and 2 will be inhibited so the J and K inputs cannot control the state of the master latch. The master latch can be in either state. At this time, the slave latch will have the same state as the master latch when the clock input is low. The output of the inverter in the clock line is binary 1, causing the gates 5 and 6 to be enabled during this time. Therefore, the state of the master latch is simply transferred to the slave latch. For example, if binary 1 is stored in the master latch, the output of gate 3 will be high and the output of gate 4 will be low. This will make the output of gate 5 low and the output of gate 6 high. This low on the input to gate 7 will force its output high, thereby setting the slave latch and storing a binary 1.

Now if the clock T goes high, gates 1 and 2 will be enabled. The output of the inverter will inhibit gates 5 and 6. The master latch cannot further change the slave latch. But now with gates 1 and 2 enabled, the J and K inputs can affect the state of the master latch. The JK flip-flop outputs Q and $\overline{Q}$ are fed back around to gates 1 and 2 where, along with the J and K inputs, they will also determine the state of the master latch.

If both J and K inputs are low, the outputs of gates 1 and 2 will be held high, so no change takes place in the master latch.

If the J and K inputs are both high (or open), then the state of the master latch will be determined by the Q and $\overline{Q}$ outputs. For example, if the slave latch is set, the master latch will be reset. If the slave is reset, the master will be set. The reason for this is the way the outputs are crisscrossed back to gates 1 and 2. Remember that with the J, K and T inputs high, the state of the master latch will be determined by the Q and $\overline{Q}$ outputs.

Now let's consider the effect of the J and K inputs. These inputs are analogous to the set and reset inputs on a latch. If J is 1 and K is 0, we will set the master latch. If J is 0 and K is 1, the master latch will be reset. Remember, the T input line must be high for this to happen.

The state of the JK flip-flop is the state of the slave latch. The state of the slave latch is determined by that of the master latch. The state of the master is, in turn, determined by the J and K inputs. And to top it off, the clock input determines *when* each of these latches will be affected. With the clock input high, only the master latch will be affected. The inverter on the clock line blocks gates 5 and 6 so the slave latch is not disturbed. The states of the JK inputs will ultimately determine the output state but only at a specific time. When the clock line switches from high to low (trailing edge), the state of the master latch is transferred to the slave latch.

When the clock (T) is high, gates 1 and 2 will be enabled therefore the master latch will be changed by either the Q and $\overline{Q}$ outputs or by the J and K inputs. When the clock goes low, the state of the master latch is transferred to the slave latch through gates 5 and 6, which are enabled at this time. Gates 1 and 2 are inhibited so the J and K inputs have no effect.

If the JK inputs are high or open, the flip-flop will change state each time the clock input switches from high to low. To show this, assume that the clock input is high, the JK inputs are high, and the slave latch is set. The Q and $\overline{Q}$ lines fed back to gates 1 and 2 cause the master latch to be reset. Then when the trailing edge of the clock pulse occurs, (clock switches from 1 to 0), the reset state in the master is transferred to the slave. The JK flip-flop is now reset. When the clock again goes high, the slave latch then sets the master latch. As the clock goes low, the set state in the master is transferred to the slave. As you can see then, with the JK inputs high, the flip-flop complements itself each time the clock switches from high to low (trailing edge). We call this operation toggling.

Assume the J and K inputs are open or high. The waveform in Figure 6-31 represents the normal flip-flop output.

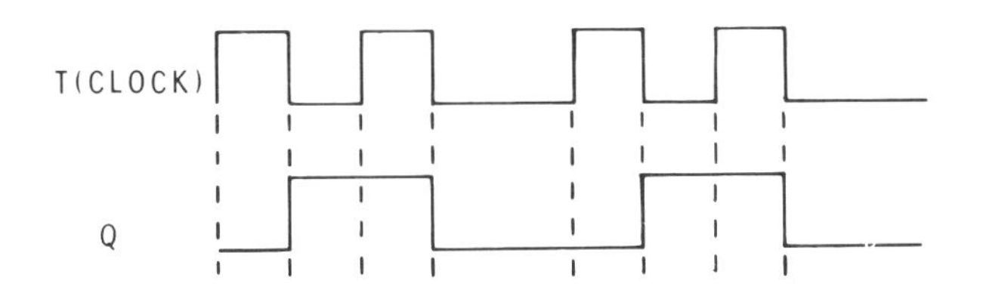

Figure 6-31

When the clock switches from 1 to 0, the state of the flip-flop changes. The output is not affected during the 0 to 1 transition (leading edge).

If you will look at the clock and output waveforms in Figure 6-32, you will see a definite relationship. The Q output has a frequency one half the T input. The reason for this is simply that the flip-flop changes state on only the trailing edge or every other transition of the clock. Therefore, the JK flip-flop in its toggling mode is a two-to-one frequency divider. It halves any input frequency applied to the clock input. If an input of 50 KHz is applied, the output will be one-half or 25 KHz. Cascading JK flip-flops permits frequency division by any factor of 2 (2, 4, 8, 16, 32, 64, etc.). The frequency division ratio is 2^n where n is the number of flip-flops cascaded.

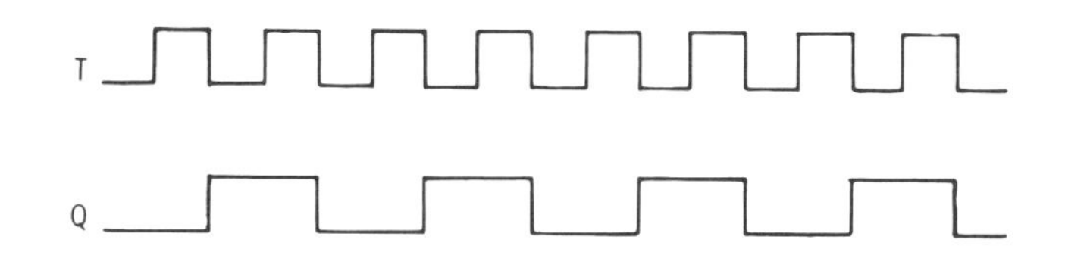

Figure 6-32

We have now considered all of the modes of operation of the JK flip-flop, but let's review them each briefly. Refer to Figure 6-30.

First, there are the S and C inputs. The effect of these can be summed up by the truth table below.

INPUTS		OUTPUTS	
S	C	Q	$\overline{Q}$
1	1	X	$\overline{X}$
0	1	1	0
1	0	0	1
0	0	1	1

This is exactly the same truth table we established for the NAND latch. Yes, the JK flip-flop does have an ambiguous state. If both S and C inputs are low, both the Q and $\overline{Q}$ outputs will be high. Therefore, care should be taken to see that this condition cannot occur.

The set (S) and clear (C) inputs are used to preset the flip-flop to some desirable condition prior to another operation. The most common operation is to reset it. For that reason many IC JK flip-flops have only a C input line. Use of the S and C inputs is referred to as asynchronous operation. The state of the flip-flop changes immediately upon the application of the appropriate input level. No other conditions are necessary. This is not true of the J and K inputs. Their effect is dependent upon the state of the clock signal. Therefore, we call the J and K inputs synchronous because they cause state changes only on the occurrence of a specific clock transition, that is in synchronism with the clock.

When the clock input switches from 1 to 0, state changes occur. It is on this transition that the contents of the master latch is transferred to the slave latch. For some types of JK flip-flops, toggling occurs on the leading or positive edge of the clock signal. Be sure to check the manufacturer's data sheet for details on any device you are using.

The synchronous operation of the JK flip-flop is summed up in the truth table below. Note that only the normal (Q) output condition is shown, but it is given twice, once prior to a clock pulse (t) and then after one clock pulse (t + 1). The output state X can represent either set (1) or reset (0).

INPUTS		OUTPUTS	
J	K	Q(t)	Q(t + 1)
0	0	X	X
0	1	X	0
1	0	X	1
1	1	X	$\overline{X}$

Refer to the truth table. When the J and K inputs are both low, the clock can change all it wants to but it will not affect the state of the flip-flop. The flip-flop simply retains its previous condition which can be either set or reset. This is an inhibit mode.

To reset the JK flip-flop, apply a 0 to the J input and a 1 to the K input then apply a clock pulse. The flip-flop will reset. To set the JK flip-flop you apply a 1 to J and 0 to K and again apply a clock pulse. The flip-flop will set on the trailing edge of the clock.

With the J and K inputs both at binary 1, the flip-flop toggles or complements each time the clock switches from 1 to 0. The flip-flop acts as a 2 to 1 frequency divider. Modern integrated circuit flip-flops are available in a variety of configurations. Some ECL flip-flops can toggle at rates as high as 1 GHz.

That completes the basic operation of a JK flip-flop. The symbol used to represents it is shown in Figure 6-33.

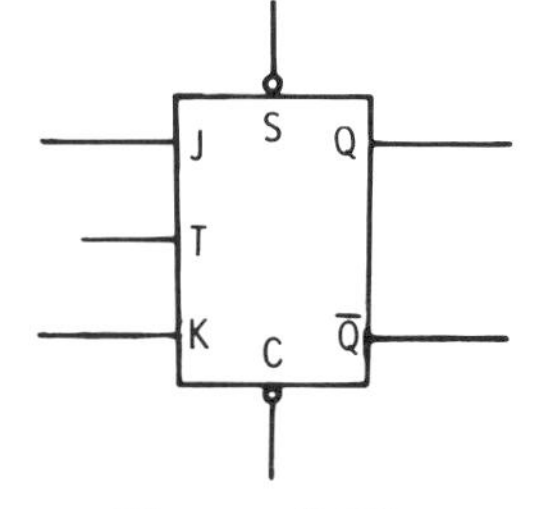

Figure 6-33

As a final check of your understanding of this important device, consider the input waveforms shown in Figure 6-34.

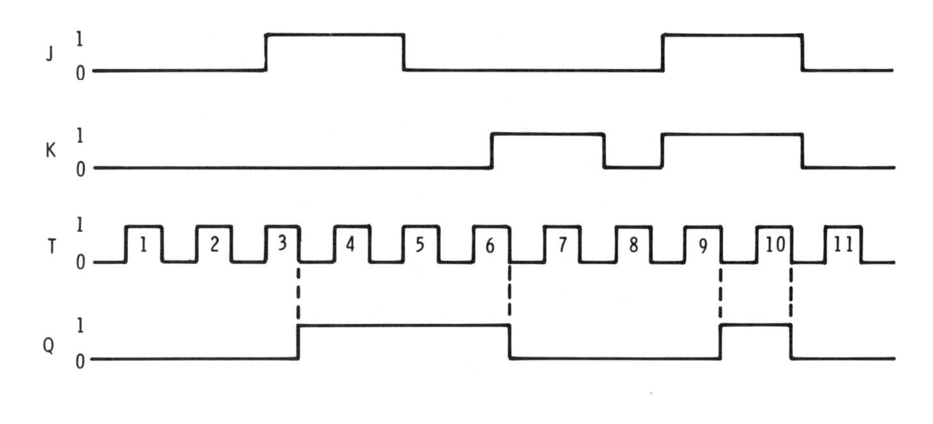

Figure 6-34

The J and K inputs affect the flip-flop state, but state changes occur only on the 1 to 0 transition of the clock pulse. This is synchronous operation.

In Figure 6-34, the normal output of the flip-flop is low prior to the occurance of the first clock (T) pulse. Pulses 1 and 2 occur but since both the J and K inputs are low, the flip-flop is inhibited and no state change takes place. Then, the J input goes high. On the trailing edge of the next clock pulse (3), the flip-flop sets. When pulse 4 occurs, J is still high so the flip-flop would remain set. The J input goes low, then clock pulse 5 occurs. With both J and K low, the trailing edge of pulse 5 has no effect. The flip-flop remains set. Next, the K input goes high and J remains low. On the occurence of the 1 to 0 transition of pulse 6, the flip-flop resets. Pulse 7 tries to reset it again. The K input goes low. Pulse 8 occurs and since J and K are low, the flip-flop remains reset. The J and K inputs go high simultaneously. Pulses 9 and 10 then toggle or complement the flip-flop, 9 setting it and 10 resetting it. After this J and K go low inhibiting the flip-flop. Pulse 11 has no effect.

The JK flip-flop is highly versatile. They are widely used in storage registers, shift registers, frequency dividers and counters. You will learn more about each of these circuits in a later unit.

Self-Test Review

17. The asynchronous inputs to a JK flip-flop are designated:

    a. J and K.
    b. S and C.
    c. Q and $\overline{Q}$.
    d. T.

18. The JK flip-flop operates as a NAND latch when which inputs are used?

    a. S and C.
    b. J and K.
    c. T.
    d. none of the above.

19. On a JK flip-flop the S and C inputs are high, the J input is high, the K input is low. What is the state of the flip-flop when one clock pulse occurs on the T input?

    a. reset.
    b. set.
    c. ambiguous.
    d. insufficient information given to determine the state.

20. The state of the JK flip-flop changes when the clock signal on T switches from:

    a. high to low.
    b. low to high.
    c. either a. or b.

21. The following conditions exist in a JK flip-flop: J = K = 1, S = C = 1, $\overline{Q}$ = 1, Q = 0. What is the binary contents of the flip-flop after three clock pulses occur?

    a. binary 0.
    b. binary 1.
    c. insufficient data given to determine state.

22. Both J and K inputs are held low. The S and C inputs are high. The Q output is 0. What is the state of the flip-flop after three clock pulses?

    a. binary 0.
    b. binary 1.
    c. insufficient information given.

23. Which of the following conditions will reset a JK flip-flop? (indicate all choices that apply):

a. J = 1, K = 0, S = 1, C = 1, T changes.
b. J = 1, K = 1, S = 1, C = 1, T changes.
c. J = 0, K = 1, S = 1, C = 1, T changes.
d. J = 0, K = 0, S = 1, C = 0, T changes.
e. J = 1, K = 1, S = 0, C = 1, T changes.
f. J = 1, K = 0, S = 0, C = 0, T changes.

24. Disregarding the S and C inputs, a JK flip-flop changes state when:

a. J changes.
b. K changes.
c. J and K change.
d. when T switches from 1 to 0.

25. In a JK flip-flop, J = K = 1, S = C = 1. The T input is a 330 KHz square wave. The Q output is a:

a. binary 0.
b. binary 1.
c. 165 KHz square wave.
d. 330 KHz square wave.

26. In a JK flip-flop, J = K = 1, S = C = 1. The T input is at 2 MHz with a duty cycle of 30 percent. What is the frequency and duty cycle of the Q output?

a. 2 MHz, 30 percent.
b. 2 MHz, 15 percent.
c. 1 MHz, 15 percent.
d. 1 MHz, 30 percent.
e. 1 MHz, 50 percent.

NOTE: The duty cycle is the ratio of the pulse on (binary 1) time to the period of the signal times 100 percent

$$\text{percent duty cycle} = \frac{\text{pulse on time}}{\text{period}} \times 100 \text{ (period} = 1/f)$$

27. A JK flip-flop could be used for switch contact bounce buffering?

a. True.
b. False.

Summary

The flip-flop is a basic digital storage device. The term flip-flop means a bistable multivibrator. Bistable means the device has two stable states, which in digital terms means 0 or 1. A bistable device is capable of storing one binary bit.

There are 3 basic types of flip-flops commonly used in digital circuits. They are the RS (set/reset), D, and JK. All flip-flops are capable of set and reset. Normally the set condition means the flip-flop is storing a 1. Reset, means the flip-flop is storing a 0. Flip-flops provide two outputs which are complementary. When one of the outputs is at binary 1, the other output will be at binary zero. The set and reset outputs are the inverse of each other. The set output is usually labeled as Q and the reset output is labeled $\overline{Q}$. Remember, that the NOT sign means inverted.

The RS flip-flop is usually used as a latch. Once the flip-flop is in a stable condition another pulse to the same input will have no effect on the output. The inputs have to be alternately triggered or the input trigger must be alternately polarity inverted. The RS flip-flop can have ambiguous states, this occurs when both outputs are high or low at the same time. The RS flip-flop is usually used as a switch debouncer. The RS flip-flop contains 2 logic gates.

D flip-flops have a data input and a toggle input. The input trigger is usually routed to the toggle input and the input pulses are of alternate polarity. The D flip-flop does not have the ambiguity problem that the RS flip-flop has. The outputs of the D flip-flop are always complementary. The flip-flops can be arranged in serial or parallel circuit configurations. The D flip-flop contains 4 logic gates and an inverter.

The JK flip-flop can do all of the functions of both the RS and D flip-flops, plus many other functions. It is by far the most versatile flip-flop. It contains 4 NAND gates, 1 inverter, and 2 flip-flops (each flip-flop contains 2 logic gates). The flip-flops are called the master and the slave. First you program the master and it programs the slave.

Therefore, there is isolation between inputs and outputs. The inputs (J, K, and T) can all be controlled or programmed. The JK flip-flop outputs can both be high when the S and C inputs are both low. The S (set) and C (clear) inputs are used to set the flip-flop to a predetermined state. Care must be exercised, that both the S and C inputs are never low at the same time. In some JK flip-flops the S and C inputs may be labeled S and R (reset).

Most flip-flops have a C or clear input. This input is usually used to preset the flip-flops to zero. In the case of a counter or register, all of the clear lines will be tied together so that, all of the counter stages can be preset at one time. There are times when the clear line will be connected to the set inputs. For example, a backward counter, or count down register will initially be set to all ones.

Remember, that a bistable device only stores 1 binary bit. Therefore, to have a BCD register or counter, requires 4 flip-flops for every digit. Many frequency counters contain a 6-digit readout. In this case, 24 flip-flops are required.

Most flip-flops are edge triggered. That means, that the flip-flop changes states either on the leading or trailing edge of the input pulse. This characteristic of a particular flip-flop can be found on its data sheet (manufacturer's specifications sheet). Its pin out, transient response time, voltage and current limits, and thermal characteristics are also supplied on most data sheets.

Solid-state semiconductor integrated packages have been developed with hundreds of flip-flops in a single package. Many devices using flip-flop storage use these integrated circuits and simply refer to them as memory chips.

Counters and registers make up parts of every digital computer. Most of the mathematical problem solving done by computers is done by registers. Nearly every function that the computer does is regulated or counted by flip-flops.

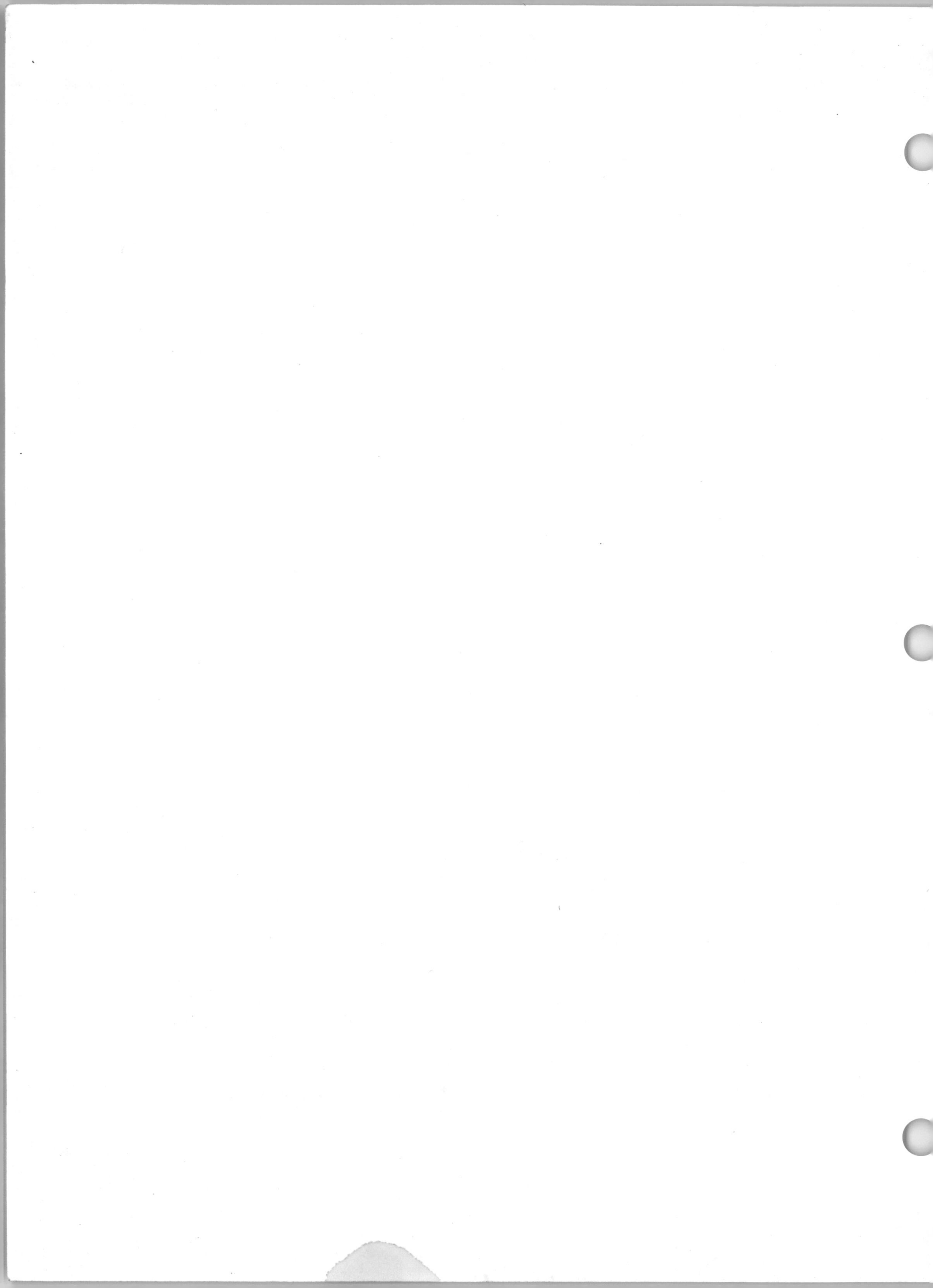